Beer, Bed & Breakfast

Great accommodation in over 500 UK real ale pubs

CAMPAIGN FOR REAL ALE

JILL ADAM & SUSAN NOWAK

Published by Campaign for Real Ale
230 Hatfield Road
St Albans
Hertfordshire AL1 4LW

www.camra.org.uk/books

ISBN 978-1-85249-230-4

A CIP catalogue record for this book is available from the British Library

Printed and bound by www.print-with-ipp.com

Head of Publications: Joanna Copestick
Project Editor: Emma Lloyd
Editorial Assistance: Debbie Williams
Copy Editor: Ione Brown
Designer: Alison Fenton
CAMRA Illustrations: John Simpson
Maps: Russell Bell

Jill Adam and Susan Nowak would like to thank the CAMRA branches and individual members for their help in compiling this guide, Roger Protz for the use of his beer styles feature from the Good Beer Guide, and would particularly like to thank Emma Lloyd at CAMRA HQ for her constant support and backup

CAMRA would like to thank the following for permission to reproduce photographs: 12 White Horse, Brancaster Staithe; Soughton Hall, Northop; 16 Burts Hotel, Melrose; 17 Tollgate Inn, Holt; 18 Queens Arms, Corton Denham; 19 Unicorn, Kingwood Common; 20 Talbot, Knightwick; 21 Stein Inn, Waternish; 23 Kirkstile Inn, Loweswater; 29 Knife & Cleaver, Houghton Conquest; 33 Swan, Inkpen; 38 Gamekeepers Lodge, Chesham; 45 Albion Inn, Chester; 56 New Inn, Veryan; 62 King's Arms, Hawkshead; 63 Kirkstile Inn, Loweswater; 65 King's Head Hotel, Ravenstonedale; 66-67 Cross Keys Hotel, Milnthorpe; 90-91 Anchor Inn, Ugborough; 94 Poachers Inn, Piddletrenthide; 98-99 Langdon Beck Hotel, Forest-in-Teesdale; 104 Donkey & Buskins, Layer-de-la-Haye; 106 White Horse Inn, Ridgewell; 120 Old Court Hotel, Symonds Yat; 122 Stagg Inn, Titley; 132 Chequers Inn, Laddingford; 134 Beacon, Rusthall; 140-141 Scarisbrick Hotel, Southport; 145 Stilton Cheese, Somerby; 149 Masons Arms Hotel, Louth; Houblon Inn, Oasby; 151 Harrison, King's Cross, London; 153 New Inn, St John's Wood, London; 163 Crown Hotel, Worthington; 165 White Horse, Brancaster Staithe; 174 Ship Inn, Oundle; 185-188 Unicorn, Kingwood Common; 196 Queen's Arms, Corton Denham; 198-199 Martlet Inn, Langford Budville; 210 Angel, Lavenham; 223 Five Bells, West Chiltington; 224 Ship Inn, Whitemans Green; 228 Old Bakery, Kenilworth; 237 Tollgate Inn, Holt; 246 Bants, Upton Snodsbury; 248 Bell Hotel, Driffield; 249 Ship Inn, Dunswell; 254-255 White Lion Inn, Cray; 256-257 Durham Ox, Crayke; 259 Duke of Wellington, Danby; 261 White Hart Inn, Hawes; 262 Blacksmith's Arms, Lastingham; 274 Tunnel End Inn, Marsden; 276 Alma Inn, Sowerby Bridge; 282-283 Burts Hotel, Melrose; 285 Castle Campbell Hotel, Dollar; 286 Winnock Hotel, Drymen; 291-292 Cross Keys Hotel, New Galloway; 301 Anderson, Fortrose; 302 Old Inn, Gairloch; 306 Stein Inn, Waternish; 311-312 Castlecary House Hotel, Castlecary; 316 Stair Inn, Stair; 317-318 Ardneil Hotel, Troon; 328 Baglan Hotel, Treherbert; 333 Wye Valley Hotel, Tintern; 337 New Inn, Bwlch

Additional photography: 15, 24-26, 69-70, 87-89, 212 Fran Nowak; 193, 238, 271 Vanessa Courtier; All other photographs from the CAMRA archive

Contents

INTRODUCTION

Welcome

It's no surprise that so many adventures, fictional and in real life, start in a pub. Centuries ago inns were one of the few places where travellers, sometimes weeks on the road, could lay their weary heads.

In the 14th century Chaucer's pilgrims on their way to Canterbury stayed at several pubs along the way. It is amusing to note that ale loosened their tongues to tell their tales, just as it does in the public bar today.

Dickens' novels abound with fabulous pubs, often in the context of travel and holidays – most notably in Pickwick Papers when that happy band of chums relished each arrival at a carefully chosen tavern where a roaring fire, hearty victuals and bed for the night awaited.

Jamaica Inn by du Maurier is a prime example of a pub where a spine chilling yarn of smuggling and murder unfolds – and surely the Hobbits had a final merry pint in their local before they set out on the Ring quest?

Maybe this is why so many inns provide a room with a view today. Coaching inns, some dating back to the 16th, 17th and 18th centuries, still stand in pretty old town squares or on a jutting headland or winding road over the moor where coaches no longer go because the modern version is racing along a motorway.

Whatever the reason, in this guide you will find B&B pubs in some spectacular settings. Overlooking mountains and lochs in Scotland, granite outcrops and still lakes in Cumbria, valleys in Wales. There is the pub where you can see the sun rising in a blaze of glory over Morecambe Bay, the pub 1,000 feet up on Snake Pass in the Peak District, the pub on the Isle of Skye; not the sort of location where you find the modern chains of soulless identi-rooms.

These purpose-built hotels are often at motorway service areas or by retail parks on the edge of town – while pubs are in places people want to be and provide real ale, good food, and a bit of idiosyncrasy. Here you will find character and diversity and, of course, well kept pints of real ale – sometimes in a pub with its own brewery or one of the increasing number to offer beers from the region or local micro-breweries.

As we worry about climate change and air travel, the sort of inns you can visit in this guide provide the ultimate incentive to stay in the UK. If summers are going to be as hot as they have been in recent years, why go to the Med when you can stay here at a friendly harbourside pub, a thatched Cotswold inn or weathered hostelry in the Yorkshire Dales?

If a city break appeals, you'll find pubs in centres from York to Birmingham, Glasgow to London, Durham to Oxford, including a few on CAMRA's national inventory of pubs with notable historic interiors.

And as you cut air miles, you can cut food miles. A growing number of pubs in this guide source local produce even for breakfast. It would be good to see more – there are still pubs where you wake up to baked beans and tomatoes out of tins, frozen hash browns, bland mass-produced sausages and watery bacon. Let this be a wake up call to those publicans. Many of your competitors are now seeking out regional black pudding, meaty bangers from their butcher, locally-cured bacon, free-range eggs from farms. Full marks to those publicans who take the trouble to prepare real porridge, and offer grilled kippers, locally-smoked poached haddock or salmon with scrambled eggs as alternatives to the full English.

The majority of accommodation in this guide is now en-suite; nearly all have TVs, tea and coffee trays, even Internet connection. Pubs are moving with the times. But fulsome facilities never make up for poor standards of cleanliness. A pub room can be basic and simple and guests will not mind – as long as the bed is comfortable, sheets and pillow cases freshly laundered, furniture and paintwork gleaming, the carpet thoroughly vacuumed, bathroom pristine and hygienic.

The bedroom may have beams and a four poster – and we love that – but dust and dinginess should never be confused with character. How unpleasant is it to wrestle open a sticking wardrobe door and find a couple of wire coat hangers and a folded old blanket? Why are mirrors sometimes blotchy or precariously balanced – or missing altogether?

No-frills travel chains may be bland but they do get the basics right – a set standard of cleanliness, hanging space for clothes, lights where you need them, including by the bed. And no clutter. It's a fine line between boring, empty surfaces and wall-to-wall bric-a-brac with no space to empty your bag. Pictures of local views or history on the walls are lovely, so is helpful information about places to visit – but not a selection of the landlady's cast off romantic novels.

Pubs are not doing enough to help the less physically able. It is too easy to use the get-out clause of an unwieldy old building as an excuse to do the minimum, or nothing. Even when licensees boast that all rooms have recently been renovated, or add a new accommodation annexe, too often no provision is made for wheelchair users or those with disabilities, or just one token room is adapted. When pubs do offer wheelchair accessible rooms, guests with special needs are still advised to check that the accommodation is appropriate for them.

More pubs are achieving wheelchair access into the bar and public rooms (albeit not always the WC, no joke when you've had a beer), so what's the message – 'You can come in for a pint and a ploughman's but you can't stay the night'?

As guest accommodation gets ever more expensive in the UK, especially in comparison with French leave across the Channel, on the whole pubs are competing well. A fair number of pubs in Beer, Bed and Breakfast are still charging under £55 a night for a double en-suite room; some peg the price at around £20 per person, generally those with shared bathrooms. And when you consider that in the majority of cases this includes a full, cooked breakfast it's a bargain compared to the budget chains, where food is an added extra.

There are some pubs that now charge a very high price indeed for a room – sometimes, of course, because it is a four-star hotel in a prime location that happens to be committed to great beers in the bar. It's all down to value for money. If a publican is charging upwards of £120 per night for a room, as some do, then the whole experience has to be comparable to a luxury hotel or a chic country house destination.

Thank goodness there is this richness of choice, from the little hillside inn with just one letting room to the real ale hotel with 40 rooms. Whatever your pleasure, you'll find it in these pages.

In our regulated lives, adventure is getting harder to find. In planning a B&B pub crawl you won't be buying a package holiday from a tour operator, you'll be going on a safari that could take you to some far-flung places...in your very own country.

The adventure starts here. Cheers!

Jill Adam

Susan Nowak

HOW TO USE THIS GUIDE

Pub listings are arranged alphabetically by county in England and Wales, and by region in Scotland. Some counties have been combined, for instance Lancashire & Merseyside and Fife & Tayside. County names appear at the top of each page. Greater Manchester appears under M, Greater London appears under L, East and West Sussex are under S and the four counties of Yorkshire under Y. West Midlands appears under W. The maps at the back of the book will help readers locate pubs, but are no substitute for a decent road map. Rooms are listed as single, double, twin or family rooms. In most cases pubs do not have single rooms and many, unfortunately, do not offer reductions for single occupancy of a double room. A family room may be a room with at least three single beds, a double and a single or bunks, or simply a double room where an extra bed can be added. Cots are sometimes available (check when booking).

Locality		DODDISCOMBSLEIGH
Pub name	☆	**Nobody Inn**
Address		EX6 7PS
Directions	▶	Off A38, 3 miles from Exeter racecourse
Telephone	T	(01647) 252394
Fax	F	(01647) 252978
E mail	E	info@nobodyinn.co.uk
Website	W	nobodyinn.co.uk
Real ales available		Otter Ale; guest beer
Accommodation		Five double, two twin rooms, five en-suite
Price range	£	£-£££
Main meals served		Snacks and meals daily, lunchtime and evening
Credit cards accepted		Accepted
Facilities		Q ♣ P

KEY TO SYMBOLS

☆ Outstanding pub for beer / bed / breakfast

Real fire

Q Quiet pub

Pub family room

Outdoor drinking area

Public bar

Wheelchair access to public areas

♣ Traditional pub games

Real draught cider

P Pub car park

Oversized lined pint glasses

On bus route

Near rail station

Every effort is made to ensure the accuracy of information contained in this Guide, but no responsibility can be accepted for errors and it is inevitable that some pubs will change their character during the currency of this Guide.

PRICES

Pubs often charge per room, rather than per person and for the purpose of this book we have given price bands which refer to charges per room, per night, based on two people sharing, for bed and breakfast (usually a cooked meal) as follows. If the rate given is for the room only (no breakfast), we say so on the individual entry.

£ Under £55 ££ £55-£75 £££ £75-£100 ££££ Over £100

Children sharing a parent's room are generally charged a reduced rate or are included in a family room price that is normally higher than for a double/twin. In some cases no charge is made at all for young children. Some pubs quote on the spot, according to the number and ages of the children. Single rooms are usually cheaper than doubles/twins; single people occupying a double room are sometimes charged the full room price, but many pubs offer a reduction. Some pubs accept pet dogs and may charge for their accommodation – always check in advance. Any prices quoted in the text were correct at time of writing but may be subject to change.

BREAKFAST AND OTHER MEALS

Most of the pubs listed include breakfast in the room price. This is usually a full (cooked) English breakfast, but may be a simpler continental style, or a different choice. Some pubs charge just for the room, as they believe customers should have the option of paying for breakfast only if required; while others offer a complete breakfast menu and you pay for what you order. The majority of inns featured here offer meals other than breakfast. Some pubs have restaurants with excellent reputations, often under the command of a top chef. Many are humbler establishments offering simple pub fare of pies, pasties and ploughman's lunches. At popular destinations you may need to book lunch or dinner in advance. Some of the pubs listed also feature in CAMRA's Good Pub Food so they make ideal culinary destinations.

SPECIAL NEEDS

Unfortunately very few pubs have rooms adapted for wheelchair users. This is mainly because of the inaccessibility of first-floor bedrooms, particularly in old buildings, where it is impractical to install a lift. Many old pubs cannot even admit the wheelchair-bound into their bars. However, it is disappointing that, even when new accommodation is added, not enough consideration is given to the needs of less able guests. Some pubs state that their accommodation is suitable for guests with disabilities, but in fact this often only implies that there is a ground-floor room, which although accessible, might not be specially adapted. For this reason, where we indicate rooms may be suitable for guests with disabilities, we would strongly recommend that you check facilities meet your requirements when booking.

NB - The symbol for wheelchair access at the foot of each entry simply indicates that the public areas are accessible, and even then the pub may not have a dedicated WC. It does not apply to guest rooms unless stated in the accommodation details.

STAR RATED PUBS

Look out for the pubs listed below, these pubs are star rated to pinpoint some of the very best pub accommodation and real ale in Britain.

ENGLAND

Swan, Inkpen, Berkshire

Ivy House, Chalfont, Buckinghamshire

Farndon Arms, Farndon, Cheshire

Trengilly Wartha, Nancenoy, Cornwall

Driftwood Spars, St Agnes, Cornwall

Manor Arms, Broughton, Cumbria

Queens Head, Troutbeck, Cumbria

Bay Horse, Ulverston, Cumbria

Old Poets, Ashover, Derbyshire

Mill Wheel, Hartshorne, Derbyshire

Masons Arms, Branscombe, Devon

Ring O Bells, Chagford, Devon

Nobody Inn, Doddiscombsleigh, Devon

Maltsters Arms, Tuckenhay, Devon

Victoria, Durham

Sun Inn, Dedham, Essex

Bell, Horndon, Essex

King's Head, Bledington, Gloucestershire

Green Dragon, Cockleford, Gloucestershire

New Inn, Gloucester, Gloucestershire

Halfway House, Brenchley, Kent

Beacon, Rusthall, Kent

Red Pump, Bashall Eaves, Lancashire

White Hart, Lydgate, Greater Manchester

Berkeley Arms, Southport, Merseyside

White Horse, Brancaster Staithe, Norfolk

King's Head, Great Bircham, Norfolk

Odfellows, Shifnal, Shropshire

Queen's Arms, Corton Denham, Somerset

Angel, Lavenham, Suffolk

Anchor, Walberswick, Suffolk

Griffin Inn, Fletching, E Sussex

Keelmans Lodge, Newburn, Tyne & Wear

Old Fourpenny Shop, Warwick, Warwickshire

Dove, Corton, Wiltshire

Tollgate Inn, Holt, Wiltshire

Check Inn, North Wroughton, Wiltshire

Admiral Rodney, Berrow, Worcestershire

Talbot, Knightwick, Worcestershire

Bants, Upton Snodbury, Worcestershire

Ferry, Cawood, N Yorkshire

New Inn, Cropton, N Yorkshire

Duke of Wellington, Danby, N Yorkshire

Cover Bridge Inn, East Witton, N Yorkshire

Maypole, Long Preston, N Yorkshire

Strines, Bradfield, S Yorkshire

Beehive, Bradford, W Yorkshire

Haworth Old Hall, Haworth, W Yorkshire

SCOTLAND

Burts, Melrose, Borders

Anderson, Fortrose, Highlands

Fisherman's Tavern, Broughty Ferry, Tayside

WALES

Angel, Abergavenny, Gwent

Clytha Inn, Clytha, Gwent

Cherry Tree, Tintern, Gwent

Soughton Hall, Northop, NE Wales

Bull's Head, Beaumaris, NW Wales

Kinmel Arms, St George, NW Wales

STAR RATED FOR ACCOMMODATION

Driftwood Spars, St Agnes, Cornwall – 'Old Cornwall in the new Millennium' is the pub's maxim. Its wonderful guest rooms, beautifully decorated in soft shades of blue, mostly enjoy sea views; some have a private garden, while the family suite has its own deck.

Mill Wheel, Hartsbourne, Derbyshire – luxury at budget prices, under £50 for a double en-suite room in recently opened cottage accommodation in a converted millhouse pub with working water wheels; serves full ranges of Oakham and Tollgate breweries' ales.

Victoria, Durham – on CAMRA's National Inventory of Heritage Pubs, the Victoria has a listed interior retaining the original layout of snug and two rooms, with a separately listed balcony above the bar, authentic Victoriana, a great breakfast, high quality bedrooms and off street parking close to Durham Cathedral.

Sun Inn, Dedham, Essex – the unloved inn was restored with panache in 2003 to provide guests with enormous beds in rooms with neutral fabrics and stylish fixtures and fittings; the bathrooms are luxurious, too.

White Horse, Brancaster Staithe, Norfolk – the pub's plain frontage is deceptive; eight lovely bedrooms are in a curved annexe built into the contours of the land with their own private terraces overlooking the tidal marshes; a birdwatcher's paradise, the guest room at the top of the pub is equipped with its own telescope.

OPPOSITE, ABOVE LEFT AND RIGHT: White Horse, Brancaster Staithe, Norfolk. BOTTOM: Soughton Hall, Northop, NE Wales

Duke of Wellington, Danby, North Yorkshire – in wonderful walking country on the River Esk, the pub gets top marks for providing excellent ramblers' leaflets of different walks starting from the pub to places including Danby Castle, Beacon Hill and over the high moors to Little Fryup Dale (plus big fry up breakfast!), with safety and countryside conservation tips.

Strines, Bradfield, South Yorkshire – in a spectacular away-from-it-all setting 1,000 feet above sea level on Snake Pass in the Peak District – but conveniently close to Bradfield Brewery. Four-poster bedrooms with patchwork quilts and breakfast brought to your room in a pub where parts date back to the 13th century.

Old Hall Inn, Haworth, West Yorkshire – grandeur that won't break the bank at an imposing Tudor manor house with studded oak front door, mullioned windows and baronial bar. Just two beautiful letting rooms in Yorkshire Tourist Board's Yorkshire Pub of the Year 2006, in Haworth, close to all the Brontë visitor sites.

Soughton Hall, Northop, NE Wales – beautiful country house hotel, originally a bishop's palace. Expensive, but worth it for the gracious surroundings. The rooms are individually named and styled, with antique furnishings and sumptuous fabrics.

Kinmel Arms, St George, NW Wales – a stylish destination, both in the public areas and the guest accommodation. There are four luxurious suites where the individual décor in each room is influenced by paintings created by owner Tim Watson; each room has a private balcony or patio.

STAR RATED FOR BEER

Old Poets' Corner, Ashover, Derbyshire – a wide range of well-kept real ales from their own small brewery plus regional and micro-breweries, as well as Belgian beers; the Old Poets Corner bedecks its beams with hops, holds seasonal beer festivals, and was local CAMRA Pub of the Year in the national Village of the Year 2006.

Halfway House, Brenchley, Kent – when the landlord took over here a few years ago he rearranged the pub's layout to give space at the back of the bar for the casks as all his beers are on gravity dispense. A changing range of mostly local ales is supplemented by Kentish cider; two beer festivals are held annually.

Berkeley Arms, Southport, Merseyside – eight real ales are always guaranteed at the Berkeley, served in prime condition, from a beautifully balanced beer list at one of the area's very few outlets for Hawkshead Bitter. Pair them with the pub's pizzas hand-made in the kitchen down to the yeast dough for the base.

The Anchor, Walberswick, Suffolk – legendary Cellarman Mark Dorber ensures the cask ales which have travelled just a few miles down the coast from Adnams Brewery are enjoyed in their prime, and matches Belgian, Czech, Bavarian, Dutch and American beers with the fabulous local produce on his wife Sophie's menu.

Old Fourpenny Shop, Warwick, Warwickshire – one house beer – RCH Pitchfork – but around 1,500 different guest beers have been drunk at the Old Fourpenny, 16 consecutive years in the Good Beer Guide. Four different teas at breakfast, too – and handy for Warwick Castle.

Check Inn, North Wroughton, Wilts – check in and check out the bar without delay! CAMRA's national Pub of the Year runner-up in 2005 always offers 10 real ales and the range changes on a daily basis, with a good smattering of local brews.

The Talbot, Knightwick, Worcestershire – home of Teme Valley Brewery serving its regular ales This, That and T'Other as well as seasonal beers alongside some of the best pub food in the UK, with home-made bread and black pudding at breakfast time. The 14th-century hotel hosts an annual Green Hop beer festival of ales made from the new season's hops.

Cover Bridge Inn, East Witton, North Yorkshire – this multiple CAMRA award winner is often referred to as a 'mini beer exhibition', stocking an excellent range of Yorkshire ales from Black Sheep, Copper Dragon and Taylor, plus three guest beers. The B&B is good value, leaving you plenty to spend on the ale.

Anderson, Fortrose, Highlands – owned by an American beer writer, the Anderson is a mecca for real ale lovers. He has showcased over 100 independent breweries in three years and also stocks more than 80 Belgian bottled beers, plus a good choice of malt whiskies.

Fisherman's Tavern, Broughty Ferry, Tayside – a favourite of local CAMRA members, the beer choice here can change daily. It stocks the largest range of real ales in the Dundee area and regularly offers brews from local micros, Moulin and Inveralmond.

OPPOSITE: Anderson, Fortrose, Highlands

the
ANDERSON
01381 620 236
UNION STREET
NEW TAPAS MENU
in the Whisky Bar!

STAR RATED FOR BREAKFAST

Ivy House, Chalfont, Bucks – an award-winning pub in the Chilterns where the breakfast menu offers everything from simple scrambled eggs on toast, to a full English, taking in omelettes and toasted waffles with maple syrup on the way; other options such as a meat and cheese platter are available if ordered in advance.

Trengilly Wartha, Nancenoy, Cornwall – a two page breakfast menu at a multi-award winning hotel where chef/landlord Mike Maguire believes in "sustainable and sympathetic food tourism". Black pudding, bacon and sausages are locally made, the kippers from Porthleven, sea trout and haddock locally smoked, Seville marmalade and damson jam made on the premises.

Queen's Head, Trout Beck, Cumbria – breakfast in the shadow of towering Garburn Pass, on Welsh rarebit flavoured with real ale from the bar, rich porridge with a nip of whisky, toasted banana bread topped with bananas, honey and toasted almonds, pancakes with scrambled eggs, crisp bacon and maple syrup – oh, and the full English including black pudding produced in the pub kitchen.

Bay Horse, Ulverston, Cumbria – be dazzled by dawn coming up over Morecambe Bay, then by a trencherman's breakfast of griddled kidneys, white as well as black pudding, Cumberland sausages, bacon from famous Woodall's of Waberthwaite, garnished with fried apple rings – butter carved into swans, and home-made lemon curd.

Burts, Melrose, Borders

Tollgate Inn, Holt, Wiltshire

Red Pump, Bashall Eaves, Lancs – set in the Ribble Valley, this is one of the few pubs to offer proper kedgeree for breakfast, with smoked haddock and basmati rice, or you can try the 'Lancashire Hit', including Bowland bacon, sausages made to the inn's own recipe and local free range eggs; the jams and preserves are home made.

Tollgate Inn, Holt, Wiltshire – a gem of a pub serving a gem of a breakfast with provenance on all the ingredients – locally smoked kippers, free range eggs from the pub's own hens, Valley Smoke House smoked salmon with scrambled eggs on toasted brioche, Sandridge Farm bacon, Church Farm sausages, Bury black pudding, sautéed Bromham new potatoes, home-made bread, jam and marmalade.

Bants, Upton Snodbury, Worcs – you have to pay a supplement for the 'luxury' breakfast here but it is more adventurous than most. Choose between a smoked salmon and prawn platter with a glass of Buck's Fizz or medallions of fillet steak with fried eggs, sauté potatoes and mushrooms, washed down with a glass of port.

Clytha Arms, Clytha, Gwent – the former dower house of the Clytha Estate offers a full Welsh breakfast. They must be a hungry lot, the Welsh, to manage it all: wild boar sausage, black pudding, laver bread and cockles as well as the usual eggs and bacon; they offer a vegetarian alternative, too.

Burts, Melrose, Borders – the hotel caters for shooting parties and provides substantial breakfasts to fortify its guests for a day out in the fresh air. An excellent buffet offers fruit, oatcakes, yogurt and fruit compotes, then there's porridge, grilled kippers or a full cooked breakfast featuring bacon, sausages and black pudding supplied by Ramsay's of Carluke.

Anderson, Fortrose, Highlands – choose from Scottish, English or American breakfasts at a pub where the landlord is also an American beer writer, his wife a New Orleans chef. Free range, organic eggs come from two local farms, sausages, black pudding and hog's pudding or a slice of fried haggis from local butchers, decorated with fresh strawberries. Muesli, marmalade and jam are home-made, Free Trade coffee beans freshly roasted in the kitchen.

GO TO BED IN A BREWERY

If a hop pillow ensures sweet dreams, then going to bed in a brewery must surely turn you into the Sleeping Beauty.

The number of micro-breweries in the UK grows each year, and quite a few of them are in pubs. But how many pubs brew their own beer and provide B&B accommodation as well? Only a handful, so it is well worth seeking them out in the pages of this guide to enjoy the ultimate experience for real ale lovers – a night spent under the same roof as the place where the beer is actually brewed.

Not literally the same roof – it's probably across the yard – but I did once visit a pub where the ale was brewed in a sort of tower brewery in the pub itself, with the fermenting vessels next to the guests' bedrooms. A night to remember!

And there is the comforting knowledge that if you have a winter break in a remote brew pub halfway up a craggy peak and it snows heavily, you can't be cut off from your pint. And that's no small beer.

So who are these heroes who set the yeast fermenting before they rush into the pub kitchen to fry up a brewer's breakfast, then change the duvet covers and run a feather duster along the picture frames?

Well, one of them resides at the Isle of Purbeck Brewery on Studland Bay looking across to the Isle of Wight, where you get sea air and a room with a view as well. The brewery is in the ground of Bankes Arms Country Inn, set in a picture postcard village at the start of the Jurassic Coast.

Beers with names like Fossil Fuel, Solar Power and Studland Bay Wrecked as well as IPA are produced in a 10-barrel plant formerly in Poole Brewery. And if you're not content with those four (plus winter's Thermal Cheer), the old stone inn provides three frequently-changing guest ales too. Find one to match the smoked mackerel at breakfast.

Far away up north, as you're rolling out of bed at the New Inn, Cropton in North Yorkshire, they'll be rolling out the barrels at their award-winning Cropton Brewery. Beer has been brewed in Cropton since 1613, illegally at first, with wrongdoers sent to York gaol. It is believed

that local women helped, and these 'ale wives' were roundly cursed for a bad brew. In 1984 the craft returned to the village when the New Inn's family owners founded their brewery in the cellar. A decade later their purpose-built brewery was established on farmland behind, and within a year production doubled.

The brewery has a visitor centre and tours, so there is plenty to see. And after a day spent in some of the country's most beautiful walking country, you can choose from the 10 different ales they brew including award-winning Two Pints and Scoresby Stout – and take some away with you, bottle-conditioned.

One of the smartest brewery pubs offering B&B is the Keelman, home of the Big Lamp Brewery, in a converted grade II listed water pumping station in a country park by the Tyne. Launched in 1982, Big Lamp relocated to its present 55-barrel plant in 1997 and is the oldest micro-brewery in the North East, producing some half dozen regular ales plus seasonal beers, including award-winning Summerhill Stout, Prince Bishop Ale, and Blackout at 11 per cent. Should it produce that effect, you can collapse into bed in the purpose-built guest lodge.

Strines Inn does not have its own brewery, but does stock beer from Bradfield Brewery based at Watt House Farm four miles away. With only three double rooms, this is a splendid place to spend a night. Though close to Sheffield, it is high up on Snake Pass in the Peak District national park surrounded by uplifting moorland scenery. Strines is an old English word meaning 'meeting of the water' and the inn is exactly 1,000 feet above sea level, surrounded by eight reservoirs. Originally a manor house, parts date back to 1275, though

Talbot, Knightwick, Worcestershire

most of it was built in the 16th century, and the lovely bedrooms have four posters with patchwork quilts, with breakfast served in the room at a table for two.

During your stay you'll enjoy a visit to family-run Bradfield Brewery, originally a dairy farm. Crystal clear Peak District water from its own borehole at Millstone Grit is used to produce the Farmers ales – Bitter, Blonde, Brown Cow, Milk Stout, Belgian Blue and Pale Ale, two of them also bottle conditioned. There is a brewery shop open Monday to Saturday afternoons, and a new room upstairs where you can sample the wares.

The words 'romantic' and 'brewery' seldom go together, but perhaps they do at the Moulin Hotel just outside Pitlochry, amid lochs and peaks on the way to the Highlands. Pretty, intimate bedrooms with four poster beds are in the 'newer' part of the hotel, added a century ago, but Moulin Brewery opened in 1995 in a converted stable to coincide with the hotel's 300th anniversary. Four ales are brewed, a straw-coloured Light at 3.7 per cent, Braveheart, malty Ale of Atholl, and Old Remedial, a robust, dark brown beer. Perhaps they should introduce a Belgian style red so they can call it Moulin Rouge. You can enjoy their beers both here and at sister hotel the Atholl Arms in Blair Atholl, near Blair Castle. Brewery tours are available and the shop is open daily from noon, where you can buy a bottle-conditioned version of Ale of Atholl to take away.

No serious brewery B&B tourist should miss the chance of staying at the Talbot in Knightwick, Worcestershire. A local CAMRA Pub of the Year, it has a kitchen garden supplying some of its award-winning food, fine produce from local producers, comfortable en-suite rooms, outstanding breakfasts with black pudding and preserves made in the kitchen, and the Teme Valley micro-brewery at the back. When the owners opened the brewery in 1997 it amused them to call their beers This and That as in, 'I'll have a pint of this and a half of that'. T'Other was then added. The joke is slightly lost in CAMRA guides where beers are listed by strength, so appear as Teme Valley T'Other, This and That, but never mind.

You can feast on fabulous old-fashioned dishes, then sit by a roaring fire sipping the regular and seasonal ales. An especially good time for beer buffs to visit is early October when the brewery hosts a Green Hop festival of beers made with the new season's hops.

HOLIDAY AT HOME

WHY go jetting off to Prague, Budapest, Milan or Vienna for a trendy city break, adding to the destruction of the planet, when you can let the train take the strain and explore our own historic centres, with the added bonus of a British pint? You can easily spend a few days in places such as York, Canterbury, Chester and Oxford – all with superb B&B pubs in this guide – and still not see everything there is to see.

By shopping around for rail fares as you would for airline tickets, you can often find a good deal. Even going by road to discover a rural idyll or Beer-on-Sea is still 'greener' than flying abroad, especially if you fill your car with friends or family. And should you want to tour pubs at the far end of the UK – and you will once you've taken a look at these pages – consider travelling by train then hiring a car to stay at out-of-the-way pubs.

Want to shop till your drop, enjoy architecture and culture, or go to a show or a play? A city break can offer all that, and the sort of pubs that create memories. Let's begin in England's number one tourist destination, London. Sanctuary House Hotel in Westminster is a capital place to stay, at the very heart of where it's at, close to the Houses of Parliament, Westminster, Buckingham Palace and the London Eye.

While others seek out hotels or boarding houses in the suburbs, your nearest tube is St James's Park, and you can collapse at the end of a day's sightseeing with a pint of Fuller's. This traditional Victorian-style pub offers a glimpse of history, with a mural depicting the story of the monks who found refuge there. And you too can find sanctuary in one of the beautifully refurbished townhouse rooms upstairs.

Another place where the attractions are within walking distance is the Albion in Chester, a sight in its own right. Looking out onto the city wall, this beautifully preserved Victorian pub is a monument to the Great War – the passion of landlord Mike Mercer. Serving the sort of beers the troops liked to march on, the menu of delicious home cooking includes the kind of dishes

Stein Inn, Isle of Skye

they might have eaten, too – traditional Victorian-style boiled gammon with pease pudding, savoury minced beef and tatties, and their ever-popular McConickie's corned beef hash. Dine under a poster of Kitchener proclaiming 'England expects...' The pub's luxury guest accommodation was recently completed, and it is a great place to set out from to walk the city walls of historic Chester.

Another Victorian gem, this one with a silver star listing in CAMRA's national inventory of heritage pubs, is the Victoria Inn, just a few minutes' walk from Durham Cathedral. The listed interior retains the original layout – a tiny snug and two main rooms with original features including three coal fires and separately listed balcony above the bar. Essentially a beer house, the pub provides no food other than for its B&B guests who are offered a hearty spread of local sausages, black pudding and free-range eggs.

In Warwick take your ease at a haven for real ale lovers, the Old Fourpenny Shop – 16 consecutive years in CAMRA's Good Beer Guide. With one regular ale, RCH Pitchfork, its guest beer tally is now around 1,500. Near the racecourse, the inn was once popular with canal navvies for cheap coffee and rum – hence the name. Before you head for Warwick Castle close by, fortify yourself from a huge cold buffet table plus the full English, grilled kippers or poached smoked haddock.

If dreaming spires are your pleasure, what better than a handsome real ale pub slap on the Thames near the centre of Oxford? The Head of the River at Folly Bridge has a big beer garden attracting both tourists and students, with guest accommodation overlooking the river.

Or follow Chaucer's pilgrims (a group renowned for enjoying a drop of ale along the way) to Canterbury and the King's Head, a grade II listed building 10 minutes' walk from the cathedral and city centre.

During a Glasgow city break you'll be spoiled for great pubs to drink in, but for B&B it has to be the inimitable Babbity Bowster (a lewd 18th-century dance). Enjoy gutsy Scottish and French fare and a changing range of Scottish beers in a beautiful bar with high ceilings designed by Robert Adam, warmed by a peat fire.

If stirring moorland and high hills beckon, set off on a B&B crawl of North Yorkshire inns, four of them star rated in this guide. Start in York at the Masons Arms on the river Ouse. In a super city full of tourist accommodation, the Masons scores for its friendly welcome, good guest beers, outstanding home-made food and location. If you're driving, it has the bonus of a private car park. But it is within walking distance of the station, city walls, Clifford's Tower, Jorvik Viking Centre and most of York's historic and tourist attractions, not forgetting York brewery. You'll need at least two days here.

Those who arrive by rail will then need to hire a car, and drive about 15 miles south to Cawood. The Ferry Inn, also on the Ouse, boasts five real ales, historic connections to Cardinal Wolsey, budget-priced attractive rooms, and one of the most imaginative breakfast menus in the guide.

From here head back up the A19 to York, east round the ring road, along the A64 to Malton, then the A169 to Pickering, left onto the A170, and Cropton is signed on the right. Here you'll find the New Inn housing Cropton Brewery (see brew pubs feature, page 18).

Choose your own route over the North York Moors through stunning vistas to Danby and the Duke of Wellington on the River Esk (south of the A171). A recruiting post during the Napoleonic Wars, today you'll find a warm welcome, comfortable rooms and interesting ales including Copper Dragon Scotts 1816. It is also a base for splendid rambles, best discovered with the help of the pub's excellent leaflets of walks to Danby Castle, Beacon Hill and across the high moors to Little Fryup Dale.

It is a short but picturesque drive to the King's Head at Newton-under-Roseberry, North East Tourism's best B&B 2006. Look across to 'the Matterhorn of Cleveland' as you tuck into a breakfast that won an award for use of local produce.

Our island nation is encircled by sensational seaside pubs, be they erstwhile smugglers' haunts on dramatic Cornish cliffs, or holding lonely vigil on the Isle of Skye. But for our final stop in this beer tour, we'll head for the jolly Suffolk coast.

The Anchor at Walberswick is the relatively new venture of Mark Dorber and his chef wife, Sophie. Mark ran one of the UK's most famous pubs, the White Horse at Parsons Green in London, until 2006. The Anchor is fast gaining its own recognition for fabulous food created by Sophie from local produce, game and fish, matched with English, Belgian and US beers. It's the sort of place you associate with childhood seaside holidays of bracing beach walks and sand castles. Adults can enjoy their own bracing walk to quaint Southwold over the estuary where Mark's favourite brewery, Adnams, produces the cask ales meticulously cared for in his cellar.

Kirkstile Inn, Loweswater, Cumbria

BREAKFAST – THE FULL MONTY

As we try to lead healthier lifestyles, for many of us the traditional cooked breakfast has been abandoned in favour of cereals, fruit, porridge or just toast. But there is nothing like the smell of bacon frying, and we can enjoy the full English much more as an occasional treat. And when better to indulge than during a weekend break – especially if we've slightly over indulged the ale the night before.

There is nothing better than a fine English breakfast to start the day: how sad, then, that this simple meal often falls very short of fine. Sausages, bacon, tomato, mushrooms, eggs and fried bread. The basics. How can you go wrong?

Let's begin with the bangers. We all know how easy it is to find good sausages today. Made by your local butcher perhaps, or a regional speciality – Cumberland, Lincoln, Suffolk... So why do so many inn keepers bulk buy cheap and nasty bangers, with unpleasant pink fillings that look and taste like plastic, when real sausages cost so little more?

Likewise bacon – do you prefer mass-produced rashers that fill the pan with watery scum, or locally cured bacon from a free-range rare breed pig? Some small specialist producers even put beer in the curing liquor.

Tomatoes – fresh, not tinned, please, and cooked until slightly caramelised to bring out the sweetness. Even in pricey hotels let alone motorway service stations, I so often push an almost raw tomato to the side of my plate. Please don't serve canned or frozen mushrooms. Fresh button fungi are fine but, for my taste, a big flat portobello goes best with breakfast. Fried bread should be cut from a decent loaf, then shallow-fried until crisp – not the deep-fried brittle slice you can't even break, let alone eat.

And why do the majority of B&Bs serve toast alongside the fry-up? Toast is for after, with delicious local honey or home-made marmalade. Does it have to be white sliced? Why can't we have a thick wedge of fresh granary bread to spread with butter (from a little pot, not foil wrapped rectangle)?

Queen's Head, Troutbeck, Cumbria and breakfast (above right)

I'm glad to say you will find plenty of pubs in this guide providing good, hearty breakfasts that will set you up for the day, and keep you going through a host of energetic activities or sight seeing.

But I would like to see a lot more imagination on the pub breakfast table. Where is the kedgeree? Where are the griddled kidneys, the coddled eggs, the potato pancakes with slices of home-baked ham? And with today's new emphasis on food miles and local produce, why are more pubs not taking advantage of our brilliant British charcuterie to dish up a breakfast featuring the tastes of their region?

Happily, a fair number of publicans do make that extra effort to seek out their locally-made sausages and black pudding. In fact, some even make their own – take a bow the Queen's Head at Troutbeck in Cumbria. When you've opened the curtains on a stunning view across to Garburn Pass, it's down to breakfast. Delicious pork sausages and black pudding are made in the kitchen, and one of the Cumbrian real ales served in the bar is an ingredient of grain mustard rarebit topped with a large field mushroom. Of course, you might prefer toasted banana bread with fresh bananas, honey and toasted almonds, or pancakes topped with scrambled eggs, crisp bacon and maple syrup. And you can request a drop of whisky in the rich porridge cooked with cream and maple syrup.

Wherever you breakfast in the UK, so often it's simply the full English. But at one place in Wales you're sure of a full Welsh – the Clytha Arms at Clytha in Gwent. At a pub that has won local CAMRA pub of the year more often than any other, landlord Andrew Canning not only makes his own cider and perry but also finds time to cook a breakfast that puts laverbread (Welsh seaweed) and cockles on the same plate as wild boar sausage, black pudding, eggs and bacon. For vegetarians he makes laverbread rissoles and marmite fritters. If you fancy fish, kippers and smoked haddock are on the menu, too.

At The Anderson, a remarkable pub at Fortrose up in the Highlands, you have the option of a full Scottish, English or American breakfast. Landlord Jim Anderson, formerly a US beer writer, told me: 'We like to use local produce as long as we think it's the best'. So the hog's

Breakfast at the Anderson, Fortrose, Highlands

pudding, a creamy mix of oatmeal and suet, comes from Sandy Jack in the village, but the black pudding comes from Charles Macleod in Stornoway over on the Isle of Lewis. The sausages are made by Gordon Moir along the coast in Rosemarkie, but the dry cure bacon is Dutch because Jim thinks it tastes better than any he's found close to home. Guests often get a slice of haggis fried with their breakfast, too, as well as two free-range eggs, baby tomatoes, delicious white and brown toast wrapped in a warm serviette, a few fresh strawberries and coffee made from Fair Trade beans roasted in the hotel kitchen.

Bob Lyons, chef/proprietor of the Bay Horse in Ulverston, Cumbria, fills a whole platter with local produce – delicious little kidneys, Cumberland sausages and beer-cured bacon from famous Woodalls of Waberthwaite, all garnished with fried apple rings. The butter arrives carved into two graceful swans, and you can spread home-made lemon curd or marmalade on your toast, while gazing across Morecambe Bay.

At the Swan, Inkpen in Berkshire, which has its own herd of cattle, breakfast is both local and organic down to the fruit juice and porridge. Sausages are home made on the premises and sold in the pub's shop, along with the locally cured bacon. Another inn raising its own meat is the Queen's Arms at Corton Denham in Somerset where they keep pigs for sausages and bacon, and Maran hens lay eggs for breakfast.

Home-laid free-range eggs are on the menu at Tollgate Inn near Holt in Wiltshire too, and smoked salmon and kippers from Valley Smoke House nearby, as well as Sandridge Farm bacon and Church Farm sausages. Even the fried new potatoes are from Bromham, the jam and marmalade home-made.

But perhaps one of the most exciting breakfast menus is to be found at a modest pub on the Ouse in Yorkshire. At the Ferry Inn, Cawood, with just four guest rooms, for breakfast you can enjoy eggs Benedict, or honey-roast ham and poached eggs on a muffin, eggs Florentine of fresh baby spinach and poached eggs, smoked salmon with scrambled eggs and mushrooms on brown toast, or the full Monty if you must.

And if the pub has sought out local produce for your breakfast, it's a good indication that the ingredients for your evening meal won't have travelled too far to reach your plate either – and hopefully there will be a pint of local ale behind the bar.

England

Bedfordshire

ASTWICK

Tudor Oaks Lodge

1 Taylors Road, SG5 4AZ

- ▶ Alongside A1 northbound 1 mile past jct 10
- T (01462) 834133
- F (01462) 834133
- W tudoroakslodge.co.uk
- Beer range varies
- Eleven double, one twin, two single rooms, all en-suite
- £ ££-££££
- Lunchtime and evening meals
- Accepted

The buildings of this mock-Tudor pub, restaurant and lodge are set around an attractive courtyard. Chalet-style rooms are individually decorated, some featuring a four-poster bed and jacuzzi. The price of a room varies according to the facilities – one room has a deluxe bath/shower/sauna, with foot massager and aromatherapy – but all include TV and free Internet access. The rooms are on the ground floor so they are suitable for guests with limited mobility. Children are welcome.

A wide choice of real ales, often from East Anglian breweries such as Charles Wells or Nethergate and micro-breweries around the country, is served in the open plan, heavily beamed bar.

The restaurant offers excellent food, good enough to win the inn a place in CAMRA's Good Pub Food guide. Fresh fish and seafood such as oysters and lobster are specialities, but the chef also offers international cuisine including curries and Mediterranean dishes, and vegetarians and vegans can be catered for. At breakfast there is a choice of full English, eggs on toast, kippers or smoked salmon and scrambled eggs.

Q ❀ ♿ P

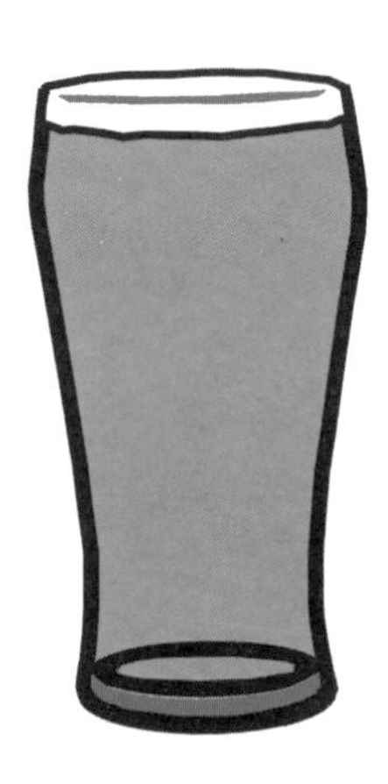

HOUGHTON CONQUEST

Knife & Cleaver

The Grove, MK45 3LA

- ▶ Off A6 5 miles S of Bedford
- T (01234) 740387
- F (01234) 740900
- W knifeandcleaver.com
- Bateman XB; Potton Village Bike
- Four double, four twin, one family room (all available as singles), all en-suite
- £ £££
- Snacks and meals daily, lunchtime and evening
- Accepted

This 17th-century country inn is believed to be the model for House Beautiful in Bunyan's Pilgrim's Progress. Across the fields from broad-leaved woodland, the Knife and Cleaver is near English Heritage's Wrest Park, Woburn stately home and safari park, the Shuttleworth old aircraft collection and the Swiss Gardens at Old Warden.

Accommodation is set in a flowery orchard garden. Fresh milk and home-made biscuits as well as tea and coffee are provided in en-suite rooms with satellite TV, direct dial phone with modem connection, hairdryer and refrigerator.

Three bedrooms in a converted stable block provide more spacious accommodation – all are at ground level, so wheelchair accessible, and all en-suites have a bath with power shower attachment. Two bedrooms are no-smoking; dogs are welcome but must stay in your room.

At breakfast you can try local sausages from Ingles of Ampthill as part of the full English, plus home-made marmalade and jam, prunes, apricots and grapefruit, as well as cereals. At other times enjoy an award-winning menu in the Victorian conservatory-style restaurant specialising in seafood from Loch Fyne oysters to silver bream and whole lobsters. There is an exciting and very reasonably priced bar menu, too.

Q P

IRELAND
Black Horse
SG17 5QL

▶ Off A600 between Shefford and Bedford, near Old Warden
T (01462) 811398
F (01462) 811398
W blackhorseireland.com
Fuller's London Pride; Potton Village Bike
Two en-suite double rooms
£ ££
Lunchtime and evening meals
Accepted

Theories abound as to how the tiny hamlet of Ireland got its name. It may have something to do with the Irish navvies who worked on the now long disused railway line. The Black Horse was a cottage until they arrived and needed refreshing after their labours, when it was converted into an ale house. It is now probably better known for its food, which enjoys a fine reputation, than the beer (although that is fine, too).

Much of the pub – the Oak Room and the Garden Room – is given over to dining and meals are also served in the bar. Full of character throughout, it features exposed brick and beams, a big fireplace and comfortable seating. The guest rooms, in an annexe, have their own entrances from the garden. Attractively decorated, they include a television, fridge, tea/coffee making facilities and a trouser press. Children are welcome.

Breakfast is continental-style: croissant and jam, fresh fruit and yogurt. Indulge in a three-course meal here the night before (the puddings are not to be missed) and you may not even be able to manage that.

The Shuttleworth Collection at Old Warden and Swiss Gardens are nearby.

P

SALFORD
Red Lion Hotel
Wavendon Road, MK17 8AZ

▶ Two miles north of M1 jct 13
T (01908) 583117
E redlionhotelmk@hotmail.com
Wells Eagle, Bombardier
Six double en-suite rooms, wheelchair accessible
£ £
Lunchtime and evening meals
Accepted

Close to the M1, the Red Lion is an ideal stop-off for motorway travellers, particularly if you have business in Milton Keynes. A small country pub on the outskirts of the village, it offers well furnished guest accommodation with three rooms in a 400-year-old cottage and another three in a converted stable block overlooking the apple orchard and pub garden; some rooms boast four-poster beds. Children are welcome to stay and the large garden has a safe play area. The pub has won awards for its food, so the breakfast comes from a recommended kitchen. You can choose from a full English or lighter continental meal.

This Charles Wells house has twice won the Morning Advertiser's Wine Pub of the Year, so expect a good choice of wine to accompany the excellent food. Meals can be taken in the dining room or the bar, a pleasant place to while away some time by the open fire with a pint.

Nearby Milton Keynes has much to offer visitors in the way of shops, theatre, cinema and the Snowdome for winter sports; Woburn is close by with its Safari Park and prestigious golf club.

P

STREATLEY

Chequers

171 Sharpenhoe Road, LU3 3PS

▶ Off A6 between Luton and Bedford
T (01582) 882072
F (01582) 883632
Greene King IPA, Abbot, Old Speckled Hen; guest beers
Five twin rooms, all en-suite
£ ££ (£30 single occupancy)
Lunchtime and evening meals
Accepted

Handy for Luton Airport and just four miles north of Luton town itself is the peaceful village of Streatley. The Chequers stands at the village centre, next to the church. The pub is Georgian but has been sympathetically extended. A short taxi ride from Luton or Harlington railway stations (London 40 minutes), the pub is a more attractive option than the airport or town-centre hotels. Junction 12 of the M1 is just a few minutes' drive, too.

The guest rooms on the first floor can all be let for single occupancy. A full English breakfast is provided and food is served all day in the single L-shaped bar. Children are welcome and there is a play area in the pub garden, where jazz sessions take place monthly on Sunday afternoons.

One of the most notable features of Streatley is the Sharpenhoe Clappers (NT), the site of an ancient hillfort and medieval rabbit warrens. On the path of the Chilterns Way, this is great walking country, with plenty of routes – a favourite short walk is to head down the hill from the Chequers and skirt the Clappers to arrive at another pub, the Lynmore in Sharpenhoe hamlet.

Q P

WHIPSNADE

Old Hunters Lodge

The Crossroads, LU6 2LN

▶ On B4540
T (01582) 872228
W www.old-hunters.com
Greene King IPA, Abbot; guest beers
Three double, one twin, one single room, all en-suite
£ ££ (single rates available; special weekend and multi-night deals)
Bar snack and restaurant meals daily, lunchtime and evening (restaurant closed Sun eve)
Accepted (not Amex)

On the edge of Whipsnade Common, Old Hunters Lodge is one of the oldest houses in the village. Reed thatched in Norfolk style, it is said to date from the 15th century. In summer, drinkers and diners enjoy a lovely garden/patio and in winter a real log fire.

All rooms are en-suite and no-smoking with telephone, TV, tea and coffee facilities; a four-poster room is popular for special occasions (special rates at weekends). Bedrooms are accessed by narrow stairs so are not suitable for wheelchair users; children are allowed in the restaurant, dogs in the bar. Breakfast features the traditional full English.

The restaurant offers a decent selection of main dishes and a table d'hote menu plus coffee. The bar has a separate snack menu, and local ingredients include meat from the butcher in Eaton Bray and vegetables from the 'veg man'. Special dietary needs should be mentioned when booking.

Walkers, cyclists and tourists enjoy exploring the footpaths and bridleways of Dunstable Downs. Places of interest nearby are Whipsnade Zoo, Luton Hoo, the 12th-century church and Tree Cathedral.

Q P

Berkshire

BEEDON

Langley Hall Inn

World's End, RG20 8SA

▶ Off A34 near Chieveley, near M4 jct 13
T (01635) 248332
F (01635) 248571
W www.langley-hall-inn.co.uk
West Berkshire Mr Chubb's, Good Old Boy; guest beers
Three en-suite double rooms
£ ££ (£50 single occupancy)
Lunchtime and evening meals
Accepted (not Amex)

Easy access to the M4 makes the Langley a good overnight stop for motorists. You can be sure of a comfortable night here in the modern, spacious rooms (one with king-sized bed) where you can slip between pure cotton sheets. The rooms are supplied with fluffy towels, television and hot drinks-making facilities. The inn is unable to cater for children but pets can be accommodated by arrangement.

Look no further than the inn's restaurant for your evening meal – the excellent menu specialises in fresh fish delivered from Brixham and local produce. Early arrivals can enjoy the tapas served between 5 and 7pm, or round off the evening with a pint of beer from the award-winning local West Berkshire brewery. What more could you ask for?

Well, maybe breakfast in the morning. You can opt for a room-only rate if you wish, but if you get a whiff of breakfast you will be sure to succumb; the full English here includes local free-range eggs and meat (sausages, bacon and black pudding) supplied by Griffins independent butchers in Newbury.

An unusual feature here is the petanque court in the garden, built to international competition standard.

♣ P

INKPEN

☆ Swan Inn

Craven Road, Lower Green, RG17 9DX

▶ Follow signs for Inkpen from Hungerford Common
T (01488) 668326
F (01488) 668306
W theswaninn-organics.co.uk
Butts Jester Organic, Traditional; West Berkshire Maggs Mild; guest beer
Four double, three twin, two family, one single room, all en-suite
£ ££-£££ (single rate available)
Snacks and meals daily, lunchtime and evening
Accepted (not Amex or Diners)

An unashamedly foodie pub with its own organic beef herd, serving locally-raised meat, much of it cured and butchered on the premises –also available to buy in the pub's farm shop. Even breakfast is an organic experience with fruit juice, cereals, porridge, bacon and sausages (home-made), tomatoes, mushrooms and eggs – as well as organic tea and coffee. Or choose kippers or a continental breakfast.

The Swan dates back to the 17th century and received a mention in the illustrated London News in 1846 when it was struck by lightning and the kitchen maid set on fire (fortunately she survived). It retains the original open fires and beams, but the bedrooms boast modern facilities such as phone/modem, colour TV, trouser press, hair dryer, power showers, tea and coffee making. All bedrooms are no-smoking.

A mile from the world's highest chalk hill, the Swan attracts hang gliders, walkers, cyclists and tourists who can relax over pub games. Needless to say, food in the Cygnet restaurant is outstanding, from a half shoulder of Moroccan lamb tagine to the organic sirloin and fillet steaks, prices around £15-£21. But there are vegan/vegetarian choices, too, and delicious, home-made bar meals such as their own beef in a steak and ale pie.

Q ♣ P

INKPEN
Crown & Garter
Inkpen Common, RG17 9QR

- ▶ Four miles off A4, 10 mins from M4 jcts 13/14
- T (01488) 668325
- W crownandgarter.com
- Archers Golden; Arkell's Moonlight; West Berkshire Mr Chubb's, Good Old Boy; guest beers
- Six double, two twin rooms (all available as singles); all en-suite, all no-smoking; one wheelchair accessible
- £ £££
- Snacks and meals Monday evening to Sunday lunchtime
- Accepted

This beautiful 17th-century inn is set amid the quiet lanes of the Berkshire countryside. Also featuring in CAMRA's Good Beer Guide, the Crown & Garter offers an excellent choice of local ales, bound to help ensure a good night's sleep. Or you can indulge in a whisky or two from the list of malts.

The breakfast menu offers naturally-smoked haddock rarebit and home-cooked ham as well as a generous full English breakfast with choice of eggs fried, scrambled or poached, and herbal teas. Main meals include authentic Thai dishes, as well as English favourites, plus continental and veggie choices.

Overnight visitors are a motley crew – business folk, walkers, wedding guests and those going to the races (the inn is halfway between Newbury and Lambourn) – weekend breaks are available. With walking, riding and fishing close by, the pub is also well-placed for visiting Windsor, Oxford and Bath. An inn with ancient charm and character, its barn was used to lay out the bodies of murderers George Broomham and Dorothy Newman, hung at Combe Gibbet.
Q P

KINTBURY
Dundas Arms
53 Station Road, RG17 9UT

- T (01488) 658263
- W dundasarms.co.uk
- Adnams Bitter; Ramsbury Gold; West Berkshire Mr Chubb's; guest beers
- Three double, two twin rooms; all en-suite and no-smoking
- £ £££ (£10 discount single occupancy)
- Lunchtime and evening meals Mon-Sat
- Accepted (not Amex or Diners)

This 18th-century whitewashed pub is situated between the River Kennet and the Kennet and Avon Canal, opposite Kintbury station. All five spacious bedrooms are on the ground floor overlooking the river, with patio doors leading to an attractive terrace with seating.

The pub's name comes from Admiral Lord Dundas who lived in the village in the early 18th century, and sponsored the canal's construction. From a decked area you can watch horse-drawn narrowboats in summer, or drink in the small single bar, which has a counter top completely covered with polished old pennies. The inn attracts a mixed clientele including cyclists, boaters, walkers and diners who come to enjoy the excellent food.

Breakfast offers free-range bacon and sausages from a London butcher, with free-range eggs 'and whatever people want within reason'. In the pub's two dining areas visitors can savour starters such as Dorset crab, home-potted shrimps or roast asparagus with crispy bacon, followed by seared marinated salmon with pineapple and mango salsa, duck breast with cider and apple sauce, grilled organic chicken with lemon risotto or red mullet with chilli lentils. Sweet tooth puds could be apricot crème brulee and chocolate pave with coffee bean sauce. Q P

MAIDENHEAD
Portland Arms
West Street, SL6 1RL

T (01628) 634649
F (01628) 634649
Brakspear Bitter; Fuller's Chiswick, ESB
One single, one double, one twin with bunk beds, all en-suite
£ £
Lunchtime and evening meals
Accepted

The Portland is quite a rarity – a real town pub that offers accommodation. Indeed its listing in CAMRA's Good Beer Guide describes it as one of the few traditional pubs left in the area, set in a back road off the High Street. It is frequented by a good crowd of regulars who come for the beer, a chat, a game of pool or to watch a match on the large-screen TV.

The accommodation in a purpose-built extension behind the pub was completed at the end of 2005. Apart from the usual facilities such as tea/coffee making and television, the rooms benefit from air conditioning and Internet access, making it a good value stop for business travellers. Its location close to the M4 and M40 and Heathrow Airport (20 minutes' drive) is an added attraction. Street parking is difficult this close to the town centre, but there is a pay and display car park nearby and the station is just 10 minutes' walk from the pub. Local places of interest include Windsor and Henley.

A full cooked breakfast is served and meals are available at lunchtime and in the evening, although the menu is fairly standard pub fare.

♣ ≉

STANFORD DINGLEY
Bull Country Inn
RG7 6LS

▶ On Yattenden-Burnt Hill road
T (0118) 974 4409
F (0118) 974 5249
W thebullatstanforddingley.co.uk
Brakspear Bitter; West Berkshire Skiff, Good Old Boy; guest beers
Two double, three twin, one family room, all en-suite
£ £££ (discount for single occupancy)
Snacks (lunchtime); main meals lunchtime and evening
Accepted

This 15th-century privately-owned inn stands in a beautiful village in the Pang Valley, in a conservation area of outstanding natural beauty. It encompasses a traditional, cottage-style saloon and tap room, with low beams, flagstoned floors and notable wattle and daub wall. A fine range of real ale includes the local West Berkshire Brewery's light, nutty Skiff at 3.6 per cent, brewed exclusively for the pub. The Bull holds monthly folk sessions and classic car days.

Bedrooms are set in an annexe; all are no-smoking and wheelchair accessible, and carry the English Tourist Board four-diamond rating. Each has independent access, TV and radio, free Internet access and tea and coffee making facilities. A camp site is also available for caravans and tents.

Breakfast is traditional English with cereals and fruit juices, 'pub grub' is served in the bar, while the recently added restaurant offers 'posh nosh', with a daily-changing menu. Pub grub includes home-made fishcakes, beef burgers, short-crust pies, curry and broccoli and stilton pasta.

Q ❀ ♿ P

Buckinghamshire

AMERSHAM

Saracens Head Inn

Whielden Street, HP7 0HU

- T (01494) 721958
- F (01494) 728205
- W thesaracensheadinn.com
- Abbot Ale; Greene King IPA, Old Speckled Hen; guest beers
- Two double, seven twin, two single rooms, all en-suite
- £ £££
- Snacks Mon-Sat lunchtime, meals lunchtime and evening
- Accepted

Steeped in character, the Saracens Head in Old Amersham is a traditional English pub built in 1530 using timbers from old ships. According to rumour the building is haunted by two ghosts, one a young serving wench from the 17th century.

Originally a coaching inn, the building surrounds a central courtyard with the original stables now converted into bedrooms overlooking a secluded garden and barbecue area. Some of the rooms are wheelchair accessible, all are no-smoking, and have TV plus mini fridge and tea and coffee making facilities; one room features a hand-carved, mahogany four poster bed.

A continental breakfast is served, including orange juice, cereal, cheese, toast, fresh fruit, tea and coffee. At lunchtime there is a wide choice of snacks – 17 sandwich and toasted sandwich fillings ranging from Brie with bacon and avocado to ham, Gruyere and Dijon mustard. Main meals start with tempura prawns, spaghetti aioli, whitebait and all sorts of salads, around £5, then simple ham, eggs and chips, home-made lasagne and burgers, or home-made fishcakes, slow roasted lamb shank, Saracens fish pie or chicken, ham and mushroom pie, from £8-£10, rising to around £15 for sirloin and fillet steaks.

Q

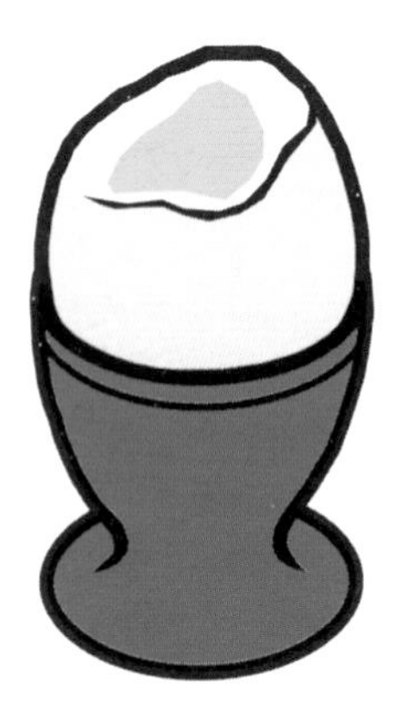

AYLESBURY
Hop Pole
83 Bicester Road, HP19 9AZ

- ▶ On A41, 10 minutes' walk from the bus and rail stations
- T (01296) 482129
- W hop-pole.co.uk
- Vale Best Bitter, Edgar's Golden Ale; guest beers
- Five single rooms sharing two bathrooms
- £ £
- Meals available all day
- Accepted

A veritable beer festival pub, the Hop Pole stocks 10 guest beers from independent micro-breweries at all times and is Aylesbury's sole outlet for Vale beers brewed in nearby Haddenham. It also keeps a good range of malt whiskies.

Not long ago this was a very run-down pub, but Vale's total refurbishment has transformed it into a beer-lovers' mecca attracting custom from far and wide. The Victorian building now has three bar areas with stripped floorboards and traditional furnishings acting as a backdrop to the collections of pictures and breweriana.

The guest rooms are simply but comfortably furnished, with hand basins and armchairs. In the morning there is a choice of a full English or continental breakfast, with cereals, toast and fruit juice. The pub is gaining a reputation for its home-cooked meals served throughout the day - again the emphasis is on simple but wholesome fare.

The Hop Pole has a good-sized function room and hosts live music every Saturday evening. Visitors should take the opportunity to visit the King's Head in the Market Square. Donated by the Rothschild Family to the National Trust in 1924, this 15th-century pub is the oldest courtyard inn in England.

CHALFONT ST GILES
☆ Ivy House
London Road, HP8 4RS

- ▶ On A413 between Amersham and Chalfont St Giles
- T (01494) 872184
- F (01494) 872870
- W theivyhouse-bucks.co.uk
- Brakspear Bitter; Fuller's London Pride; Hook Norton Hooky Bitter
- Four double, one single room, all en-suite
- £ £££
- Lunchtime and evening meals; meals served all day at weekends; cream teas 3-6pm
- Accepted

This award-winning family-run free house is a 250-year-old brick and flint building with open fires, comfy armchairs and bric-a-brac. A former coaching inn, the accommodation is probably rather more comfortable than in the early days. The rooms have been beautifully decorated and equipped to a high specification with luxurious bed linen and towels. Satellite TV, a desk, coffee/tea making facilities and a digital safe are provided in each of the rooms.

Naturally this sort of quality doesn't come cheaply, but weekend guests can take advantage of reduced prices for a two-night stay. Most rooms have fine views of the Chiltern Vale, and there is much to explore with Milton's Cottage and the Chiltern Open Air Museum minutes away. Children are welcome and the Ivy might be a fine reward for parents after a trip to nearby Legoland.

The breakfast menu ranges from plain scrambled eggs on toast or omelettes to toasted waffles with maple syrup or the full English. Other items, such as croissants, muffins and a meat and cheese platter are available by advance order. Most produce comes from local suppliers. P

CHESHAM

Gamekeepers Lodge

Bellingdon Road, HP5 2NN

T (01494) 793491
E gamekeepers.lodge@btinternet.com
Brakspear Bitter; Tetley Burton Ale; guest beers
Three rooms; shared bathroom
£ £
Snacks and meals lunchtime and evening (no food Monday or Sunday evening)
Accepted

The Gamekeepers is a traditional English community pub with two bars and the Carvery restaurant at the rear, offering meals and a Sunday roast carvery lunch. It has a large-screen TV and pool table, and is close to Chesham museum, countryside walks, the Elgiva theatre and rail links into London.

The accommodation is basic and fairly inexpensive (£30 per person, or £25 if sharing) in three letting rooms. These include a double room with an extra single bed, a room with four singles and a room with three singles. Guests share a bathroom, but each room has a TV, and tea or coffee is available if required. The price includes a full English breakfast plus cereals.

Meals are served from Tuesday to Sunday lunchtime, and sometimes include local produce as available.

DENHAM
Falcon Inn
Village Road, UB9 5BE

- ▶ Overlooking village green
- T (01895) 832125
- W falconinn.biz
- Taylor Landlord; Wells Bombardier; Young's Bitter; guest beer
- Two double, one twin room, all en-suite
- £ Mon-Thurs £££; Fri-Sun ££ (single rates available)
- Snacks and meals daily lunchtime and evening
- Accepted

Dating back to the 16th century, the inn has an unusual entrance – stone steps rise to the front door five feet above street level (no wheelchair access). The Falcon has been an ale house since Richard Curtis held it during the reign of Henry VIII; in 1623 it passed to Robert Bowyer, brother of Sir William Bowyer, who had purchased the whole Manor of Denham – and from then gained its present name from the family crest 'A Falcon Arising'. The pub retains many original features, with exposed beams in the bedrooms as well as the bar.

You serve yourself to breakfast in your room – the fridge contains orange juice, bottled water, yoghurt, butter, milk, cheese and cold meats; bread, cereals and preserves are also available as well as biscuits and tea and coffee making facilities. Each room has a safe, TV with video or DVD, books and extra pillows and blankets.

Attractions within easy distance include Windsor Castle, Legoland, Denham Marina and Aerodrome, Thorpe Park, Pinewood Studios, Chiltern Open Air Museum, Ascot and Colne Valley Park visitors' centre. Golf enthusiasts will find five courses five to ten minutes away, including the famous Denham club. Central London is 25 minutes by train from Denham. Q

SHERINGTON
White Hart
1 Gun Lane, MK16 9PE

- ▶ Close to M1 jct 14, just off A509
- T (01908) 611953
- F (01908) 618109
- W whitehartsherington.com
- Young's Bitter; guest beers
- Four double rooms, all en-suite
- £ Sun-Thurs £££; Fri & Sat ££
- Snacks and meals daily lunchtime and evening (not Sun eve)
- Accepted

Set in a converted barn, with English Tourist Board accreditation, the delightful, individually decorated rooms (two wheelchair accessible) incorporate the original exposed wooden beams. A past local CAMRA Pub of the Year, the White Hart once came close to closing but is now at the heart of the village.

Although just the other side of the M1 from modern Milton Keynes, the inn (circa 16th century) is set in a traditional village overlooking the Ouse Valley, within the perimeter of an Iron Age camp and Roman site. A century ago the landlord was a 28-stone hulk call Henry Hill; he would be in his element today - not only can you tuck into a hearty English breakfast, but the pub is renowned for its excellent food including daily specials and fresh fish.

If you just want a snack, tapas grazing dishes include Moorish lamb kebabs, spicy Canarian roast potatoes and marinated anchovies. In the high, beamed restaurant meals might start with Peking duck rolls or Orkney crab cakes, followed by gammon with Tom Boulton's local free-range eggs and chips, char-grilled chicken Caesar salad or Orkney beef fillet with shallot and brandy sauce, prices up to £16.

Q P

Cambridgeshire

ABBOTS RIPTON

Three Horseshoes

Moat Lane, PE28 2PA

- On B1090, north of Huntingdon
- T (01487) 773440
- E abbotsripton@aol.com
- Adnams Bitter, Broadside; Oakham JHB; guest beer
- Five double en-suite rooms (four wheelchair accessible)
- £ ££ (£55 single occupancy)
- Lunchtime and evening meals (not Mon)
- Accepted

Originally a tiny pub, part of the de Ramsey estate, in a picturesque village of thatched cottages, the Horseshoes has undergone a sensitive redevelopment programme over the last six years. The original pub area, with exposed oak beams and quarry-tiled floor, has been retained as an attractive family room. A new extension houses a large, comfortable lounge bar, a restaurant and the guest accommodation.

The new three-star rated bedrooms are spacious and some feature king-sized beds. All modern comforts and facilities required by guests, whether for business or pleasure, are available. Children are welcome and the rooms can be let as singles. Breakfast is served in the rooms - guests can help themselves from the fridge to fruit juices to accompany a continental breakfast of cereals, croissant, pastry, cheese, cold meat and fruit. Modern cuisine is served daily (except Monday when the pub is closed) in the elegant restaurant, and most dietary requirements can be catered for.

Not far from the A1(M), the pub is within easy reach of the East of England Showground at Peterborough, historic Cambridge, Huntingdon and St Ives.

Q P

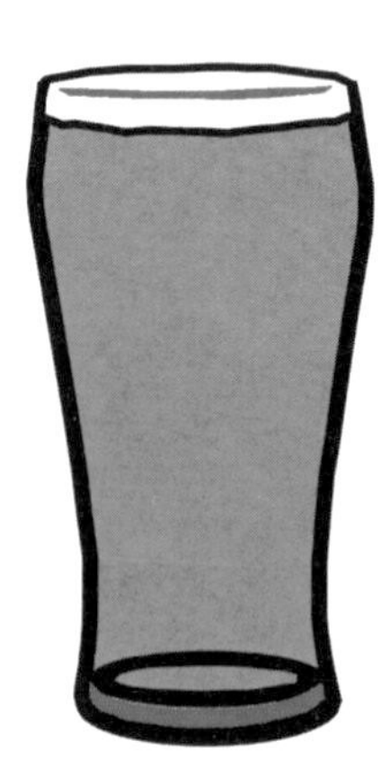

BRAMPTON
Grange
115 High Street, PE28 4RA

- ▶ On B1514, off A14 near Huntingdon
- T (01480) 459516
- F (01480) 459391
- W grangehotelbrampton.co.uk
- Greene King IPA; guest beers
- Four double, three single rooms, all en-suite
- £ £££
- Lunchtime and evening meals
- Accepted

Set in a quiet residential village and built in 1773, the Georgian building was converted to a hotel as recently as 1981; before that it served as a girls' school and as the HQ of the American Eighth Army Air Division during World War Two. Bought by the Steigers in 2000, it has now been restored to its original elegance.

The pub stocks a house beer brewed locally by Potton as well as frequently changing guest beers. It now enjoys a good reputation for its food, served in the bar and restaurant. You will always find fish on the monthly changing menu but Friday is officially 'fish night'; vegetarian dishes are available on request and other dietary requirements can be accommodated with prior notice.

The comfortable rooms are well equipped with CD players, TV and video players. One room boasts a four-poster and one can be booked for a family (children are welcome). The full English breakfast includes free-range eggs and sausages from the Denham Estate, or there is porridge or Greek yogurt with prunes. Fish such as kipper, smoked haddock or smoked salmon (served with scrambled egg) may also be available.

❀ ♿ P

ELTISLEY
Leeds Arms Hotel
2 The Green, PE19 6TG

- ▶ Off A428 between Cambridge and St Neots
- T (01480) 880283
- Wells Eagle, Bombardier; guest beers
- Three twin, six single rooms, all en-suite
- £ ££
- Snacks and meals daily, lunchtime and evening
- Accepted

So why is an inn in Cambridgeshire called after a city in Yorkshire? It isn't, actually - the name originates from the Leeds family of Croxton Park who built the pub, first licensed in 1814, on the edge of the village green. Since then it has passed through the hands of several breweries but, from 2004, has been part of Charles Wells' estate.

The bedrooms are in a single storey, chalet-style building situated in the pub's attractive garden; guests can come and go as they please. All rooms provide a TV, telephone and tea and coffee making facilities, with children and pets welcome. In the morning you can enjoy a full English breakfast or kippers, while the bar provides various snacks and meals, and the restaurant offers a menu of freshly-cooked choices using fruit and vegetables from Bedfordshire Growers, and meat from Croxton Organic Farm. Vegetarian and gluten free dishes are available.

The bar, with two large fireplaces, is a warm and friendly place to relax over a pint of real ale. The pub has a large, secure garden, excellent for families. The inn is ideally placed for visiting Cambridge with its historic buildings and colleges, and the American War Cemetery at Madingley.

Q ❀ ♿ ♣ P

HILTON

Prince of Wales

Potton Road, PE28 9NG

- ▶ Off A14 and A1198
- T (01480) 830257
- Adnams Broadside; Taylor Landlord; guest beer
- Three double, one twin, one single room
- £ £££
- Evening meals daily, lunches Friday to Sunday
- Accepted

In the triangle bounded by Cambridge, Huntingdon and St Neots, the Prince of Wales at Hilton is well placed for exploring the ancient seat of learning plus two attractive towns, and is also close to the National Trust's Houghton Mill.

Built in 1830, the white-painted hostelry with blue shutters and a beamed interior is well patronised by walkers and local villagers, as well as visitors to nearby Papworth Hospital. At the heart of the community, it adjoins the village store and post office.

The pub comprises a lounge bar with beams and open log fire, plus a public bar with pool table and TV. Outside there is a small beer garden. The comfortable bedrooms, upstairs in the pub, are all no-smoking, and offer tea and coffee making facilities, TV, hairdryer and telephone. All but one are en-suite.

All tastes are catered for at breakfast whether you want a full English or continental; at other meal times food is freshly prepared using locally grown seasonal fruit and vegetables, local eggs and meat from a traditional family butcher.

Local attractions include the Oliver Cromwell Museum and a turf maze in the village.

Q

HOUGHTON

Three Horseshoes Inn

The Green, PE28 2BE

- ▶ Off A1123 between Huntingdon and St Ives
- T (01480) 462410
- W threehorseshoesinn.net
- Greene King IPA, Old Speckled Hen; Oakham JHB; Taylor Landlord; guest beer
- Two double rooms, one en-suite, one with bathroom
- £ £
- Meals and snacks daily lunchtime and evening
- Accepted

A traditional village pub offering some of the most inexpensive accommodation you will find in this guide – just £49 for a double room (£39 for single occupancy). One of the rooms is en-suite, and has a king sized bed as well as a single bed so can be used as a family room, the other double has its own bathroom. The accommodation is mainly used by workmen during the week and tourists at weekends.

Indeed, Houghton itself is popular with tourists and this is its only pub. The village is set on the Great Ouse, with a working flour mill, canal with lock, boat hire on the river, and 14th-century church of St Mary Magdalene. The Three Horseshoes dates back to the 17th century and encompasses three bars – a restaurant area with separate conservatory, drinkers' bar and a pool room with gaming machine. There is a garden at the rear and benches at the front.

Guests can fortify themselves for the day with a full English breakfast, while lunchtime and evening meals feature products from local farms on the specials board; vegetarian, gluten free and nut allergy requirements can be catered for.

Q P

HUNTINGDON
Old Bridge Hotel
1 High Street, PE29 3TQ

- Off Huntingdon ring road
- T (01480) 424300
- F (01480) 411017
- W huntsbridge.com
- Adnams Bitter; guest beers
- Sixteen double, two twin, six single rooms, all en-suite
- £ ££££
- Snacks and meals daily, lunchtime and evening
- Accepted

Unashamedly luxurious, this handsome, 18th-century ivy-covered hotel overlooks the River Ouse on the edge of Huntingdon town centre. The individually designed rooms have exceptionally comfortable beds (two rooms have four posters), air conditioning, power showers, satellite TV and audio systems. Prices include full English and buffet breakfast, early morning tea and a newspaper. Weekend break rates are available.

The Old Bridge is renowned for its award-winning food overseen by an executive chef who is ex-Bibendeum (even the breakfast black pudding is made on the premises). Main meals include the excellent value lunch served Monday-Saturday, £14 for two courses such as vichyssoise with confit quail followed by grilled salmon with olive and tomato potato salad. Snacks include home-made crisps and hot chorizo sausage with olives; starters might be Portland crab on linguini pasta or deep fried calves' brains with sauce gribiche. Main courses might be pork and sage sausages with mash, or grilled Lincolnshire rabbit with parsley salad and sauté potatoes, prices up to £15.

P

STILTON
Bell Inn
Great North Road, PE7 3RA

- Half a mile S of jct 16 A1(M)
- T (01733) 241066
- F (01733) 245173
- W thebellinnstilton.co.uk
- Fuller's London Pride; Greene King IPA, Abbot; Oakham JHB; guest beer
- Twenty two rooms, all en-suite (three wheelchair accessible)
- £ ££££
- Snacks and meals daily, lunchtime and evening
- Accepted (not Diners)

This historic inn is the birthplace of Stilton cheese and has appeared in every edition of CAMRA's Good Pub Food guide, and what better way to enjoy it than at the end of a pleasant meal when you can retire for the night? Others before you, from Dick Turpin to Clark Gable, have done just that.

Bedrooms are built round the old courtyard, each individually designed, including two with four posters and several with whirlpool baths. All have colour TV and tea and coffee making facilities.

Breakfast includes Scotch porridge oats (sweet or salted), Grasmere ham, lightly smoked haddock with poached egg or oak smoked salmon and scrambled egg – unless you fancy the full English complete with black pudding.

As well as the stone-floored village bar with its open log fire, there is a bistro bar serving snacks and bar meals at very reasonable prices, with Stilton cheese from Quenby Hall prominent in creamy Stilton pâté or Stilton and wild mushroom soup. In the beamed, galleried restaurant a three-course meals costs £25.95, and Stilton is served to finish with the inn's famous home-made plum bread.

Q P

Cheshire

CHESTER
Albion Inn
Park Street, CH1 1RN

▶ Between Newgate and the river
T (01244) 340345
W albioninnchester.co.uk
Bateman XB; Black Sheep Best Bitter; Caledonian Deuchars IPA; Taylor Landlord; guest beers
One double, one twin room, both en-suite
£ ££
Lunchtime and evening meals and snacks
Not accepted

The Albion is an inn like no other. Insisting that it is not a 'concept pub', the landlord has nonetheless created something akin to a museum commemorating the days of the Great War, with furnishings and fittings to match, including old posters and advertising signs. Near the former Drill Hall, which was the wartime recruiting centre, the inn is the last surviving Victorian corner pub in the city. The only machine used for entertainment here is a 1928 Steck player piano.

The guest rooms are new, but have been designed in Victorian style with appropriate furnishings and full en-suite facilities of bath and shower. Families are not catered for – in fact children are positively discouraged here. The full English breakfast includes fresh fruit, muesli and other cereals, then a cooked meal with local free-range eggs and outdoor reared bacon; Manx kippers can be provided as an alternative on request.

Local produce is used as far as possible in a menu (Trench Rations) that would have warmed the hearts (let alone stomachs) of British servicemen. Alongside the boiled gammon with pease pudding and liver, bacon and onions are more exotic dishes to suit today's customers' tastes, and excellent snacks.

Q

CONGLETON

Queen's Head Hotel

Park Lane, CW12 3DE

▶ Opposite Congleton station
T (01260) 272546
Caledonian Deuchars IPA; Greene King Abbot; Wells Bombardier; guest beers
One double, one twin, one family, one single room; shared bathroom
£ £
Snacks and meals daily, lunchtime and evening
Not accepted

Full of character, this pub at Bridge 75 on the Macclesfield Canal has its own mooring and is popular with locals and boaters, as well as walkers and cyclists. The comfortable, reasonably priced accommodation is in a recently renovated cottage next to the pub.

First licensed in 1830 and reputed to be haunted, the Queen's Head is a community pub offering seven real ales including guests from small breweries such as York, Cottage, Coach House and Phoenix. It has a pool table as well as bar skittles and darts.

A full English breakfast is two rashers, two bangers, hash browns, egg, beans, tomato and toast, while main meals from the Cottage Pie menu and changing specials board are mostly home-made. Food is served in a dining area at the rear of the pub, overlooking the canal.

It is within easy reach of some of the best scenery in the Peak District, as well as being handy for Jodrell Bank Observatory, Little Moreton Hall and the Cloud beauty spot. A huge beer garden has a children's play area. Children are welcome in the overnight accommodation and so are pets 'within reason' – so leave your lion at home.

Q ❀ ♣ P

FARNDON

☆ Farndon Arms

High Street, CH3 6PU

T (01829) 270570
W farndonarms.com
Beer range changes weekly
Two double, two twin, one family, two single rooms, all en-suite
£ £
Snacks and meals daily, lunchtime and evening
Accepted

A striking black and white timbered pub formerly known as the Raven, with etched ground-floor windows carrying the original name. Local produce features at breakfast – with home-made jams, local butter, sausages and bacon from Rose Farm, mushrooms from the field (in season), farm eggs, Gloucester Old Spot black pudding and tomatoes from Manchester market. Tea and coffee are Fair Trade.

All this is included in the bargain price of £55 for a double or twin en-suite room at this family run pub boasting 'three star quality and five star service'. Facilities include colour TV, tea and coffee making and your pick of the world's newspapers (by prior request).

The award-winning Queen's Head is renowned locally for its food, with starters such as 'our famous dish of baked bananas, Cheshire Blue cheese and grilled bacon', main courses including hotch potch of pork, lamb and braised oxtail, capsicum filled with asparagus risotto or red sea bream on buttered samphire, again all excellent value for money.

Set in a picturesque valley just 200 yards from the river bordering Wales, the pub has open fires, a sun terrace, and is convenient for Chester, Manchester, Liverpool and lovely countryside.

Q ❀ ♣ P

HIGHER BURWARDSLEY
Pheasant Inn
Tattenhall, CH3 9PF

▶ Signposted from Burwardsley Post Office
T (01829) 770434
W thepheasantinn.co.uk
Weetwood Best Bitter, Eastgate Ale, Old Dog Bitter, Oasthouse Gold; guest beer
Twelve double or twin rooms, all en-suite
£ £££-££££
Snacks and meals daily, lunchtime and evening
Accepted

This old Cheshire sandstone building dates back over 300 years with open fires and a flower-filled courtyard for a drink as the sun goes down… and to carry on the romantic theme, two of the country-style bedrooms are feature rooms suitable for honeymooners or romantic getaways; all have en-suite shower and bath, TV, hairdryer, tea and coffee making.

With an atmospheric beamed bar and separate dining room, the Pheasant enjoys spectacular views across the Cheshire countryside. An ideal base for golf and angling, it is close to Chester, Oulton Park motor racing circuit and Chester racecourse.

For breakfast enjoy fresh fruit and cereals as well as the full English. The day's menus emphasise Cheshire produce, with local Cheshire cheese in the ploughman's; other snacks include fresh rope mussels and hot beef sandwiches. Traditional pub food might be cod in beer batter, bangers with mustard mash, home-made steak burgers or salmon and crab fishcakes. More elaborate main dishes include grilled sea bass on olive crushed new potatoes with beetroot crisps, slow roasted Chinese belly pork, or fresh garden pea and mint risotto – leave room for Cheshire Farm honeycomb ice cream or champagne sorbet.

Q P

KNUTSFORD
Cross Keys
52 King Street, WA16 6DT

T (01565) 750404
W knutsfordcrosskeys.co.uk
Boddingtons Bitter; Taylor Landlord; Tetley Bitter; guest beers
Eight double, two twin, three single rooms, all en-suite
£ £££
Snacks and meals daily, lunchtime and evening
Accepted

This 18th-century coaching inn has been run by the same family for 13 years, and featured in the Good Beer Guide for seven of them. In 1989 two original stables and the coach house were converted into 13 quality rooms, all en-suite, offering internet access via phone point, TV and video with Sky, tea and coffee making, and a trouser press.

Situated on an attractive shopping street, the Cross Keys is one of the town's oldest pubs, though largely rebuilt in 1909. It is notable for a fine choice of cask ales, including three constantly changing guests, dispensed from a gleaming bank of polished brass handpumps.

Breakfast is full English, as well as fruit juice and fresh fruit, with free newspapers on offer. Bar meals are available at lunchtime, as well as English and international dishes served in the small, intimate restaurant, reached by a barrel-vaulted tunnel. A sample menu offers light bites such as home-roasted ham with egg, chips and peas or lamb sausages on toasted ciabatta. Main meals include lamb shanks in port and redcurrant sauce and fisherman's stew of white fish, mussels, prawns and crab.

The pub is close to Tatton Park, Gaskill Manorial Tower and Arley Hall.

P

OVER PEOVER

Dog Inn

Well Bank Lane, WA16 8UP

▶ Off A50 at Stocks Lane and follow lane for 2.5 miles
T (01625) 861421
F (01625) 864800
W doginn-overpeover.co.uk
Copper Dragon Scotts 1816; Hydes Original; Moorhouses Black Cat, Pride of Pendle; Weetwood Best Bitter
Four double, two twin rooms, all en-suite
£ ££
Lunchtime and evening meals (all day Sunday)
Accepted (not Amex or Diners Club)

The Dog is popular with business people who would rather stay in the convivial surroundings of a real country pub than a soulless B&B in one of the towns nearby. This lively local inn started life as an ale house in 1860 and remains a focal point of village life. There is always plenty going on here, including regular live entertainment and a twice-weekly quiz. The tap room houses a pool table, dartboard and TV.

Four-diamond rated, the six comfortable guest rooms are attractively decorated with TV, hospitality tray (with free spring water), hair dryer and trouser press. Fresh fruit is provided at breakfast, along with cereals and the full English. With advance notice special dietary requirements can be catered for. The pub uses seasonal produce from local farmers and growers as available and the food here, whether you opt for a freshly-cooked main meal or just something from the 'lite bites' menu, is highly recommended.

Local places of interest include National Trust properties Tatton Park, Dunham Massey, Quarry Bank Mill and Styal Estate or, for the scientifically minded, Jodrell Bank Observatory is also nearby.
Q P

WARMINGHAM

Bear's Paw

School Lane, CW11 3QN

▶ Ten mins from M6 jcts 17/18
T (01270) 526317
W thebearspaw.co.uk
Tetley Bitter; guest beers
Nine double, two single, one family room, all en-suite
£ ££
Bar snacks, lunch at weekends, evening meals daily
Accepted

An imposing hotel built in the 1870s by the Earl of Crewe, the Bear's Paw offers a dozen comfortable en-suite bedrooms with facilities including TV and tea and coffee making, all on the first floor so not suitable for wheelchair users. The only pets allowed are guide dogs.

Set in a traditional village four miles north of Crewe, the pub was voted local rural pub of the year in 2005 by CAMRA members. It is Cask Marque accredited, always serving two guest ales, often from local brewers.

You can choose between continental and full English breakfast including sausages from the local butcher. Evening meals include some mouth-watering choices, such as cod cooked in Hoegaarden beer batter, Tennessee bourbon pork ribs, red mullet on crab mash, sweet peppers stuffed with wild mushroom risotto topped with Brie, and a full range of steaks, main courses around £10. Traditional favourites might be hand-made steak pie with shortcrust pastry topping, roast of the day with market vegetables, home-made beef lasagne or a slow-roasted shoulder of lamb with roast potatoes and mint gravy.

Children are welcomed as B&B guests, and the pub attracts a wide clientele from cyclists to tourists. Q P

Cornwall

BOTALLACK

Queen's Arms

TR19 7QS

▶ Just off B3306
T (01736) 788318
W queensarms.info
Sharp's Doom Bar; guest beers
One double (or twin) room, en-suite
£ £
Snacks and meals daily, lunchtime and evening
Accepted

Not the usual B&B pub – for a start, you make your own breakfast! The Queen's Arms has a separate self-catering apartment in a barn conversion, comprising a double or twin bedroom, bathroom with shower, lounge/dining area with colour TV and fully equipped kitchen. It costs £180-£380 per week, depending on season, but shorter breaks can be booked in winter.

The grade II listed 18th-century Cornish granite country pub makes a great base for a holiday, just a few miles from Land's End on the coastal path and close to the awesome Botallack Head cliffs, so popular with walkers and climbers. The cosy bar has a real fire and dining area, with a large family room to the rear; all the real ales are brewed in Cornwall.

Food is local, too; the pub is a member of Taste of the West and Penwith Produce. So, while you may have to make your own breakfast, there are excellent gourmet meals available at other times, from grilled whole megrim with Swiss chard and prawn sauce to pan-roast pigeon breast with wine gravy or Falmouth bay mussels. All desserts are home made, such as the old-fashioned baked rice pudding with strawberry jam and clotted cream.

Q ♣ P

CHARLESTOWN
Harbourside Inn
Charlestown Road, PL25 3NJ

- ▶ Off A390, on the harbour front
- T (01726) 67955
- F (01726) 69246
- W pierhousehotel.com
- Beer range varies
- Fifteen double, four twin, two family, nine single rooms, all en-suite
- £ £££-££££
- Snacks and meals daily, lunchtime and evening
- Accepted

Originally two cottages, the Pier House was built in 1794 in the unspoilt port of Charlestown; its new Harbourside Inn was added in 2004. Originally used by the clay industry, the harbour is now home to three tall ships and the area is frequently used for filming TV series.

Guests can stroll across the cliff tops to nearby Porthpean Beach and village, or to Carlyon Bay in the other direction. Two beaches providing safe swimming are close to the hotel, and the Eden Project is only a few miles away.

Awarded three crowns by the English Tourist Board, the family-owned hotel has a cosy bistro bar where there is occasional live music, and a full à la carte restaurant. All bedrooms have colour TV, direct dial phone, tea and coffee facilities, and many have sea or harbour views. Family rooms sleep two adults and up to three children.

Apart from the full English, breakfast may also include porridge, smoked haddock and kippers, plus a choice of cereals, yoghurt, prunes and grapefruit. At other meal times local produce and fish caught by local fishermen are specialities, not forgetting the traditional Cornish cream tea, and Sunday roast carvery lunch.
❀

CRAFTHOLE
Finnygook Inn
PL11 3BQ

- ▶ On B3247, 5 miles from Plymouth between Torpoint and Looe
- T (01503) 230338
- F (01503) 230338
- W finnygook.co.uk
- Sharp's Doom Bar; guest beer
- Two double, three twin rooms; four en-suite, one with bathroom
- £ ££
- Snacks and meals daily, lunchtime and evening
- Accepted

The 16th-century Finnygook gets its name from the ghost (gook) of smuggler Silas Finny who was throttled close by and is said to haunt not only the pub but the adjoining road to Portwrinkle. Guests can reach the pub by road – the A38 Devon expressway – or the Torpoint ferry from nearby Plymouth where you will find a host of attractions. Free luggage transfer/collection from the railway station is offered.

The five bedrooms have modern comforts including en-suite bathroom, TV, tea and coffee making, iron and hairdryer, while two enjoy spectacular views over the Tamar estuary and Whitsand Bay golf course. Visitors include walkers who tread the coastal path, tourists and naval families visiting HMS Raleigh.

Breakfast is the full Monty – egg (fried, poached or scrambled), bacon, sausage, tomato, mushrooms, hash brown, fried bread and beans, while all meat, some fish and as many vegetables as possible are local. Diners can enjoy Looe crab, steak and ale pie, local ham and eggs, and splendid Sunday lunch of roast Cornish beef, lamb, pork or chicken at around £7 for a plateful.

Finnygook Dawney Ale is brewed by Sharp's, guest ales are from Cornish brewers. ❀ P

FOWEY
King of Prussia
3 Town Quay, PL23 1AT

▶ At jct of Fore Street and Lostwithiel Road by the river
T (01726) 832694
F (01726) 834902
W kingofprussiafowey.com
St Austell Tinners, Tribute
Six double en-suite rooms
£ £££ (£55 single occupancy); reduced rate in winter
Lunchtime and evening meals
Accepted

Once owned by Walter Hicks, the founder of St Austell Brewery, and still a tied house, this 17th-century pub stands right by the river in Fowey. It attracts a good mix of customers, including families and tourists.

Contrasting with the traditional interior of the pub itself, the adjacent Little Prussia restaurant and tea room is decorated in cool modern style. The main menus offer modern British cuisine, incorporating as much Cornish produce – fish, cheeses, etc – as possible. In the afternoon you can enjoy scones, sandwiches or the chef's speciality of Fowey rarebit, washed down with a cup of tea or even a glass of Pimm's.

Breakfast is served in the pub where you can watch the river come to life as you tuck into a freshly-cooked and filling meal. The light and bright guest rooms, too, all enjoy river views. Wireless Internet connection is available. Children are welcome to stay (under-12s are free of charge).

Trips on the river and sailing are possible in Fowey, while visitors in August can enjoy the Royal Regatta, when there is also a carnival and a firework display. The popular Eden Project and local gardens are all nearby.

GUNWALLOE
Halzephron Inn
TR12 7QB

▶ Three miles S of Helston on A3083, through village, pub is on left
T (01326) 240406
F (01326) 241442
W halzephroninn@gunwalloe1.fsnet.co.uk
Organic Halzephron Gold; St Austell Tribute; Sharp's Doom Bar
Two double en-suite rooms
£ £££
Lunchtime and evening meals
Accepted

Situated just 300 yards from the South Cornwall footpath, the Halzephron is the only pub on the coastal path between Mullion and Porthleven, so is a very welcome sight for weary hikers. The free house is 500 years old and inevitably has a smuggling history; the shaft connecting an underground tunnel still exists. The pub name is derived from the old Cornish 'Als Yfferin' – cliffs of hell because of the danger to shipping along this coast and the number of wrecks.

Well preserved, with many small rooms, low ceilings, old paintings and gleaming copper, the inn offers a good choice of ales (including a vegetarian beer from the local Organic Brewery) and excellent food – breakfast will certainly set you up for a further day's walking. Fresh grapefruit and prunes are available and you can opt for scrambled eggs and smoked salmon as an alternative to the full English.

The two cosy double bedrooms, with television and hospitality tray, benefit from views across open countryside to the rear of the pub over to the Goonhilly Earth Station. Other places of interest in the vicinity include Flambards Theme Park, Cornwall Seal Sanctuary and Poldark Mine.

Q P

LOSTWITHIEL

Globe Inn

3 North Street, PL22 0EG

▶ Near bridge and parish church
T (01208) 872501
F (01208) 872559
W globeinn.com
Sharp's Doom Bar; Skinner's Betty Stogs; guest beers
Three double, one family room, all en-suite
£ ££
Lunchtime and evening meals
Accepted

Ideally situated for visitors using public transport, the Globe is just two minutes' walk from the station on the main London-Penzance line, while the Eden Project, Heligan Gardens and Lanhydrock House (NT) are just a few of the tourist sites within a 10-mile radius.

Close to the ancient river bridge in the heart of Lostwithiel old town, the pub is contemporary with the 13th-century parish church nearby. The former capital of Cornwall is dominated by the ruins of Restormel Castle, a good starting place for exploring the narrow streets and hunting out antiques.

The guest rooms have brass beds with hand-made mattresses and good quality linen. Furnishings are antique but facilities are modern with wifi Internet access, flat screen television and a fully stocked fridge in all the rooms. A hospitality tray is also provided. One room is available for families.

A full English breakfast is cooked to order, accompanied by fresh fruit and cereals. The pub is noted for its excellent food and features in CAMRA's Good Pub Food guide. Local, and organic as far as possible, produce is used in the kitchen. Most dietary requirements can be met.

NANCENOY, NEAR CONSTANTINE

☆ Trengilly Wartha

TR11 5RP

▶ Off B2391, follow signs for Gweek from Constantine
T (01326) 340332
W trengilly.co.uk
Sharp's Cornish Coaster, Doom Bar; Skinner's Betty Stogs, Heligan Honey, Keel Over; guest beers
Eight double, three twin, two family, eight single rooms, all en-suite
£ £££
Snacks and meals daily, lunchtime and evening
Accepted

The breakfast menu runs to two pages at this multi-award winning hotel. There is a choice of 10 starters from fresh grapefruit to six cereals, while the main event is full English including free-range eggs, local black pudding, bacon and sausages, or there's Porthleven kipper, scrambled eggs with smoked sea trout, and smoked haddock poached in milk. To follow is toast with home-made Seville marmalade or damson jam. Chef/landlord Mike Maguire believes in 'sustainable and sympathetic food tourism', making almost everything on the premises.

A free house with a public bar committed to real ale, the pub has a boules piste, six-acre garden, games room, residents' lounge and family room. Imaginative bar food is modestly priced, and the à la carte restaurant outstanding. Six cottage bedrooms with full facilities are in the main building; recently built garden rooms overlook their lake.

Situated in a beautiful part of Cornwall between Falmouth and Helston, the Trengilly is close to Skinner's Brewery centre, the Lizard peninsula, Flambards theme park and a seal sanctuary.

Q P

PENDEEN

North Inn

TR19 7DN

T (01736) 788417
W thenorthinnpendeen.co.uk
St Austell IPA, Tinners, Tribute, HSD
Double, twin, family, single room, all en-suite
£ ££
Snacks and meals daily, lunchtime and evening
Accepted

New purpose-built accommodation provides four bedrooms separate from the pub overlooking the garden, towards the sea, each with its own balcony. All can be used as a double, family, twin or single room, all have a bath and shower, TV, tea and coffee facilities, hair dryer and radio; one has a bathroom adapted for the disabled. Camping facilities (£3 per person per night including use of showers, no bookings taken) are also available.

The North Inn is a welcoming pub set in an old mining village halfway between Land's End and St Ives. Dating from around 1717, the former farmhouse was converted to a pub around 250 years ago. A small upstairs restaurant with impressive views of the sea serves home-made food. The authentic Indian curries including South Indian-style monkfish are favourites, and fresh fish is available, as well as vegetarian dishes. Breakfast is the full English variety. The pub was awarded Cornwall CAMRA Pub of the Year in 2003.

Set in an area of outstanding natural beauty, the inn is close to Geevor Tine Mine, now a mining museum, with cliffs, beach and coastal path close by.

PORTHLEVEN

Harbour Inn

Commercial Road, TR13 9JB

By the harbour
T (01326) 573876
W staustellbrewery.co.uk
St Austell Tinners, Tribute, HSD
Seven double, one twin, one family, one single room; all en-suite
£ ££ (£ in winter)
Meals served daily from noon until 9pm
Accepted

The hotel, known locally as 'the Commercial', stands by the harbour of this lovely old fishing port. The large open-plan bar, refurbished in a nautical style, leads to a side extension that houses the restaurant where children are welcome. The pub also has a games room with pool table.

The Harbour successfully combines a traditional atmosphere with modern facilities. The guest rooms, which benefit from sea views, are well equipped with satellite TV, hospitality tray, hairdryer, bathtubs and showers. Three double rooms have an extra bed available, while the family room is an adjoining double and twin. There is also a small self-catering flat.

A full English breakfast is served, and the main menu, of steaks and traditional pub favourites, based on local produce, is available all day. Visitors in winter can take advantage of excellent B&B rates of just £20 per person per night.

The pub hosts regular live entertainment at the weekend and there is plenty to do locally during the day. Boating and fishing trips are available from the harbour, while cycle routes and the coastal path pass nearby. Children will enjoy a trip to Flambards Theme Park (three miles) and Poldark Mine.

ST AGNES

☆ Driftwood Spars Hotel

Trevaunance Cove, Quay Road, TR5 0RT

- ▶ In St Agnes village, turn right into Peterville then follow tourist signs
- T (01872) 552428
- W driftwoodspars.com
- Driftwood Cuckoo Ale; St Austell Tribute, HSD; Sharp's Doom Bar, Own; Tetley Bitter
- Nine double, four family, one twin, one single room, all en-suite
- £ £££
- Lunchtime and evening meals
- Accepted

'Old Cornwall in the new millennium, with style, comfort and attention to detail,' is the Driftwood's claim. And with a variety of charming rooms, each with its own oceanic theme, the hotel is able to cater for all needs. Three south-facing Garden Rooms have their own private garden, two rooms together on the ground floor are perfect for an extended family, while the Top Deck is a large family suite with a private deck - this room, like many others, benefits from sea views. All have colour television and good quality refreshment tray.

The hotel was once a mine warehouse and its huge beams are said to have come from shipwrecks; the old parts are dark and mysterious, the newer areas light and airy. It has its own micro-brewery and its seafood restaurant is highly recommended. At breakfast local ingredients, including sausages or smoked fish, accompany the hotel's own free range eggs.

There is much to see and do in Trevaunance Cove and its environs. An abundance of craft and design workshops will ensure that you go home with some unusual souvenirs; you can visit the Blue Hills working tin mine and the Marine Conservation Area.

P

STRATTON

King's Arms

EX23 9BX

- ▶ Near Bude, off A39 on Holsworthy road in town centre
- T (01288) 352396
- E steve@thekingsarms.freeserve.co.uk
- Exmoor Ale; Ring O' Bells Dreckly; Sharp's Doom Bar; Theakston Old Peculier; guest beer
- Two double, one twin, two single rooms
- £ £-££
- Lunchtime and evening meals
- Accepted

Built in the 17th century to serve coaching traffic, the pub's name is an indication of the town's loyalties during the Civil War – the Battle of Stamford Hill was fought near here in 1643.

This simply-furnished establishment has retained its character in the well-worn Delabole slate floor, the large beamed fireplace and the small bread oven that was uncovered when the lounge was given a facelift. The pub is popular with locals – its Tuesday quiz is a highlight – and pool and darts are played. A second guest beer is often available in summer.

There is a large double room with en-suite facilities; the other rooms share a bathroom with bathtub, shower and WC, plus a second WC. All the rooms have tea and coffee making facilities. A full English breakfast is included, cooked by the landlord. A nearby butcher supplies meat from locally-reared animals and the eggs are all free range.

There are good walks to be enjoyed locally and the pub is just two miles from a beautiful beach. The coastal path is a 10-minute drive and the Eden Project an hour away.

P

TREWARMETT
Trewarmett Inn
PL34 0ET

▶ On B3263 between Tintagel and Trebarwith
T (01840) 770460
W thetrewarmettinn.co.uk
Sharp's Own, Doom Bar, Special; Skinner's Betty Stogs, Heligan Honey; guest beers
Four en-suite doubles, one twin with shower room
£ £
Evening meals, lunchtime in summer
Accepted

This 200-year-old inn was known by quarry workers as a 'kiddleywink' – an ale house where a wink would get you a drop of the hard stuff. Not sure if the same tactic still works today, but why would you need anything stronger with such a good range of Cornish ales to sample?

The food menu specialises in beef from the licensees' own farm a mile away at Condolden and fresh fish from Padstow or Port Isaac, while smoked cheese from Tintagel often features in vegetarian dishes. A full English breakfast is prepared by the restaurant chef, with eggs from a nearby farm, bacon and award-winning sausages from the local butcher.

A small bar with a cosy log burner is complemented by the larger restaurant; slate floors and stone chimneys add character.

The accommodation has recently been refurbished to provide light, comfortable bedrooms. The four doubles all benefit from panoramic coastal views; Trebarwith Strand and the North Cornwall coast path are easily accessible. Out of season guests can take advantage of a three-night dinner, bed and breakfast deal (£200 per couple).

Q ♣ P

TRURO
City Inn
Pydar Street, TR1 35P

▶ Near former cattle market
T (01872) 272623
F (01872) 272623
Courage Best Bitter; Sharp's Doom Bar; Skinner's Betty Stogs; guest beers
Nine rooms (four can be used as double, three as family); two are en-suite
£ £
Snacks and meals daily, lunchtime and evening
Accepted

The landlord has turned this inn into a vibrant community pub with a spacious single bar and 'sport' room. A member of CAMRA, his motto is to let the beer do the talking, and he serves a first-class pint, including guest ales from micro-breweries.

Described as 'a village pub in the city', this former traditional coaching inn 10 minutes' walk (uphill) from the city centre was originally built to serve the old cattle market. It has a white painted, part timbered frontage, with a stone and wood interior, the ceiling decorated with a huge collection of jugs. The garden has seating and a fishpond.

Accommodation is excellent value in the heart of Cornwall's capital city, famous for its beautiful cathedral, museum, and the meeting of the rivers Truro, Allen and Kenwyn. The price includes either a continental or full English breakfast with local bacon, sausages and eggs. At other times the kitchen serves wholesome home-cooked food including game in season, fish caught by fishermen who drink in the bar, and meat with full traceability to local farms.

Q ♣

VERYAN

New Inn

TR2 5QA

- ▶ Off the A3078 between St Mawes and St Austell
- T (01872) 501362
- W newinnveryan.co.uk
- St Austell Dartmoor Best, Tribute, HSD
- Two en-suite double/twin rooms, one single room with private bathroom; no children under 14 admitted
- £ ££
- Lunchtime and evening meals (not Sun eve)
- Accepted (not Amex or Diners)

Originally two 16th-century cottages, this pretty whitewashed pub stands at the centre of a picturesque village in the Roseland Peninsula, just a mile from the safe sandy beaches at Carne and Pendower. The spacious guest rooms have recently been updated and the two double rooms now have en-suite facilities; they all have television, tea and coffee making facilities and hairdryers.

Walkers are attracted to the area because of the many excellent paths surrounded by beautiful scenery and there are also facilities for sailing and horse riding nearby. There are many gardens open to the public, including Trelissick and Heligan which is a half hour drive away, close to the Eden Project.

In the pub kitchen, they rely on seasonal produce as far as possible to offer a menu that changes frequently, with plenty of fresh vegetables, along with meat and fish from local suppliers. Vegetarians, vegans and others with special dietary requirements can usually be accommodated. There is a breakfast buffet of fresh fruit salad, fruit juice, yogurt and cereals to which you can add a full cooked breakfast, or cold baked ham and eggs, kippers, smoked haddock or simply free-range eggs as you like them.

Q

Cumbria

BARROW-IN-FURNESS

Ambrose Hotel

Duke Street, LA14 1XT

T (01229) 830990
F (01229) 830991
W ambrosehotel.co.uk
Coniston Bluebird; guest beers
Five double/twin rooms, two family, one single, all en-suite
£ £
Snacks and meals daily, lunchtime and evening
Accepted

Real ale, real food and real fire is the boast of the Ambrose, a town-centre hotel opened as a public house in 1861. The hotel has a traditional feel with original beams, a panelled public bar and games room.

Bedroom facilities include colour TV, tea and coffee making, hair dryer and fridge. The full English breakfast, featuring Waberthwaite local bacon, Estuary sausage and black pudding and local free-range eggs, or a vegetarian alternative, or Manx kippers, is included in the very reasonable price for an overnight stay. At other times home-cooked meals feature local produce such as Lakeland beef, lamb and pork, and Waberthwaite Cumberland sausages.

The Ambrose offers Coniston Bluebird as its house beer, but also provides a changing range of ales from breweries in Cumbria and the north such as Ulverston, Thwaites and Rudgate.

Barrow-in-Furness has an interesting industrial heritage, situated on the coast down in the heel of Cumbria close to an island nature reserve. Nearby are Furness Abbey, the award-winning Dock museum over the original Victorian graving dock, and Dalton Castle, with the Lakes 20 minutes' drive away.

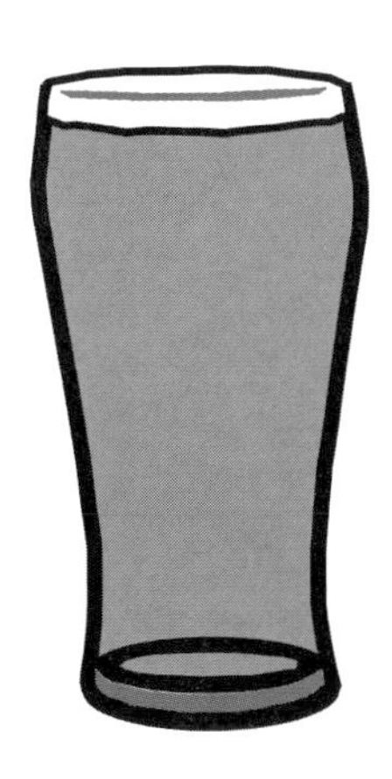

BOOT
Boot
CA19 1TG

▶ Off A595 near Gosforth
T (01946) 723224
W bootinn.co.uk
Robinsons Old Stockport, Hartleys XB, Cumbria Way, Unicorn, Double Drop
Four double rooms, three twin, one family, one single, all en-suite
£ ££
Snacks and meals daily, lunchtime and evening
Accepted

This traditional Lakeland inn stands in a magnificent setting in Eskdale Valley - described by John Ruskin as 'the gateway to paradise'. A walkers' pub with a warm and welcoming atmosphere, it is surrounded by the highest fells in Lakeland but is just a short walk from Dalegarth station on the famous La'al Ratty line. Boot is an unspoilt hamlet of ancient cottages, with a 17th-century pack horse bridge and the country's oldest working watermill.

Bedrooms overlooking the fells have recently been redecorated; there is a residents' lounge and boot room with drying facilities for the many walkers. The price per night includes a hearty cooked breakfast with local bacon, Cumberland sausage and free-range eggs from a nearby farm.

The inn specialises in traditional and hearty home cooking and baking. Main meals feature local lamb and beef, and home-grown fruit and herbs. You can dine in the16th-century beamed restaurant, in the cosy bar or in the light and airy conservatory.

The bar offers a wide-screen TV and pool table, a conservatory with play area, and separate quiet snug with roaring fire in winter. There are two beer festivals a year. Reduced rates are available in quieter months. Well behaved dogs are welcome.

Q P

BOUTH
White Hart Inn
LA12 8JB

▶ Off A590, 6 miles NE of Ulverston
T (01229) 861229
E nigelwhitehart@aol.com
Black Sheep Best Bitter; Jennings Cumberland Ale; Tetley Bitter; guest beers
Five double rooms (also available as single or twin occupancy), four en-suite, one with bathroom
£ £-££
Snacks and meals daily, lunchtime and evening
Accepted

Overnight guests can take their pick from ancient or modern – three bedrooms are in the old oak-beamed part of this 17th-century coaching inn and two were built three years ago. All have fine views; there is a TV in all rooms. Excellent value, the price includes a sturdy breakfast of Cumberland sausage, bacon, sautéed potato, beans, tomatoes, mushrooms, and eggs of your choice as well as cereals or fruit juice.

Set in the Lake District national park, the White Hart is in the village centre opposite the green. Slate floors, original beams, old farm implements and real fires give a Lakeland atmosphere, while a heated terrace offers outstanding views. Guest beers are often from Cumbrian breweries such as Coniston or Ulverston. The inn is no-smoking throughout. In the upstairs restaurant (it is advisable to book when you reserve your room, especially at weekends) beef from nearby Abbots Reading Farm is a speciality. Children's portions are available.

Local attractions include Lakeside and Haverthwaite Steam Railway, adjoining Grizedale Forest and the Lakes themselves. Pets are welcome at a fiver a night.

P

BROUGHTON-IN-FURNESS

☆ Manor Arms

The Square, LA20 6HY

T (01229) 716286
F (01229) 716729
Coniston Bluebird; Yates Bitter; guest beers
Two double, one twin room, all en-suite
£ £
Snacks only served noon to 10pm daily
Accepted

If you want to introduce someone to real ale for the first time, this is the place to take them, recommends the local CAMRA branch. Praise indeed, and well-deserved. The father and son owners, in 'a quiet, unpretentious quest after perfection', ensure that the constantly-changing selection of eight beers is kept in tiptop condition.

Breakfast is delivered to your room, and a splendid meal it is. You can choose from cereal, Cumberland sausage, smoked back bacon, mushrooms, tomato, one or two fried free-range eggs, poached eggs on toast, sausage or bacon sarnies, or smoked haddock or kippers when available. Snacks are available at any time of day.

A multi-award winning hostelry, this delightful, spotless free house is set in an imposing Georgian square at the centre of this small charter town close to Duddon Valley. Two open fires, one in an 18th-century basket fireplace, create a warm and welcoming atmosphere. Foxfield station is a mile and a half away.

Broughton-in-Furness is a noted walking centre with access from the village to local walks around the Duddon Estuary. Nearby attractions include the Swinside stone circle, Furness Abbey and the Dock Museum.

BUTTERMERE

Bridge Hotel

CA13 9UZ

▶ Off B5289 from Keswick
T (017687) 70252
W bridge-hotel.com
Black Sheep Best Bitter; Hawkshead Bitter; Theakston Old Peculier
Twelve double, seven twin, two single rooms, all en-suite
£ £££-££££
Snacks and meals daily, lunchtime and evening
Accepted (not Amex or Diners)

Though quite a large hotel – 21 bedrooms, some with four-posters – the Bridge is a real pub and an oasis of tranquillity set among breath-catching, soaring scenery. Most of the individually-decorated bedrooms enjoy superb views, and provide tea and coffee making, hair dryer and direct dial phone – but not TV due to poor reception caused by the surrounding fells.

In this marvellous location between Buttermere and Crummock Water, on a site occupied for over 1,000 years, the former coaching inn attracts walkers, cyclists, bird watchers, anglers, photographers, painters and endless visitors (including Alfred Wainwright). It has two traditional bars, a patio with stunning views, residents' sitting room and dining room.

Listed in CAMRA's Good Pub Food guide, the hotel provides outstanding cuisine featuring local flavours, and there is a separate vegetarian menu. A large buffet breakfast includes Cumbrian ham and cheese plus hot choices such as full English with Cumberland sausage and black pudding, smoked haddock or grilled Scottish kipper. Packed lunches can be provided on request.

Note that prices vary depending on the time of year and whether you want to include the five-course dinner with your B&B.

DENT
George & Dragon Hotel
Main Street, LA10 5QL

▶ Centre of the village
T (015396) 25256
E thegeorgeanddragon@tiscali.co.uk
Dent Bitter, Aviator, Kamikaze; guest beers
Five double, three twin (one with bunk beds), two family rooms, all en-suite
£ ££
Meals served all day until 9.30pm
Accepted

Dent is one of the most quaint and pretty villages in the Yorkshire Dales, with its cobbled streets and famous fountain. It enjoys a rural setting in the National Park near the head of Dentdale and the market town of Sedbergh, within easy reach of the Lake District and the west coast.

Dent Brewery was set up initially to supply the Sun Inn in the village; this lovely old pub, a favourite with local CAMRA members, is still thought of as the brewery tap and well worth a visit for a pint or two. The beers proved so popular that the brewery now supplies around 50 free trade outlets and it has also acquired the George and Dragon in the centre of the village.

Dating back to the early 1800s, the hotel features much traditional wood panelling in its two bars, pool room and restaurant. The 10 comfortable guest rooms have colour televisions and facilities for making hot drinks. Special rates are available at the weekend for dinner, bed and breakfast, and golfing breaks can be booked all year round. Breakfast is a full English affair and the kitchen makes use of locally-sourced ingredients as far as possible.

Q P

ELTERWATER
Britannia Inn
LA22 9HP

▶ Off B5343
T (015394) 37210
W britinn.co.uk
Coniston Bluebird; Jennings Bitter; Taylor Landlord; guests
Seven double, two twin rooms, all en-suite, one with bathroom
£ £££
Snacks and meals daily, lunchtime and evening
Accepted (not Amex)

Once a gentleman's farmhouse, the Britannia became an inn around 200 years ago and retains the low ceilings, original beams and stone flagging. The bar rooms have roaring fires in winter; in summer the patio provides stunning views towards the Elterwater tarns.

In keeping with the 500-year-old building, the bedrooms have their own individual character combining old world charm with modern convenience – all were completely refurbished a year ago with new shower rooms installed.

Breakfast starts with fruit juice, fresh fruit and cereal followed by eggs cooked as you like, award-winning Waberthwaite Cumberland sausage, bacon, fried bread, grilled tomatoes and sautéed potatoes. The main menu offers a wide choice of dishes, many home-made. Good, freshly-made children's meals are also available.

Situated in Langdale Valley, the pub is in excellent walking country close to Scafell, Bowfell and Langdale Pikes, with Ambleside and Grasmere a short drive. A champion of champions beer festival is held in November. Guests are offered one free visit to the leisure club on the adjoining Langdale estate.

Q ♣ P

FOXFIELD
Prince of Wales
LA20 6BX

- ▶ Opposite station on A5092
- T (01229) 716238
- W princeofwalesfoxfield.co.uk
- Beer range varies, always including a mild
- Two double, one twin room, all en-suite
- £ £
- Snacks Fri-Sun 12-7pm
- Not accepted

Mild champions Stuart and Linda Johnson put beer first at the Prince of Wales, serving ale from their two micro-breweries, Foxfield and Tigertops, plus an ever-changing range from brewers nationwide. Situated in a rural hamlet opposite towering Black Combe, the pub adjoins Foxfield station – it was built at the same time, circa 1850 – and is on a bus route. With themed beer festivals held throughout year, and six other pubs in the parish serving good ale, this is a real beer drinkers' haven.

The pub is closed on Mondays and Tuesdays and does not serve meals, but provides home-made snacks from Friday to Sunday. A traditional drinking establishment with main bar and games area, the pub's decor is, in the words of the owners, 'in need of renewal'. But the three guest rooms were recently refurbished and share a sitting room with TV, video and DVD. Bedrooms provide warm, basic accommodation with old-fashioned furniture, two with showers, the other with bath and shower.

In the breakfast room, tuck into a traditional English with famous Woodalls of Waberthwaite black pudding, the local butcher's sausages and 'Donald's eggs'. Prices are excellent value and there is a reduction for CAMRA members.

GREAT LANGDALE
Old Dungeon Ghyll Hotel
LA22 9JY

- ▶ Take B5343 off A593
- T (015394) 37272
- W www.odg.co.uk
- Black Sheep Special; Jennings Cumberland Ale; Theakston XB, Old Peculier; Yates Bitter; guest beers
- Nine double, two single, two family rooms, some en-suite
- £ £££; no single night bookings available at weekends
- Lunchtime and evening meals
- Accepted

The hotel is blessed with a spectacular setting at the head of the Great Langdale Valley in the heart of the Lake District. Catering for fell walkers and climbers, with a drying room for outdoor clothing, the hotel offers a real escape – you will find no TV, mobile phones or Internet connection here. The hotel has a comfortable residents' lounge, warmed by an open fire, but most visitors head first to the Hikers' Bar with its hard floor and bench seating, where the patio offers a splendid view of the fells.

Home-cooked meals, featuring local meat and organic vegetables when available, can be taken in the hotel bar or dining room, but gone are the days when visiting parties would sound a horn at the top of the Blea Tarn Pass to signal how many people would be arriving for a meal! A sturdy breakfast, with free-range eggs and home-baked bread, will set you up for a day out on the fells.

In the evening you will find ample hot water for a soak in the tub, although not all the rooms have their own facilities. The guest rooms are traditionally furnished with brass beds – some are four-posters.

HAWKSHEAD

King's Arms

The Square, LA22 0NZ

- ▶ Village signposted from Ambleside
- T (015394) 36372
- F (015394) 36006
- W kingsarmshawkshead.co.uk
- Black Sheep Best Bitter; Coniston Bluebird; Hawkshead Bitter, Gold, Red; guest beers
- Seven double, two family rooms, all en-suite
- £ £ per person
- Snacks and meals daily, lunchtime and evening
- Accepted

At the heart of the Lake District, close to Windermere in the beautiful Esthwaite vale, the Kings Arms has greeted visitors since Elizabethan times. One of four pubs in the village, it features a massive regal sculpture by local artist John Whitworth supporting the bar ceiling.

Set among hills and fells, the inn attracts tourists and walkers in large numbers and free fishing is available for guests. Beatrix Potter's home is a short distance away, as is Grizedale Forest, and the passenger steam launch on Coniston.

Attractively-decorated en-suite rooms vary in price depending on the season, with special mid-week breaks from £25; two self-catering cottages are also available. For breakfast porridge, fruit juice or cereal are followed by full English of Cumberland sausage, bacon, free-range egg, mushrooms and tomatoes, scrambled and poached eggs on toast, or kippers.

At lunchtime there is a choice of snacks from chip butty with onion relish to minute steak on rye bread open sarnie with beetroot and horseradish chutney. Evening meals include Esthwaite organic trout or steak and Hawkshead ale pie – beer from the local brewery is always served. Packed lunches are available on request. Well-behaved dogs and children are welcome.

LOWESWATER
Kirkstile Inn
CA13 0RU

- ▶ Off B5289, follow signs to Loweswater
- T (01900) 85219
- F (01900) 85239
- W kirkstile.com
- Coniston Bluebird; Loweswater Melbreak Bitter, Kirkstile Gold, Grasmoor Dark; guest beer
- Five double, three twin, one family room, all en-suite
- £ £££
- Snacks and meals daily, lunchtime and evening
- Accepted

Home to the Loweswater brewery, Kirkstile is a classic 16th-century Lakeland inn with low ceilings, open fires and stone walls in a stunning setting between Loweswater and Crummock Water. It has a single bar with three seating areas and a large outdoor area with views across to Buttermere valley.

Recently upgraded cottage-style accommodation includes fresh flowers, tea and coffee making trays; there are two private sitting rooms (one with TV) for residents, providing marvellous views of the fells. One room has a four-poster bed, and the family suite has a double and a twin plus bathroom.

Breakfast includes fruit, cereal or porridge followed by Cumberland sausage, bacon, tomato, mushrooms and eggs fried, poached or scrambled, or poached haddock or grilled kipper fillets. To drink, tea or coffee are both available decaff, as well as Earl Grey, camomile, peppermint or fruit teas.

An interesting home-cooked menu served in the bar and dining room offers local cheeses and fish, Lakeland meat, black pudding in beer batter, steak and ale pie with Melbreak Bitter, plus vegetarian choices.

Q P

MILNTHORPE

Cross Keys Hotel

1 Park Road, LA7 7AB

- ▶ On A6, close to M6 jcts 35/36
- T (015395) 62115
- F (015395) 62446
- W thecrosskeyshotel.co.uk
- Robinsons Hartleys XB, Dark Mild, Unicorn; guest beer
- Six double, two family rooms, all en-suite
- £ ££
- Snacks and meals daily, lunchtime and evening
- Accepted

A family-run hotel, the Cross Keys is a historic coaching inn that has recently undergone major refurbishment and modernisation. The eight well-appointed bedrooms are all en-suite, some with seating areas, and have colour TV, safe, hairdryer, direct dial phone, courtesy tray and tea making.

A Robinsons house, the pub also serves a weekly guest beer in its oak-panelled bar. It is set in the historic village of Milnthorpe with its busy Friday street market dating back to 1334. The village's heyday was from the mid-18th to 19th century when many buildings in the centre – now a conservation area – were built, including the Cross Keys. When the Kendal-Lancaster turnpike road was constructed 200 years ago the village became an important staging post. Nearby is Arnside, classed as an area of outstanding natural beauty, with walks through wooded hills and along the shore; Sandside estuary on Morecambe Bay is also close by.

The restaurant serves meat from Silverdale and Arnside butchers, as well as veggie options, and the puds are a speciality - sticky toffee is a local favourite.

OVERLEAF: Cross Keys Hotel, Milnthorpe

NEAR SAWREY

Tower Bank Arms

LA22 0LF

- ▶ On B5285, 6 miles S of Ambleside
- T (015394) 36334
- W towerbankarms.com
- Beer range varies
- Two double, one twin room, all en-suite
- £ ££
- Snacks and meals daily, lunchtime and evening
- Accepted

This traditional, historic Lakeland inn is illustrated in Beatrix Potter's story Jemima Puddleduck, and adjacent to the author's home Hill Top. With a stone-flagged floor and log fires in winter, it is a cosy, popular, friendly little country pub – there is no juke box or fruit machine. Note the photos of visiting celebrities on the walls.

Ideally placed for exploring the Lake District, the accommodation is popular with walkers, cyclists and tourists. The freshly-cooked traditional English breakfast is a highlight, featuring local produce including artisan breads. Food is hearty and reasonably priced at other times of the day, too, such as generous sandwiches with fillings from Cumbrian ham to Cumberland sausage, or a bowl of Cumbrian beef and ale stew with herby dumplings at lunchtime. The tempting dinner menu includes starters such as game terrine, poached smoked haddock or mussels steamed with chilli and lemongrass, and main courses could be pork loin stuffed with black pudding mousse or Cumbrian lamb rump with root vegetable and oranges.

The inn is close to Windermere, Esthwaite Lake, Grizedale Forest, cycle trails and walks. Constantly-changing ales are mainly from Cumbrian breweries; the small car park is reserved for residents.

Q P

RAVENSTONEDALE
King's Head Hotel
CA17 4NH

- ▶ Off M6 jct 38 near Scotch Corner
- T (015396) 23284
- W kings-head.net
- Black Sheep Best Bitter; guest beers
- One double, one twin room, both en-suite, family room with private bathroom
- £ ££
- Lunchtime and evening meals
- Accepted

The array of pump clips and four guest beer pumps in the cosy bar show how serious they are about real ale at the King's Head. A traditional cider is also always available. The inn has a games room, lounge and large dining room, all with an olde-worlde feel about them. Family-oriented, the pub welcomes walkers (and their dogs) from the nearby fells. The pub's beck-side garden is home to a rare population of red squirrels.

Guest rooms are simply but comfortably furnished and all have TV and tea and coffee making facilities. Your breakfast will be cooked to order with eggs as you please; kippers are an alternative to the usual full English. The restaurant menu has recently been revamped and offers a mix of local dishes, such as lamb from the Lakes and Dales and Ravenstonedale salmon, and international dishes, including curries and stir fries.

A sleepy, unspoilt village in the Eden Valley, Ravenstonedale boasts the remains of a 13th-century Gilbertine abbey. Hotel residents can make use of the village tennis courts and golf course, and there are facilities nearby for horse riding. Tickets for fishing – both coarse and fly – are available for rivers Eden and Lune.

Q P

ROBINSONS
CROSS KEYS
HOTEL
ROBINSONS

SHAP
Greyhound Hotel
Main Street, CA10 3PW

- ▶ Half mile from M6 jct 39
- T (01931) 716474
- W greyhoundshap.co.uk
- Hesket Newmarket Doris's 90th Birthday Ale; Jennings Bitter, Cumberland Ale; Robinsons Cumbria Way; Tetley Bitter; guest beers
- Four double, three twin, one family, two single rooms, all en-suite
- £ ££
- Snacks and meals daily, lunchtime and evening
- Accepted

Westmorland CAMRA Pub of the Year in 2004 & 2005, the Greyhound is a spacious former coaching inn dating from 1684. It has been welcoming guests for well over 300 years (including Bonnie Prince Charlie in 1745) but nowadays offers accommodation with more modern comforts including colour TV and hostess tray in the 10 en-suite rooms.

Coast-to-coast walkers night-stopping at the Greyhound are fortified by a hearty breakfast including local butcher Nick Bellas' world championship Cumberland sausage and Westmorland black pudding, free-range eggs laid by Vera-next-door's hens, bacon, tomatoes and mushrooms. Porridge is an option.

You can eat in the bar or in one of the two restaurants, where the same commitment to local produce prevails, including meat from local farmers, all butchered in-house, and fresh fish from Fleetwood. Meal choices include cod in beer batter, pot-roasted Fell-bred brisket, and veggie options, all under £10, with small portions available.

Shap is a popular village near Shap Abbey, Lowther Park, Rheged Discovery Centre, Ullswater, Lakeland fells and valleys, and historic Penrith and Kendal.

P

STAVELEY
Eagle & Child
Kendal Road, LA8 9LP

- ▶ Off A591 between Windermere and Kendal
- T (01539) 821320
- F (01539) 821320
- W eaglechildinn.co.uk
- Beer range varies
- Two double, two twin, one family room, all en-suite
- £ ££
- Snacks and meals daily, lunchtime and evening
- Accepted

With a huge commitment to local ales, many from micros, the Eagle and Child offers a choice of beers from Hawkshead, Barngates, Tirril, Dent, Coniston and Hesket Newmarket regularly on handpump. The pub also holds two beer festivals a year. The upstairs function room is in the style of a medieval banqueting hall and the pub benefits from two gardens, one of them next to the River Kent on the other side of the road.

Cosy bedrooms, all with colour TV, are economically priced, and there are special rates in winter. Featuring in CAMRA's Good Pub Food guide, the inn offers a full English breakfast, including locally-made sausages from Hayton's. Local produce is always a speciality and main meals could include slow-braised Kentmere lamb shank on mustard mash, chicken breast stuffed with Hayton's Cumberland sausage, fresh local trout or beef in ale gravy with Yorkshire pudding.

Situated in the Lake District national park, the hostelry is also within easy reach of the Yorkshire Dales, attracting tourists, families, walkers and cyclists. Buses to Kendal and Ambleside stop outside.

P

TROUTBECK

☆ Queen's Head Hotel

LA23 1PW

▶ On A592 (Kirkstone Pass road)
T (015394) 32174
F (015394) 31938
W queensheadhotel.com
Coniston Bluebird; Hawkshead Red; Jennings Cumberland Ale; guest beers
One twin, fifteen double rooms, all en-suite
£ £££-££££
Snacks and meals daily, lunchtime and evening
Accepted (not Amex or Diners)

A truly outstanding Cumbrian breakfast awaits overnight visitors to the Queen's Head. You can even start your day with a drop of real ale, an ingredient in the grain mustard rarebit topped with grilled field mushrooms. Or you can have a nip of whisky in the rich porridge cooked with cream and golden syrup. But there's also toasted banana bread with fresh banana, honey and toasted almonds as well as pancakes topped with scrambled eggs, crisp streaky bacon and maple syrup. Not forgetting the black pudding and pork sausages made on the premises. It's no surprise that the inn gained a star for outstanding food and ale in CAMRA's Good Pub Food guide.

Rooms are tasteful, too, including the master bedroom with a four-poster bed. The main bar has a massive open fireplace, the bar itself is made from an Elizabethan four-poster from Appleby Castle, and there are oak beams and stone flagged floors throughout.

The inn has stunning views across the Troutbeck valley to towering Garburn Pass and is ideally placed for visiting Windermere and Ullswater.

P

ABOVE TOP: Bay Horse, Ulverston, Cumbria. ABOVE BOTTOM: English breakfast at the Bay Horse

ULVERSTON
☆ Bay Horse
Canal Foot, LA12 9EL

- ▶ Follow signs for Canal Foot from A590
- T (01229) 583972
- W thebayhorsehotel.co.uk
- Jennings Cocker Hoop; guest beers
- Six double, three twin rooms, all en-suite
- £ £££-££££
- Snacks and meals daily, lunchtime and evening
- Accepted

Six of the comfortable rooms at the Bay Horse (little touches include home-made biscuits) are sea facing with balconies, giving a panoramic view across the estuary to the Lakeland Fells.

Chef/proprietor Bob Lyons, once head chef at the Miller Howe, provides exciting, award-winning food with the emphasis on local ingredients such as Morecambe Bay shrimps and saltmarsh lamb. He dishes up one of the best English breakfasts in this guide – kidneys, white as well as black pudding, and fried apple rings, all in a huge platter alongside locally cured bacon, Cumberland sausage, fried egg, mushrooms, tomato and fried bread. Or you might prefer grilled Scottish kippers, naturally-smoked haddock, eggs as you like them, followed by wholemeal toast with home-made marmalade or lemon curd.

Patronised by walkers, bird watchers, tourists, families and business people, the Bay Horse has a traditional bar plus conservatory restaurant and is handy for Holker Hall, Lake Coniston, Ulverston Golf Club and the Laurel and Hardy Museum. Guided walks are available across the sands of the Levens Estuary and Morecambe Bay.

♣ P

ULVERSTON
King's Head
14 Queen Street, LA12 7AF

- ▶ From jct 26 of M6 follow A590 towards Barrow
- T (01229) 588064
- Jennings Cumberland Ale, Cocker Hoop, Sneck Lifter; guest beers
- One double, three twin rooms, sharing two shower rooms
- £ £
- Lunch Thu-Sat, evening meals Tue-Sat
- Accepted

Built around the middle of the 17th century, this old coaching inn, with exposed beams and open fires, has maintained its traditional atmosphere and there are even rumours of the presence of a ghost. However, the possibility of unearthly companionship does not deter tourists, walkers and contract workers from taking advantage of the budget accommodation.

Breakfast is generous – egg, bacon, sausage, mushrooms, tomatoes and black pudding make up the full English, along with cereals, toast and marmalade. The main meals are also good value. If you eat in the dining room look out for the well that was uncovered during refurbishment and is now illuminated under a glass floor.

The pub has a garden where you can enjoy a fine pint of local Jennings ale in summer while you watch a game of bowls on the bowling green – now a rare amenity in English pubs. Ulverston stands at the start of the Cumbria Way on the edge of the Lake District, with a beach, wildlife park and Buddhist priory all nearby; Holker Hall and Muncaster Castle are both worth a visit.

Q

Derbyshire

ALDERWASLEY
Bear Inn
DE56 2RD

T (01629) 822585
F (01629) 826676
Draught Bass; Black Sheep Bitter; Greene King Old Speckled Hen; guest beers
Ten double rooms, all en-suite
£ £ per person
Snacks and meals daily, lunchtime and evening
Accepted (not Amex)

Originally a coaching inn dating from the late 16th or early 17th century, the Bear's interior retains original stone and low beams, and is furnished in keeping with its age. All rooms are en-suite, fitted with antique furniture, while 'superior' rooms have four-poster beds.

Happy to cater for all dietary requirements, the Bear uses almost entirely local produce from nearby farms for its home-prepared food, from the full English breakfast to the à la carte menu and Sunday carvery. Home-made bar snacks are popular with the real ale drinkers. Apart from the regular beers you might find guests such as Whim's Hartington and Taylor Landlord.

This popular pub welcomes visitors from regulars to tourists to walkers (and their dogs). There is a function room and beer garden, and even a helicopter pad. It is handy for the Heights of Abraham, Chatsworth House, Carsington Water, Bakewell and Matlock Bath. Alderwasley's claim to fame is that the yachtswoman Ellen MacArthur was born here.

Q P

ASHBOURNE
Green Man
St John Street, DE6 1GH

- T (01335) 345783
- Leatherbritches Dr Johnson; Greene King Abbot; guest beers
- Ten double, one twin, nine single rooms, all en-suite
- £ ££
- Snacks and meals daily, lunchtime and evening
- Accepted

Ashbourne is famous for its spring water but if you stay at the Green Man you may prefer to try the real ales. House beer Dr Johnson, brewed exclusively by Derbyshire micro Leatherbritches, is £2 a pint, and guest beers are from local breweries including Whim, Falstaff, Peak Ales, Thornbridge and Derby Brewing Co. The Green Man hosts the annual Ashbourne Beer Festival at August Bank Holiday with 40 ales, five ciders and 10 bands.

This 17th-century, privately-owned, town-centre coaching inn with gallows sign outside has 20 'olde worlde' rooms, all en-suite, with colour TV, tea and coffee making and direct dial phone. There are two bars: the traditional, oak-panelled Boswell bar with log fires, and larger, livelier Johnson bar, with leather sofas, pool, darts and games machines, attracting younger customers. Outside are two beer gardens for alfresco drinking.

A full English breakfast includes bacon, sausage, free-range egg, tomatoes, mushrooms, fried bread and baked beans (vegetarian sausages are available). The inn is a member of Peak District Cuisine and uses local produce as far as possible – the 'pie and pasty' offer includes a pint of Dr Johnson plus Derbyshire beef and local ale pasty for just £3.95.

Ashbourne is close to the Peak District National Park, Alton Towers, Chatsworth House, Buxton and Heights of Abraham.

Q P

ASHOVER
☆ Old Poets' Corner
Rutts Road, S45 0EW

- T (01246) 590888
- W oldpoets.co.uk
- Greene King Abbot; Kelham Island Pale Rider; Oakham JHB; guest beers
- Three double, one twin room, all en-suite
- £ ££
- Snacks and meals daily, lunchtime and evening
- Accepted

With the redoubtable Kim and Jackie Beresford at the helm, the Old Poets' Corner goes from strength to strength – twice Chesterfield CAMRA Pub of the Season, in 2006 it was Pub of the Year. Originally a 17th-century coaching inn, it burnt down and was rebuilt in mock-Tudor style. A delightful building, it has beams and open fires inside, and is decorated with old village photos and hops over the bar. Eight beers are always available including the regulars and changing guest ales – and now ales from the pub's own micro brewery.

Comfy olde-worlde style bedrooms have brass beds, colour TV, tea and coffee making facilities, and a holiday cottage attached to the pub sleeps eight. The landlord himself cooks an ample breakfast few can finish – cereal or juice followed by two eggs, fried bread, sausage, bacon, black pudding, beans and tomatoes – but if you want something different, just ask. Featuring in CAMRA's Good Pub Food guide, the pub serves tasty, traditional meals including a monster 19-oz haddock in real ale batter, pork and black pudding sausages with mash, and authentic curries.

An attractive place to discover, Ashover was 2006 national Village of the Year, and is popular with walkers and cyclists. Bargain breaks are available.

Q P

CHESTERFIELD
Portland Hotel
West Bars, S40 1AY

- ▶ Off the smaller of the town's two market squares
- T (01246) 293600
- Greene King Abbot, Marston's Burton Bitter; Theakston Best Bitter; guest beers
- Twelve double, six twin, two single, one family room
- £ £ (room only)
- Meals and snacks available all day
- Accepted

Chesterfield is the largest town in Derbyshire and this traditional Victorian hotel dating from 1899 in the town centre is ideally situated for both business travellers and tourists. It is a convenient base for exploring the Peak District and Sherwood Forest as well as stately homes such as Chatsworth and Hardwick Hall. Another must-see in the town itself is the church of St Mary and All Saints with its famous crooked spire, a local landmark. The pub gets busy on market days.

The Portland, once a railway hotel, is now a Wetherlodge and offers the usual Wetherspoon's range of beers, though you may be lucky to find a brew from Wentworth in nearby Rotherham as a guest. Meals and snacks are served all day.

Accommodation here is in good-value rooms rated two-star by the ETC. At the weekend you can stay three nights for the price of two. Tea and coffee making facilities, television, hair dryer, trouser press and modem point are all provided as standard. Breakfast is extra. Children are welcome.

Q P

DERBY
Alexandra Hotel
203 Siddals Road, DE1 2QE

- ▶ Short walk from Derby station
- T (01332) 293993
- W tynemill.co.uk
- Beer range varies
- Three twin, one single room, all en-suite
- £ £
- Snacks and meals at lunchtime
- Not accepted

The birthplace of Derby CAMRA in 1974, the Alexandra Hotel – affectionately dubbed the Alex – offers a budget deal on all fronts. Comfortably refurbished twin en-suite rooms with shower, TV, tea and coffee making, are priced at just £40 per room per night including a light, continental style breakfast.

At lunchtime, snacks and plain meals are all good value – filled baguettes with salad or chips, jacket potatoes and salad, bangers and mash with onion gravy, shepherd's pie with chips, or the working man's lunch of sausage, egg, chips and beans, all below £4.

Originally the Midland Coffee House, the two-roomed hotel with central bar was named after the Danish princess who became the wife of Edward VII. Built in 1871 for rail passengers, memorabilia reflects strong railway links. It has been part of the Tynemill group of pubs for 18 years, and is a champion of micro-breweries, as well as selling continental and bottled beers.

There is always a warm welcome for a mixed clientele: train buffs to CAMRA members, walkers to cyclists, and everyone visiting historic Derby with its many places of local interest. The pub has its own secure car park.

P

GREAT HUCKLOW

Queen Anne Inn

Main road, SK17 8RF

- ▶ Signposted off Tideswell-Bradwell road
- T (01298) 871246
- W thequeenanne.net
- Beer range varies
- One double, one twin room, both en-suite
- £ ££
- Snacks and meals daily, lunchtime and evening
- Accepted

The only pub in this pretty village, the Queen Anne was originally a farmhouse selling ale as early as 1577, but was formally licensed in 1704, so celebrated its tercentenary in 2004. A mellow, stone-built inn, inside there are low ceilings, beams and brasses, with a high backed settle and open fires. Beers are often from Storm Brewery and bottle-conditioned beers are stocked.

The inn has just two guest rooms overlooking the pub garden, with wonderful views; rooms have colour TV and tea and coffee making facilities.

Local produce features in both the full English breakfast and other meals on a menu offering excellent value for money. Dishes such as steak and ale pie with vegetables, Cumberland sausages or beef stew in a giant Yorkshire pudding, or lamb madras, are all around £7; the grills (except the 16-oz T-bone steak) are below £10.

Great Hucklow thrived on lead mining in the 18th century and was also on a salt route from Cheshire to Yorkshire. At the heart of the Peak District National Park, with pleasant pastures and ancient stone walls, it is a haven for ramblers.

There is much to discover close by: Hope Valley, the Blue John mine and caves, Peak Rail, the starting point of the Pennine Way, and stately homes Chatsworth and Haddon Hall.

Q P

HARTSHORNE

☆ Mill Wheel

Ticknall Road, DE11 7AS

- ▶ On A514, near Burton upon Trent
- T (01283) 550335
- W themillwheel.co.uk
- Greene King Abbot Ale; Oakham range; Tollgate range; guest beers
- Four double rooms, all en-suite
- £ £
- Snacks and meals daily, lunchtime and evening
- Accepted

The Mill Wheel, a converted millhouse with working waterwheel, offers quality accommodation at a rock bottom price. In 2004 it opened its adjoining B&B cottage with four double en-suite rooms, costing around £50 per room per night, including continental or full English breakfast, fitted with hand-made pine furniture, and offering colour TV and tea and coffee facilities. One ground floor room is wheelchair accessible and adapted for disabled use.

There was probably a corn mill on the site in the 17th century but the present building dates from the late 18th century when wooden screws were manufactured on lathes turned by one waterwheel. In 1987 the brick building was converted to a pub with the 23-foot waterwheel restored and now a feature of both the traditional bar with open fire and the beamed restaurant.

A tempting menu offers a good-value lunchtime two-course meal, with dishes such as medallions of beef with wild mushrooms, or grilled mackerel with polenta cake and gooseberry puree, followed by warm Belgian waffle. The evening menu also has some mouth-watering specialities. The full range of Oakham ales is served.

Local attractions include Calke Abbey, Ashby Castle, Bass Museum, Donnington Park and East Midlands airport.

Q P

HATHERSAGE
Plough Inn
Leadmill Bridge, S32 1BA

- ▶ On B6001, 1 mile from Hathersage village and rail station
- T (01433) 650319
- W theploughinn-hathersage.co.uk
- Adnams Bitter; Theakston Best Bitter, Old Peculier; guest beers
- Five double/twin rooms, all en-suite, one wheelchair accessible
- £ £££-££££
- Lunchtime and evening meals
- Accepted

In the heart of the Peak District, the Plough Inn stands in its own grounds – all nine acres of it stretching alongside the banks of the River Derwent.

The guest rooms are comfortable and well appointed with television, hospitality tray and hairdryers. Two luxury bedrooms are in the newly converted September Cottage, across the cobbled courtyard from the pub. The cottage has been carefully renovated using exposed beams and brickwork and offers a full bathroom and sitting area with video and hi-fi.

Breakfast is generous, whether you choose the continental or full English. Cereals and fresh fruit are always available as well as smoked salmon or smoked haddock. Main dishes, served in the cosy bar or relaxing restaurant, are a mix of modern European and traditional favourites. The owners source as much of their produce locally as possible and can cater for any dietary requirements.

Set within the National Park, the Plough is an ideal base for exploring the Peak District: the famous Blue John Mine at Castleton is a 10-minute scenic drive along the Hope Valley, while Chatsworth and Haddon Hall are both nearby. Q P

HOPE
Cheshire Cheese Inn
Edale Road, S33 6ZF

- ▶ Take Edale road from A6187 in Hope
- T (01433) 620381
- F (01466) 620411
- W cheshirecheesehope.co.uk
- Black Sheep Best Bitter; Wentworth Pale Ale; Whim Hartington Bitter; guest beers
- Two double, one twin room, all en-suite
- £ ££
- Lunchtime and evening meals; all day Sun until 8.30pm
- Accepted

This small country pub with a relaxed, unspoiled, olde-worlde atmosphere dates back to 1573. It gets its name from the time when it served as a stopover on the salt route across the Pennines from Cheshire to Yorkshire, when payment for lodging was made in cheese, and you can still see the original cheese hooks. Its three seating areas are simply furnished with upholstered chairs and benches; the lower section doubles as a restaurant at mealtimes.

Guest rooms are comfortably furnished. One double has an adjacent lounge where a futon can accommodate a third person, the other contains a double and a single bed.

Ale lovers appreciate the choice of beers from micro-breweries in Derbyshire, Cheshire and South Yorkshire, while diners enjoy the good home-cooked fare and hearty cooked breakfasts.

The Cheshire Cheese is popular with walkers exploring the delightful Hope Valley. Castleton, famous for the Blue John Mines, and the stately home of Chatsworth are both worth a day trip. The Peak District is also much favoured by mountain bikers with plenty of routes.

Q

HULLAND WARD
Black Horse Inn
DE6 3EE

▶ On A517 between Ashbourne and Belper
T (01335) 370206
Beer range varies
Four double rooms, all en-suite
£ ££ double, £ single
Snacks and meals daily, lunchtime and evening
Accepted

Dating from the 1690s, the Black Horse is a traditional inn on the edge of the Peak District in some of the area's most picturesque countryside. It offers an ever-changing range of real ales from four handpumps on a central bar in a split level, multi-roomed drinking area with low, beamed ceilings and quarry-tiled floors.

The en-suite rooms all have four-poster beds plus colour TV and tea and coffee facilities; the price includes a rib-sticking full English including black pudding and fried bread. Children aged 14 and over are welcome.

At other meal times the focus is on local game in season with specials such as pigeon and walnut or hare casserole, rabbit stew, sweet and sour pheasant or pheasant jalfrezi. Meat is reared within a 10-mile radius of Ashbourne, served in an eat-as-much-as-you-like Sunday carvery of pork, beef and lamb at £8. There is also an excellent vegetarian menu offering a choice of 13 dishes.

Close to Carsington Water with its fishing, sailing, walking and pony rides, the pub is also near Alton Towers, Chatsworth and Dovedale.

P

NEWTON SOLNEY
Unicorn Inn
Repton Road, DE15 0SG

▶ On B5008 near Burton Upon Trent
T (01283) 703324
W unicorn-inn.co.uk
Draught Bass; Marston's Pedigree; guest beers
Six double, two twin rooms, all en-suite
£ ££ double, £ single
Snacks and meals daily, lunchtime and evening
Accepted

A coaching inn dating back 300-400 years, the Unicorn recently underwent extensive refurbishment and now has a smart, modern wine bar style interior, featuring open gas fires and offering four real ales, including two changing guests.

The accommodation (including two family rooms) is split between traditional old cottage style and contemporary. All rooms have TV and trouser press; the price includes either a full English or continental breakfast. Four of the rooms are wheelchair accessible, children are welcome and small dogs, too.

The 25-seater dining room provides budget lunches including freshly-filled baguettes with salad and hand-cut chips. At night the restaurant offers a mix of contemporary cuisine and traditional home-cooked dishes.

Newton Solney in the Trent Valley has links to the brewing dynasties of nearby Burton upon Trent, and boasts a church dating back to the 11th century. Close by are Repton, the ancient capital of Mercia, Calke Abbey, Bass Museum, Teycross Zoo and the site of the battle of Bosworth.

P

RIPLEY

Moss Cottage Hotel

Nottingham Road, DE5 3JT

- ▶ On A610, near Sainsbury's
- T (01773) 742555
- W mosscottage.net
- Beer range varies
- Eleven double, three twin, two family rooms, all en-suite; the family room on the ground floor is wheelchair accessible
- £ £ (room only)
- Lunchtime and evening meals
- Accepted

The Moss Cottage has a traditional bar and an adjacent cottage-style restaurant. The hotel was added just two years ago, so offers modern amenities. The lounge has a plasma television and there is a pool table in the bar. Guest rooms are well appointed, with television including Sky News, free wifi Internet connection and tea and coffee making facilities. For a touch of luxury, book the executive/bridal suite with a jacuzzi bath.

Rates are charged for the room only, then you can choose between a continental breakfast or the very full English version, which will certainly set you up for the day – eggs cooked to your taste, bacon, sausage, beans, mushrooms, hash brown and grilled tomato. The restaurant has a good selection of steaks and other pub favourites and offers a children's menu.

The bar offers up to five guest beers at any time, as well as a traditional cider or perry. The pub is a good choice for transport fans as the Butterley Railway Centre and the Crich Tramway Museum are both nearby; Denby Pottery and Gulliver's Kingdom are also among the local attractions. CAMRA members are offered a 10 per cent discount on room prices.

Q ❀ ♿ ♣ P

YOULGREAVE

George Hotel

Church Street, DE45 1WW

- ▶ Off A6 between Matlock and Bakewell
- T (01629) 636292
- Greene King Old Speckled Hen; Theakston Mild; guest beers
- Two twin, one family room, all en-suite
- £ £ (per person)
- Snacks and meals daily, lunchtime and evening
- Accepted

This unspoiled, award-winning 17th-century listed pub runs a modest B&B operation with just three letting rooms. A friendly village inn offering a warm welcome, the premises are unmodernised and promise no juke boxes or gaming machines.

The three bedrooms are fairly spacious and attractively decorated in pastel shades; all are en-suite with TV and tea or coffee making. Children and pets are welcome. Excellent value, the price includes a full English breakfast.

The George features in CAMRA's Good Pub Food guide, and dishes use local produce as much as possible, including game in season. Specialities might be wood pigeon casserole or jugged hare; meat suppliers are name-checked on the blackboard. The award-winning steak and Old Peculier pies are 'the best in the Midlands', but vegetarians are catered for too with dishes such as a giant Yorkshire pudding filled with vegetable stew. At lunchtime the two-course mix and match menu is just £6, and there is a Sunday roast.

Close to Bakewell, Chatsworth Hall and Hoddan Hall, the George is opposite a 12th-century church and visitors can enjoy fine walks nearby.

Q ❀ ♿ ♣ P

Devon

BLACKAWTON

George Inn

Main Street, TQ9 7BG

- ▶ Off B2212
- T (01803) 712342
- F (01803) 712640
- E george@thegeorgeinn.biz
- Palmer's Copper Ale; Princetown Jail Ale; Teignworthy Springtide Ale; guest beers
- Two double, one twin, one family room, all en-suite
- £ £
- Snacks and meals daily, lunchtime and evening
- Accepted

This traditional village inn has spectacular views over rolling Devon countryside towards the sea from some of its bedrooms while others overlook the street. It was originally built to provide accommodation for monks from the nearby church, though the building was rebuilt in the 1930s following a fire.

The en-suite bedrooms are excellent value, with colour TV, tea and coffee making facilities, and access to fax and Internet. The price includes breakfast with a choice of fried or scrambled egg plus two rashers of bacon, sausage, black pudding, mushrooms, baked beans and fried bread. The George is also popular with diners at other times of day, serving local produce as far as possible, including meat from Luscombes butcher's in Totnes and vegetables grown locally; special dietary requirements can be catered for. Packed lunches are provided.

Popular with visitors and locals alike, the main bar is partly timbered and has a real wood burner lit in winter months, a bay window in the end lounge with 'the best view ever', according to the landlord, and there is a pleasant, quiet beer garden. There are many sandy beaches, coves and nearby fishing villages to explore, as well as historic Slapton Sands, Dartmoor, Dart Valley railway and delightful Dartmouth.

Q ♣ P

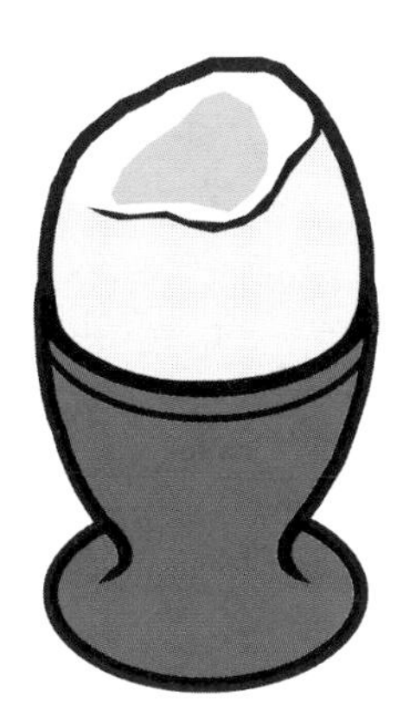

BRANSCOMBE

☆ Masons Arms

EX12 3DJ

▶ Off A3052 between Sidmouth and Seaton
T (01297) 680300
W masonsarms.co.uk
Branscombe Vale Branoc; Otter Bitter; guest beers
Fourteen double, four twin, one family room; seventeen en-suite, two with shared bathroom
£ ££-££££
Snacks and meals daily, lunchtime and evening
Accepted (not Amex)

A stunningly beautiful pub in a gorgeous village. Accommodation is divided between the pub and a cottage annexe; all rooms have recently been refurbished to a very high standard, some with open beams, four poster and jacuzzi, private terrace and views across the valley to the sea beyond. Prices vary depending on the room but include full English breakfast, grilled kipper or poached smoked haddock.

This family-run, 14th-century, creeper-clad inn with slate and thatched roofs was originally a cider house and haunt of smugglers. Inside is a stone-walled bar, ancient ships' beams, slate floor and a fireplace used for weekly spit roasts. The house beer, Mason's Ale, is brewed by Otter.

Meals are good enough to put the Masons in CAMRA's Good Pub Food guide, featuring local fare from lobster and crab landed on Branscombe beach to organic Branscombe beef and lamb. Bar meals include beef and horseradish sausages and Asian-style slow roasted belly pork. A separate à la carte restaurant menu is available evenings only.

The National Trust old bakery, Manor Mill and forge are in the village, the beach and South West Coastal Path half a mile away.

Q P

BUTTERLEIGH

Butterleigh Inn

EX15 1PH

▶ Off M5 jct 28, take road to Cullompton then follow Butterleigh signs
T (01884) 855407
F (01884) 855600
W thebutterleighinn.com
Butcombe Bitter; Cotleigh Tawny; Greene King Abbot; guest beers
Two double, two twin rooms, all en-suite
£ ££
Lunchtime and evening meals
Accepted

For 400 years this wonderful, traditional Devonshire cob building has been dispensing a warm welcome to locals and travellers alike. New landlords the Franklyns took over in 2006 and have continued to maintain the inn's reputation for a relaxed, friendly atmosphere and fine hospitality. The inn and its surroundings are delightful; the open fire in the bar and woodburner in the lounge make it cosy and inviting in winter, while in summer the pleasant secluded garden offers views of rolling hills.

The pub's modern dining room is well known for its food and the Franklyns aim to carry on the tradition of using produce sourced locally to make daily specials. Special events such as hallowe'en and St George's Day are celebrated with themed menus. Vegetarians and vegans can be catered for, and the extensive breakfast menu includes a cooked vegetarian alternative. The guest rooms are simply but comfortably furnished and equipped with TV, telephone, hospitality tray and bottled water.

Butterleigh is less than five miles from the nearest station at Tiverton Parkway, for trains to Exeter. Other places of tourist interest in the vicinity include Bickleigh Castle and Bickleigh Mill Visitor Centre.

Q P

CHAGFORD

☆ Ring O' Bells

44 The Square, TQ13 8AH

▶ From A30 Whiddon Down roundabout follow signs to Chagford
T (01647) 432466
W ringobellschagford.co.uk
Butcombe Bitter; Teignworthy Reel Ale; guest beer
Three double, one twin, one single room
£ £
Snacks and meals daily, lunchtime and evening
Accepted

This 400-year-old country inn was once the Stannary Courts and holding prison for miscreants on their way to Okehampton Assizes. Full of character, it retains an oak bar, exposed beams and huge open fireplace; a pretty courtyard garden is to the rear.

Spotlessly clean and cosy bedrooms, some en-suite, some with shared bathroom, all recently redecorated, are equipped with TV, tea and coffee and snacks, and have delightful views of Castle Drogo, Chagford Square or the pub garden. Excellent value, the room rate includes a full English breakfast with organic eggs and bacon, black pudding and sausages from the local butcher, not forgetting 'world class poached eggs!' Residents also have their own guest lounge where real ale from the bar will be brought to them – and there is a drying room and a lock up for bicycles.

The Ring O' Bells also serves a good menu featuring local produce at other times of day, from a light lunch menu including west country cheese ploughman's, to the evening menu with locally-sourced tuna or Devonshire mussels in local cider and cream.

Close to Dartmoor, local attractions include the Mythic Garden, House of Marbles and Lydford Gorge. No under 12s are permitted, dogs by arrangement.

CHITTLEHAMPTON

Bell Inn

The Square, EX37 9QL

▶ Off B3227, opposite church
T (01769) 540368
F (01769) 540110
W thebellatchittlehampton.co.uk
Beer range varies
Two double rooms, one twin, all en-suite
£ £
Snacks and meals daily, lunchtime and evening
Accepted (not Amex)

A genuine free house, run by the same family for the past 30 years, the Bell has overlooked the main square since 1888. A real focal point for the village community, you can take your pint outside and look across to historic St Hieritha's parish church. The central bar serves up to 10 real ales (three on handpump, the rest on gravity), and Sam's Dry Cider from Winkleigh – not forgetting 150 whiskies. Shove ha'penny, skittles and darts are played here. There is a dining conservatory, beer garden with play area and orchard where alpacas roam.

Accommodation is all en-suite in newly-converted rooms above the pub, two with colour TV, all with tea and coffee making facilities, and there is free Internet access. A full English breakfast is included.

The Bell has a good reputation for its food, mainly local produce on a changing blackboard menu, including steaks from a nearby farm, home-made pies and vegetarian choices.

Popular with walkers, cyclists, golfers – excellent golf courses are nearby - cricket enthusiasts and locals, the pub makes a good base for exploring north Devon.

CHULMLEIGH
Old Court House
South Molton Street, EX18 7BW

- ▶ 200 yards from town centre
- T (01769) 580045
- F (01769) 581417
- W oldcourthouseinn.co.uk
- Cotleigh Tawny; Princetown Dartmoor IPA; guest beer
- Two double, two family rooms, two en-suite
- £ £
- Snacks and meals daily, lunchtime and evening
- Accepted

Dating from 1633, this grade II listed, thatched country inn serves three real ales – the guest chosen by locals – in its cosy bar. It has an Internet café and outside is a pretty cobbled beer garden where you can dine in fine weather. Regular quizzes support charities, there is a skittle alley, and you can also play darts, karem, shove ha'penny, shut-the-box and k'nobbling.

Accommodation is under the ancient thatched roof of The Old Court House. Charles I stayed here in 1634 on his first tour of the west country in a wheeled carriage. Charlie's Room has a four-poster bed in a room built within the upper levels of the Great Hall, and is dominated by Charles I's seven-foot-square coat of arms. Although not en-suite, the bathroom is close by on the shared landing. And the en-suite Family Room is in an ancient room suspended above the very old carriageway entrance. All rooms provide colour TV, hair dryer and tea and coffee making, and the generous traditional breakfast (if you want black pudding, order in advance) is included in the price. To the rear is a self-catering holiday flat in a modern barn conversion.

Q

CHULMLEIGH
Red Lion Hotel
East Street, EX18 7DD

- ▶ At town centre, off B3096
- T (01769) 580384
- F (01769) 580384
- W redlionchulmleigh.co.uk
- Barum Original; St Austell Dartmoor; guest beers
- Two double, one family room, all en-suite
- £ £-££
- Lunchtime and evening meals and snacks
- Accepted

It is always good to discover a pub that caters properly for families, especially if it offers a menu that doesn't just consist of chicken nuggets and chips. The Red Lion offers excellent choices for younger diners and will provide small portions of some items from the main menu. It also has highchairs in the restaurant, a playroom with games and colouring books and baby-changing facilities.

The imaginative meals served here are excellent for all ages and short on 'food miles', too – nearly everything comes from within a 10-mile radius, much of it direct from farms. The breakfast menu is varied: black pudding or hog's pudding accompanied by sausage and eggs, or you can order ham with grilled tomato, kippers or scrambled eggs with smoked trout.

This 300-year-old grade II listed pub houses a large bar that stocks Thatchers Cheddar Valley cider alongside its real ales, a restaurant and a function room with skittle alley where local teams play on Monday and Thursday evenings. There is also a new patio garden. The guest rooms are modern with fairly plain furnishings, but they all have a comfy sofa. The family room has a double and bunk beds.

P

DODDISCOMBSLEIGH

☆ Nobody Inn

EX6 7PS

- ▶ Off A38, 3 miles from Exeter racecourse
- T (01647) 252394
- F (01647) 252978
- W nobodyinn.co.uk
- Otter Ale; guest beer
- Five double, two twin rooms, five en-suite
- £ £-£££
- Snacks and meals daily, lunchtime and evening
- Accepted

Alcohol is very much on the menu even at breakfast time at the Nobody Inn. 'Champagne,' it reads, 'is traditionally a breakfast wine but please not mixed in orange juice as it ruins the flavour of both.' Fizz is good with eggs – but after extensive testing they have decided that at breakfast it must be dry white wine with good acidity if the meal includes egg, a light dry red if there is no egg. Porridge lends itself to a wee dram in which 'we have found a use for Baileys Irish Cream as a substitute for milk'. Kippers were made for Islay malts ('in fact we think some Islay malts are made from kippers'). With coffee, 'a simple Spanish brandy will out perform Cognac at this time in the morning'. Shame they don't mention beer – not even house beer Nobody's brewed by Branscombe – but nobody's perfect.

Dating back to 1591, this delightful pub has low ceilings, blackened beams, inglenook fireplace, antique furniture and unspoilt olde-worlde charm. The traditionally-styled, attractive bedrooms are in the pub itself and Town Barton, a manor house 200 yards away. Breakfast, includes Crannacombe farm apple juice, bacon, organic eggs and sausages, plus black pudding and hog's pudding.

Q P

HEXWORTHY

Forest Inn

PL20 6SD

- ▶ Off B3357 between Ashburton and Tavistock
- T (01364) 631211
- F (01364) 631515
- W theforestinn.co.uk
- Teignworthy Reel Ale, Beachcomber; guest beers
- Six double, two twin, two family rooms; seven en-suite, three share bathroom
- £ ££
- Lunchtime and evening meals and snacks
- Accepted

Lying within Dartmoor Forest, the inn not only offers you a room for the night but one for your horse, too (four stables are available by arrangement). Dogs are also permitted. A real rural retreat, the pub is frequented by walkers, riders and anglers. The forest also offers opportunities for other outdoor pursuits such as canoeing, bird watching and cycling.

After an active day you can relax in one of the comfy sofas in the bar or head for the Huccaby room or more formal dining room for meals prepared with local produce such as meat from Brimpts Farm and cheeses from Tavistock. An inventive menu offers two courses for around £18. A good range of ploughman's, sandwiches and jacket potatoes is also available. In the morning, you can enjoy a full English breakfast (vegetarian sausages on request) or choose from a list of alternatives, including kippers.

The original Forest Inn was almost completely destroyed by fire in 1912. The current building dates from 1914 and the slightly old-fashioned decor in the guest rooms is in keeping with the style of the pub. The pub also has a 20-bed bunk house equipped with showers and a kitchenette.

P

IDDESLEIGH
Duke of York
EX19 8BG

- ▶ Off B3217, next to church
- T (01837) 810253
- F (01837) 810253
- Adnams Broadside; Cotleigh Tawny; Sharp's Doom Bar; guest beers
- Five double, one twin, one family room, all en-suite
- £ £ (per person)
- Snacks and meals daily, lunchtime and evening
- Accepted

This remote 15th-century village free house set in rural mid-Devon has no fruit machine, juke box or karaoke night, so you're guaranteed to find a little peace and quiet. Inglenook fireplaces, old beams and a warm welcome add to the traditional atmosphere. There is space outside for alfresco drinking. Accommodation includes a full English breakfast – two eggs, bacon, sausage, mushrooms and tomato.

As well as locals and business people, the Duke of York attracts families, cyclists and walkers, many of them enjoying the long-distance walking and cycling route the Tarka trail nearby.

The pub's main meal menus include dishes such as sea bass with smoked bacon and pine nuts, pork with apple and cider sauce, Stilton and port pâté, spiced leek and parsnip cake with minted yoghurt for vegetarians, and some delicious products from Dartmouth smokehouse – salmon, trout fillet and chicken breast smoked with tarragon. A set menu includes some rather tempting desserts such as Congress tart or Boodles orange fool , and Sunday lunch features roast sirloin, stuffed leg of lamb or chicken with all the trimmings. The cider is Sam's Dry from nearby Winkleigh.

Q

KINGSTON
Dolphin Inn
TQ7 4QE

- ▶ Off A379 between Plymouth and Kingsbridge, follow brown signs
- T (01548) 810314
- F (01548) 810314
- E info@dolphininn.eclipse.co.uk
- Courage Best Bitter; Princetown IPA; Sharp's Doom Bar; Teignworthy Reel Ale
- Two double, one twin room, all en-suite; all available as singles
- £ ££
- Lunchtime and evening meals daily
- Accepted

The Dolphin dates all the way back to 1520 and was built by stonemasons to live in while constructing the adjacent church. Originally three cottages, it has slowly evolved into the fine establishment it is today, full of character with inglenooks, beams and exposed stone. In winter you can sit by a blazing fire and in summer head out into the large garden.

The guest accommodation has been converted from a barn across the road, a listed building with some exposed stone walls, centrally heated in winter. An extra bed can be added to a double room for a child. Facilities for making hot drinks are provided and in the morning you head back to the pub for a full English breakfast cooked to your liking. Excellent home-cooked meals are available every day; the menus incorporate local produce as available and can be washed down with ales from Devon and Cornwall.

Kingston is a charming south Devon village of thatched cottages near Wonwell beach. Visitors can enjoy walks along the coastal path, stroll alongside the River Erme or make for the moors. Kingsbridge, Plymouth and Modbury are all within a short drive. Q P

LAKE

Bearslake Inn

EX20 4HQ

- ▶ On A386
- T (01837) 861334
- F (01837) 861108
- W bearslakeinn.com
- Beer range varies
- Four double, two family rooms, all en-suite
- £ ££
- Snacks and meals daily, lunchtime and evening (closed Sun eve)
- Accepted

A real picture postcard pub believed to date back to the 13th century, the main building is a traditional thatched Devon longhouse, originally a working farm. The interior is full of character, featuring exposed beams and timbers, flagstone floors and low ceilings, while the bedrooms – also beamed – are all individual in their decoration. Room rates include a full English breakfast made with west country bangers and bacon. The family-run pub offers a good selection of regional ales such as Otter, Cotleigh, Teignworthy and St Austell.

Using as much local produce as possible, the daily changing menu might start with Falmouth Bay scallops, before going on to rack of west country lamb, local beef fillet stuffed with Devon blue cheese, venison with cranberry sauce and marmalade duck, prices around £15. Four west country cheeses, including luscious Sharpham Brie, grace the cheeseboard.

With good access to Dartmoor and the Granite Way, as well as Lydford Gorge, the Bearslake has fine views of rugged landscape and granite tors. Attracting walkers, cyclists, horse riders and anglers, it has a delightful garden with a stream, overlooked by High Willhayes and Yes Tor in the distance. Q P

RINGMORE

Journey's End Inn

TQ7 4HL

- ▶ Off A379 between Kingsbridge and Modbury
- T (01548) 810205
- Cottage Golden Arrow; Sharp's Doom Bar; South Hams Devon Pride, Eddystone
- Two double en-suite rooms
- £ ££
- Lunchtime and evening meals
- Accepted

Situated at the end of the road, at the bottom of a hill, this pub in a pretty South Hams hamlet is indeed a fine place to end your journey. With several footpaths running from here to meet the long-distance south west coastal path a mile away, the pub is popular with walkers as well as cyclists, locals and visitors enjoying Ringmore's secluded beach Ayrmer Cove.

The Journey's End dates back to the 13th century and was originally built to accommodate workers constructing the parish church. The snug, oak-panelled bar offers local ale from South Hams Brewery, situated close by near Kingsbridge. There is also a lounge, dining room and conservatory. The delightful beer garden is very popular in summer.

The guest rooms are quaint, furnished with double bed, dressing table and TV. Children and pets are welcome. Breakfast is a choice of full English or continental.

Burgh Island is a good walk or short drive away and the market towns of Modbury and Kingsbridge can be reached in 10 minutes, while the bustling, fashionable resort of Salcombe is well worth a visit.

Q P

SANDY PARK

Sandy Park Inn

TQ13 8JW

- ▶ Off A30 Whiddon Down, on A382 to Chagford
- T (01647) 433267
- W sandyparkinn.co.uk
- Otter Ale; St Austell Tribute; guest beers
- Four double, one twin room; two en-suite, three with bathrooms
- £ £ (per person)
- Snacks and meals daily, lunchtime and evening
- Accepted

A thatched 17th-century free house in Dartmoor National Park five miles from Castle Drogo, the Sandy Park is a welcoming, unspoilt inn with stone-flagged floor, log fire, exposed beams and pews, and charming snug. With glorious views over Dartmoor and walks along the Dartmoor Way or river to Fingle Bridge, it is a mile away from the pretty town of Chagford.

The bedrooms are comfy and welcoming, all providing flat-screen TV, CD player, and tea and coffee making facilities. A full Devonshire breakfast with Barry Moore's well-known sausages from nearby Moretonhampstead is included.

Food is also local at other times on a daily-changing blackboard menu – fish from Brixham, beef and lamb from moorland farms, game in season, dishes including grilled lemon sole or braised lamb shank. Cask Marque accredited, there are always four regional real ales on handpump including two guests such as O'Hanlon's Royal Oak or Yellowhammer, or Exe Valley's Devon Glory.

The pub attracts walkers and cyclists, and has a 12-mile stretch of the Upper Teign for fly fishing. The landlord is happy to arrange horseriding for you at nearby stables, and use of the 18-hole championship golf course, spa, pool and gym at Bovey Castle.

TUCKENHAY

☆ Maltster's Arms

Bow Creek, TQ9 7EQ

- ▶ Signed from A381, Totnes-Kingsbridge Road
- T (01803) 732350
- W tuckenhay.com
- Princetown Dartmoor IPA; guest beers
- Five double rooms, all-en-suite
- £ £-£££
- Snacks and meals daily, lunchtime and evening
- Accepted (not Amex or Diners)

This renowned pub has bedrooms all flamboyantly designed to different themes by celebrity chef Keith Floyd when he was the landlord more than a decade ago. Since then the inn has regularly featured in both the Good Beer Guide and Good Pub Food under the enthusiastic ownership of Denise and Quentin Thwaites.

Accommodation rates vary according to the room and season, but always include a fine full English or Quentin's speciality, the veggie alternative with sautéed bananas and baby corn. Or there is a choice of smoked haddock, kippers or scrambled eggs with smoked salmon, and toast and local honey from Ashprington. Card-carrying CAMRA members get a 10 per cent discount on accommodation.

Overlooking Bow Creek, many visitors arrive by boat (there are moorings for those staying overnight) and could find a beer festival, canoe rally, barbecue or music event in progress. The pub also fields a cricket team.

Well known for fine food, served in both bar and dining room overlooking the water, you could find lobsters from Dartmouth, salmon from the Dart, River Exe mussels, Yealm oysters, local venison, pheasant, pigeon and rabbit. Places to visit locally include Paignton Zoo, Totnes and Torquay.

Q P

ABOVE AND NEXT PAGE: Maltster's Arms, Tuckenhay, Devon

THE
MALTSTERS
ARMS

TURNCHAPEL
Boringdon Arms
Boringdon Terrace, PL9 9TQ

- ▶ On Plymouth Sound, opposite Plymouth
- T (01752) 402053
- W bori.co.uk
- Draught Bass; Butcombe Bitter; Otter Ale; RCH Pitchfork; South Hams Devon Pride; Summerskills Best Bitter; guest beers
- Two double, one twin, three family rooms; one en-suite
- £ £
- Snacks and meals daily, lunchtime and evening
- Accepted (not Amex)

A former regional CAMRA Pub of the Year, the 18th-century Boringdon Arms has been sympathetically renovated over the past few years, with accommodation upgraded. Three rooms have sea views, including the en-suite dormer room, while the other rooms share two showers and two WCs. A full English with eggs cooked as you like them is included.

The Bori, as it is generally called, offers a splendid range of well-kept real ales, and beer festivals are held on the last weekend of every other month. It is also known for good, inexpensive food including its speciality, 'heroic' pies, and gigantic cod fillets in home-made beer batter.

Set in a terrace of Georgian houses in a conservation village, the pub was originally a quarry master's house – the garden is hewn out of the redundant quarry. A large front bar has an open fire, on the other side a smaller bar is used for dining.

Adjoining a yachting marina, the pub is on the South West Coast Path and is visited by walkers, sailors and divers as well as locals. A 10-minute drive from Plymouth, the historic Barbican can also be reached by water taxi from nearby Mount Batten.

UGBOROUGH
Anchor Inn
1 Lutterburn Street, PL21 0NG

- ▶ Off B3210 close to A36, 10 miles east of Plymouth
- T (01752) 892283
- F (01752) 690534
- W anchor-ugborough.co.uk
- Draught Bass; Courage BB; guest beers
- Two double, one twin, one family, one single room, all en-suite
- £ £
- Snacks and meals daily, lunchtime and evening
- Accepted

The Anchor in Ugborough was the limit of the marauding press gangs' range from Plymouth - the nautical pub name intended as a warning to the unwary. The centre of village social life, this welcoming historic 16th-century inn has a public bar with oak beams, leaded window, open fire and traditional oak floor. Draught Bass is served straight from the barrel, and three guest ales often include one from the Ring O' Bells

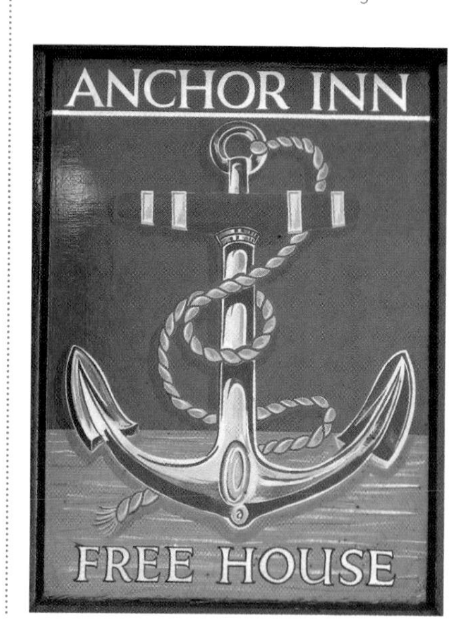

brewery in Cornwall.

Located to the rear of the pub, the self-contained, en-suite bedrooms provide colour TV, tea and coffee making, plus a private car park. Budget-priced accommodation includes a full English breakfast, and food at other times is made with as much local farm produce as possible. A bar menu offers cod in home-made beer batter, hand-made burgers and freshly-made pizzas. In the 40-seater à la carte restaurant you can enjoy locally-caught seafood and organic meat, dishes including king scallops with monkfish tail, guinea fowl, fresh mussels, pan-fried pigeon breast and char-grilled steaks.

The Anchor is popular with locals as well as cyclists, walkers and tourists visiting Dartmoor and Plymouth.

P

WOODLAND

Rising Sun

TQ13 7JT

- ▶ Take Woodland turn off the A38 southbound
- T (01364) 652544
- F (01364) 654202
- W risingsunwoodland.co.uk
- Princetown Jail Ale; guest beer
- Two double, one twin, one family room, all en-suite
- £ ££
- Lunchtime and evening meals, Tue-Sun
- Accepted (not Amex)

The Rising Sun is renowned for its award-winning food and is listed in CAMRA's Good Pub Food guide. Ninety per cent of the produce used in cooking comes from local suppliers and the home-made pies (available to take home) have been recommended in Henrietta Green's A Food Lover's Guide to Britain. Local Luscombe cider is available alongside the Jail Ale brewed by Princetown in Dartmoor, either of which would be a perfect accompaniment to the ploughman's served with a choice of four west country cheeses and home-made chutney.

The pleasant guest rooms have colour TV and tea and coffee making facilities. Breakfast is a very full English affair including bacon, sausage, sautéed potatoes, black pudding and hogs pudding, a Devon speciality. Eggs are cooked to your taste or if you prefer you can have kippers or smoked haddock.

This friendly inn with a cosy log fire adding winter warmth is surrounded by glorious countryside on the edge of Dartmoor so you are assured of wonderful walks. It is within easy reach of Exeter, Plymouth and Torbay. With a public family room and play area in the garden, children are welcome here, as are dogs.

Q P

Dorset

BUCKHORN WESTON

Stapleton Arms

Church Hill, SP8 5HS

- ▶ Wincanton exit off A30 or A303
- T (01963) 370396
- F (01963) 370396
- W thestapletonarms.com
- Butcombe Bitter; Taylor Landlord; guest beer
- Four double, one twin, one family room; all en-suite
- £ ££££
- Lunchtime and evening meals
- Accepted

The Stapleton, which dates from the 18th century, is now the only hostelry remaining in the village and serves its community well. And with a recent refurbishment, the landlord intends to continue to cater for locals and visitors alike for many years to come.

Guest rooms include all the modern amenities: comfortable beds, television and DVD and wireless Internet access. The pub has a bar area and separate dining room. It benefits from a lovely garden and, by the time the guide is published, should also have a paddock for horses.

Guest beers come from regional breweries and the superb menu relies heavily on local produce, such as fish from Samways on the south coast, meat from Wincanton, cheese from Longmans of North Cadbury and fresh salad and veg from an award-winning producer near Ilminster. The classic English breakfast includes Wiltshire cured bacon, local sausages, field mushrooms and roasted vine tomatoes, or you could choose eggs on toast, cooked to your preference, boiled egg and soldiers or Dorset kippers with vine tomatoes.

Walkers can explore the Blackmore Vale; the towns of Shaftesbury and Sherborne are nearby. Discounts on accommodation apply for longer stays. Q P

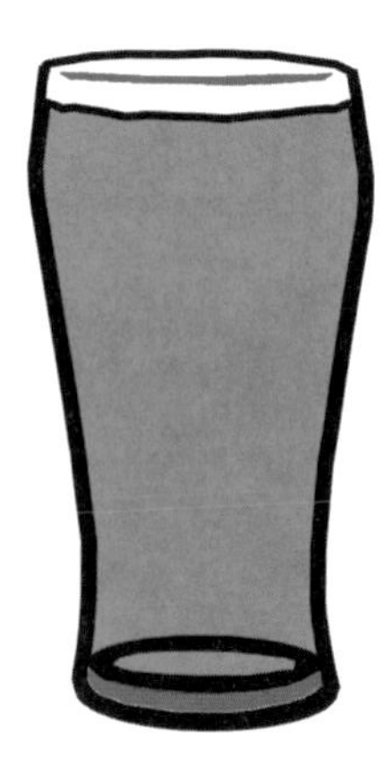

FARNHAM

Museum Inn

DT11 8DE

▶ Off A354, north-east of Blandford Forum
T (01725) 516261
W museuminn.co.uk
Taylor Landlord; guest beers
Eight double/twin rooms, all en-suite
£ £££-££££ (10% discount for single occupancy)
Lunchtime and evening meals
Accepted

This delightful part-thatched country pub was built in the 17th-century by a famous archaeologist to accommodate visitors to the local museum. The inn's best guest room (and its most expensive) is named the General's Bedroom in his honour. This luxurious, generously proportioned room with a four-poster is one of four in the main building - all are fairly spacious. The stable rooms are smaller but they all have bath and power shower, TV and use of a charming residents' sitting room.

The owners, who took over and carried out a major refurbishment around five years ago, take care to provide little extras that make a difference, such as home-made biscuits and organic chocolates on the hospitality tray, current magazines to browse through and a daily newspaper to read as you tuck into the full English breakfast.

In the public areas original features such as flagged floors, cosy nooks and a large inglenook remain, but the bar has a wonderful open airy feel. Two rooms off the bar and a conservatory serve excellent food made from the freshest seasonal produce. Poultry is free range, fish from the south coast, game from neighbouring estates and where possible organic vegetables are used. There is usually a guest ale from a local independent brewery to sample.

Q P

MIDDLEMARSH

Hunter's Moon

DT9 5QN

T (01963) 210966
W huntersmoon.co.uk
Beer range varies
Four double, four twin, four family, one single room, all en-suite
£ ££
Snacks and meals daily, lunchtime and evening
Accepted

Owner Brendan Malone and his family have used local craftsmen to transform the 400-year-old derelict former White Horse into a beautiful country inn with rustic interior and genuine warm welcome. The L-shaped bar is decorated with brewery memorabilia, jugs, cups and tankards hanging from the ceiling, with little alcoves and corners breaking up the room. Outside is a well-kept beer garden.

The old stables, skittle alley and log store have been converted into charming accommodation, each room different and spotlessly clean, with a comfortable couch to watch the TV. Prices include a full English breakfast. No smoking and no pets are house rules. The restaurant offers a taste of local produce including – appropriately for the Hunter's Moon – game in season. It is advisable to book for the popular Sunday carvery.

The beer range changes but most are local from Palmers in Bridport, St Austell and Sharp's in Cornwall. Attractions nearby are the three miles of sandy beach at Studland Bay, the Durdle Door rock arch and Jurassic Coast, Lulworth Cove and Corfe Castle.

Q P

PIDDLETRENTHIDE

Poachers Inn

DT2 7QX

- ▶ On B3143, by River Piddle
- T (01300) 348358
- W thepoachersinn.co.uk
- Butcombe Gold; Fuller's London Pride; Otter Head; guest beers
- Eighteen twin/double rooms, three family, all en-suite
- £ £ (per person)
- Snacks and meals daily, lunchtime and evening
- Accepted

Farmers in boots mingle with tourists staying at the Poachers who have come to explore Thomas Hardy country and Dorchester six miles away, or visit the Cerne Abbas giant or Monkey World, or simply wander round a village dating back to the Domesday Book.

The inn has been much improved since the current owners took over in 2004, and includes quality accommodation in 21 contemporary en-suite bedrooms, most with bath as well as shower, hairdryer and tea and coffee. The Queenie suite also has mini-fridge, king-size double bed and Jacuzzi. The price includes a choice of full English breakfast, scrambled or poached eggs on toast, or smoked kippers with fried bread and tomato. In summer guests can also enjoy a heated outdoor pool in the suntrap garden.

The Poachers is noted for its excellent cuisine. Typical specials could be sea bass on rosti with caper butter, pork and leek sausages with mustard mash, seafood salad of prawns, mussels and baby calamari or venison and Guinness pie; main dishes are reasonably priced at around £10.

The pub lawns run down to the Piddle which is, incidentally, Anglo Saxon for 'a clear stream....'

Q P

SHROTON
Cricketers
Main Street, DT11 8QD

- ▶ Off A350
- T (01258) 860421
- W (01258) 861800
- Badger First Gold; Greene King IPA; guest beers
- One double, en-suite
- £ ££
- Snacks and meals daily, lunchtime and evening
- Accepted

The Cricketers has just one letting room (twin/double), but it is rather special, award-winning accommodation. It is in the 'Pavilion' – a separate garden room with bay window overlooking a clematis-covered arbour, featuring super-king size bed, delightful furnishings, shower room, mini-fridge, complimentary chocolates and mineral water, and tea and coffee making facilities. Breakfast is a choice between full English with organic eggs and locally-made sausages, or continental with preserves from the farmers' market. The room rate includes breakfast, with three-night break rates available.

Overlooking the village green and cricket pitch, the pub has a cricketing theme with handpumps in the style of cricket bats and memorabilia adorning the walls. The hub of the village and focal point for cricket teams after weekend matches, the light and airy inn at the foot of Hambledon Hill is also popular with walkers on Wessex Ridgeway. It has a large public bar with games area, and is known for its good food.

Close to Blandford Forum, the Hall and Woodhouse brewery centre makes an interesting outing, as do the Jurassic coastline, Royal Signals Museum, Salisbury Cathedral and Sherbourne.

STUDLAND
Bankes Arms Country Inn
Manor Road, BH19 3AU

- ▶ On B3351, five miles east of Corfe Castle
- T (01929) 450225
- F (01929) 450307
- Isle of Purbeck Fossil Fuel, Solar Power, Studland Bay Wrecked, IPA; guest beers
- Seven double, two twin, one single room; eight en-suite, two rooms share a bathroom
- £ ££-£££
- Lunchtime and evening meals; all day in summer until 9.30pm
- Accepted

Fresh sea air and freshly-brewed ales – the perfect combination for a good night's sleep in one of the Bankes Arms' cottage-style rooms. The inn has views over the Solent to the Isle of Wight and five of the guest rooms overlook the sea. There is a residents' lounge/dining room and all rooms have television, hair dryer and tea making facilities. Children are welcome. For breakfast you can pretty much order whatever you fancy, from poached, scrambled or boiled eggs, or smoked mackerel, to a full English.

This old stone inn – some parts dates back to the 15th century – stands in a picturesque village at the start of the Jurassic Coast world heritage site, offering superb cliff-top walks and lovely long sandy beaches with good swimming and water sports. Horse riding and golf can also be enjoyed nearby.

The cosy inn is the home of the Isle of Purbeck Brewery, which supplies around 50 local outlets with its fine ales. The bar also stocks three frequently-changing guest beers, so ale lovers have plenty of choice here. In August there is a four-day 80-barrel beer festival with live music and entertainment.

TARRANT MONKTON
Langton Arms
DT11 8RX

▶ Between B3082 and A354 near Blandford Forum
T (01258) 830225
W thelangtonarms.co.uk
Hidden Pleasure; Ringwood Best; guest beers
Three double, three twin rooms, all en-suite
£ £££
Snacks and meals daily, lunchtime and evening
Accepted (not Amex or Diners)

Sadly, the original chocolate box thatched pub burned down in a major fire in 2004 but the inn has now been beautifully rebuilt, including a fine thatched roof – hence the pub sign depicting a phoenix. The pub now has a tap room with pool table, large dining and function room, separate restaurant (licensed for weddings) and skittle alley.

The six guest rooms are built in rustic brick around a courtyard, all at ground level with their own entrance, so wheelchair accessible, and with bay windows overlooking the Dorset countryside. Single occupancy is available or beds can be added for families. Furnished to a high standard with colour TV and tea and coffee making, a full English breakfast is included in the price.

The pub is popular for dining; meals feature as much local produce as possible including Tarrant Valley beef and other meat from a nearby farm shop. A selection of rustic breads with locally-produced farmhouse butter and home-made hummus and olives can be served while you decide what to order, perhaps Dorset game such as rabbit, pigeon, pheasant and venison pie or local faggots in onion gravy. The house beer, Langton Arms Bitter, is from Hop Back.

P

WAREHAM
Duke of Wellington
7 East Street, BH20 4NN

T (01929) 553015
W dukeofwellington.biz
Camerons Castle Eden Ale; Isle of Purbeck Fossil Fuel; Ringwood Best Bitter; guest beers
One family room
£ £-££
Lunchtime and evening meals and snacks
Accepted (not American Express)

This busy pub is centrally situated for the town and tourist sites and easily accessible by public transport. There is just one family-sized room, big enough for four (one double bed and two singles), with a separate bathroom. There is plenty to see and do in the vicinity for all the family, including Swanage steam railway, Corfe Castle, the Jurassic coastline and the RSPB reserve on the Arne Peninsula.

The guest bedroom is equipped with a television, but the main pub, which dates back to the 16th century and is Grade II listed, is free from TV, juke box and fruit machines to suit its largely middle-aged clientele. Always popular, visitors come to enjoy the varied selection of real ales – three guest beers on handpump as well as the regulars – and the extensive menu. There is always a good choice of fresh fish here, as well as traditional English and international dishes and daily additions to the main menus. 'Sizzlers' are a house speciality. Overnight guests are offered a hearty cooked breakfast, complemented by fresh orange juice, cereals and toast.

Q P

Durham

CROXDALE

Daleside Arms

Front Street, DH6 5HY

▶ On B6288, 3 miles S of Durham, off A167
T (01388) 814165
E daleside.croxdale1@barbox.net
Beer range varies
One double, one twin, one single room, all en-suite
£ ££
Evening meals only, plus Sunday lunch
Not accepted

This family-run local shows how a country pub can succeed by making the effort to do simple things well. Clean, comfortable accommodation is in three light and airy en-suite rooms, all with tea and coffee making facilities, and there is a secure car park, locked at night.

The hearty breakfast includes bacon, eggs, mushrooms, tomato, fried potatoes, beans and toast, or you can choose continental at a reduced rate. All pub meals here incorporate local produce sourced from the same suppliers for the past 25 years. An interesting range of real ales is served - the permanent house ale is brewed by Wear Valley.

Built in 1870, the Daleside was used as a community hostel until 1929, then it became a guest house until 1959, and was re-licensed in 1993. Sporting relics decorate the bar, which has a TV showing sport and hosts regular quiz nights. There is a separate restaurant, a large family area outside and delightful, prize-winning floral arrangements.

In a rural location just south of Durham city, the Daleside attracts locals as well as tourists and ramblers. Nearby attractions are the Beamish Museum and scenic walks on the Wear.

Q ❀ ♿ ♣ P

DURHAM
☆ Victoria Inn
86 Hallgarth Street, DH1 3AS

T (0191) 386 5269
W victoriainn-durhamcity.co.uk
Big Lamp Bitter; guest beers
Three double, two twin, one family, two single rooms, all en-suite
£ £ (per person)
Lunchtime meals served
Accepted

An absolute gem, the Victoria is an authentic, unspoiled, immaculately-kept brick-built local with Silver Star listing in CAMRA's National Inventory of heritage pubs. Its listed interior retains the original layout with a tiny snug and two main rooms. Many original features remain including three coal fires, the off-sale hatch, walls decorated with original paintings and pictures, and the balcony above the listed bar filled with Staffordshire and Victoria & Albert figurines.

The overnight accommodation is up-to-date and high quality; delightful bedrooms are all en-suite with TV and tea and coffee making facilities, plus free off-street parking for guests – invaluable in central Durham. The hearty breakfast includes local sausages, black pudding and free range eggs.

Just five minutes' walk from Durham Cathedral and market place, the Victoria makes an atmospheric, inexpensive base for exploring the city. Superb real ales from small local breweries are sold alongside three dozen Irish malts at a pub with no music, TV or pool, run by the same licensee for 30 years. It was awarded Durham CAMRA Pub of the Year in 2003 and 2005.

FOREST-IN-TEESDALE
Langdon Beck Hotel
DL12 0XP

▶ On B6277, 6 miles W of Middleton-in-Teesdale
T (01833) 622267
W langdonbeckhotel.com
Black Sheep Best Bitter, Emmerdale; Jarrow Rivet Catcher; guest beers
Two double, three twin, two single rooms; twin rooms en-suite plus two shared bathrooms
£ £ (per person)
Snacks and meals daily, lunchtime and evening
Not accepted

An isolated country pub built around 1820, the Langdon Beck is high in the Pennines with stunning views of some of the country's finest scenery. It has two cosy bars, three open fires burning logs and coal, a large lounge and dining room, and offers a warm country welcome.

An excellent, traditional breakfast features local black pudding and sausages, bacon, local eggs, mushrooms, tomatoes and fried bread – vegetarians and vegans can be catered for. Food is good at other times, too, from a big bowl of mussels with home-made bread, to local Teesdale T-bone and sirloin steaks, traditional Sunday lunch, or home-made vegetable rissoles, followed by home-made desserts from sticky toffee pudding to apple pie.

The hotel is popular with walkers, cyclists, botanists, geologists and bird watchers. It has a 24-hour licence so there is plenty of time for guests to relax and enjoy fine ales including two guests from local micros after a day spent walking the Pennine Way or visiting the spectacular High Force and Cauldron Spout waterfalls. Packed lunches are available on request.

HARTBURN
Parkwood Hotel
64-66 Darlington Road, TS18 5ER

▶ Off A1027, near A66
T (01642) 587933
Camerons Strongarm; Greene King Abbot; guest beer
Four double, one twin, one single room, all en-suite
£ ££
Snacks and meals daily, lunchtime and evening
Accepted

A converted Victorian house built in 1865 as residence to the Ropners, a local ship building family and civic benefactors, the Parkwood became a pub after the war, and is virtually unchanged in outward appearance. Set in a leafy, suburban area but convenient for Teesside International Airport, the hotel has an open-plan bar, restaurant, conservatory and attractive beer garden with decking.

Spacious, well-appointed accommodation includes colour TVs and tea and coffee making facilities. The full English breakfast starts with fruit juice, cereal or fresh fruit, or kippers if preferred. Lunchtime and evening meals are served in the bar or separate dining room from an à la carte menu. All meat and vegetables are sourced locally and special dietary needs can be catered for.

Parties of all sizes are catered for to celebrate special events, with children and pets welcome. But the licensee is determined to keep the bar as a real pub for lovers of quality real ales and does not allow diners to take it over (no meals served on Sunday evenings). Children and pets are welcome. ❀ P

OVINGTON
Four Alls
The Green, DL11 7BP

▶ 2 miles S of Winston and A67
T (01833) 627302
Tetley Bitter; guest beer
One double, two twin, two single rooms; three en-suite, two sharing a bathroom
£ ££
Evening meals only
Accepted (not Amex)

The pub is the home of the Four Alls brewery but this one-barrel micro cannot brew enough to satisfy demand, so its half dozen ales alternate with a guest. The traditional, stone-built 18th century inn overlooks the green in what is known as the 'Maypole village'. It comprises a bar decorated with fresh hops and sparkling horse brasses, games room and dining room, plus an outside drinking area.

The five bedrooms looking out onto the green or the pub garden each have their own character; three are en-suite with one single and one twin room sharing a bathroom. All have tea and coffee making facilities and a continental breakfast or hearty full English with black pudding is included in the price.

Simple, good value meals are served in the evening, with braised beef, house curry and chicken and ham or steak, kidney and ale pies all home-made, plus a choice of local steaks. The pub welcomes walkers and cyclists and is near High Force, Raby Castle and Peel House. Note the unusual Victorian sign denoting the Four Alls.
Q ❀ ♣ P

Essex

COLCHESTER

Rose & Crown Hotel

East Street, CO1 2TZ

- ▶ Follow signs to Roller World, hotel stands opposite
- T (01206) 866677
- F (01206) 866616
- W rose-and-crown.com
- Adnams Broadside; Tetley Bitter; guest beers
- 38 double/twin rooms, all en-suite; two rooms are wheelchair accessible
- £ £££ (single occupancy £85)
- Lunchtime and evening meals
- Accepted

Now owned by the Best Western group, the Rose and Crown dates back to the 14th century and is said to be the oldest coaching inn in Britain's oldest recorded town. The building is heavily beamed throughout with many original features, though the amenities the hotel offers are up to the minute.

Most of the rooms (some with four-poster beds) are in the old building but nine stylish executive suites have recently opened in a new wing with modern facilities such as air conditioning, luxurious bathroom fittings and flat-screen plasma television. All rooms have a pay per view system allowing guests to surf the Internet, check emails, order a movie, play games or simply listen to the radio. Guests can choose either a continental or full English breakfast. Children are welcome.

Although the Rose and Crown is first and foremost a hotel, non-residents are always welcome for a meal or just a pint of real ale. The wonderfully atmospheric Tudor Bar/Brasserie is in the oldest part of the hotel and offers a traditional menu. In contrast, the East Street Grill is much more modern in mood and flavour with a contemporary cooking style.

Q P

DEDHAM

☆ Sun Inn

High Street, CO7 6DF

- ▶ Take Stratford St Mary exit from A12 westbound
- T (01206) 323351
- W thesuninndedham.com
- Adnams Broadside; Crouch Vale Brewers Gold; Earl Soham Victoria; Green Jack Grasshopper; guest beers
- Five double rooms, all en-suite (one with bath, four showers)
- £ £££-££££
- Lunchtime and evening meals
- Accepted

Piers Baker obviously knew what he was doing when he acquired the rather unloved Sun Inn in 2003. He has spared no expense in restoring the premises with style and panache. The public spaces – a comfortable seating area, bar and dining room – combine traditional features of open fires, exposed beams and oak floorboards with modern touches. The guest rooms have been beautifully equipped with enormous beds – super king size, four poster or tester – natural fabrics and stylish furniture and fittings. The en-suite facilities are equally luxurious.

The same attention to detail is found in the kitchen where an imaginative menu, based on locally sourced and often organic produce, is changed daily. The spacious restaurant is noted for its extensive wine list, while the bar stocks real ales from local micro-breweries. Rather than offer the usual full English at breakfast, the Sun serves a continental version with a twist, including two different fruit salads, fruit bread and frittatas alongside the croissants and toast.

Convenient for visiting Flatford Mill and Constable Country, other places of interest nearby include the Beth Chatto Gardens and Sir Alfred Munnings Museum. P

EAST MERSEA

Mersea Vineyard Courtyard Café

Rewsalls Lane, CO5 8SX

- ▶ Off B1025 from Colchester, follow brown tourist signs
- T (01206) 385900
- F (01206) 383600
- W merseawine.com
- Mersea Island Mud Mild, Yo Boy Bitter, Skippers Bitter
- Three double/twin rooms, all en-suite
- £ ££
- Snacks served 11-4pm, not Tue
- Not accepted

The Courtyard Café is not a pub, but it does supply beer, bed and breakfast. The café is part of the Mersea Vineyard and brewery; the vineyard was established in 1985 and the brewery 20 years later. It is one of the rare outlets for the growing Mersea Island beers. Accommodation is provided in the Hop Loft in three twin-bedded rooms, available either for B&B or self-catering, with a lounge and kitchen area. A smaller unit, Vine Cottage, is also self catering and sleeps up to four people. Children are welcome. Breakfast – full English plus fresh fruit salad, yogurt and cereal – is served in the café.

Snacks – baguettes, sandwiches and jacket potatoes – are available during the day and nearby Colchester has plenty of places where you can eat out in the evening.

Mersea Island lies between the Blackwater and Colne estuaries, and the café and accommodation enjoy good views. Tours of the brewery and vineyard can be arranged. P

GREAT DUNMOW

Saracens Head Hotel

High Street, CM6 1AG

▶ Town centre, off A120
T (01371) 873901
W thesaracenshead.biz
Greene King IPA, Ruddles County; Mighty Oak Maldon Gold; guest beers
Ten double, eleven twin, six family, four single rooms, all en-suite
£ £££
Lunchtime and evening meals
Accepted (not Diners Club)

Dating from 1560, the hotel building is an amalgam of Georgian and Tudor architectural styles behind an 18th-century frontage. Now family run, the owners have recently completed major works on the premises, including a more spacious bar (the Flitch) and a barn conversion providing additional guest accommodation, with a sumptuous bridal suite. The remaining rooms have been renovated in keeping with the olde-worlde charm of the building.

Room-only rates are available (breakfast is £6.50 per person); children are welcome and pets are accommodated. All the rooms are comfortable and spacious; those on the ground floor are accessible to wheelchair users. A varied continental breakfast buffet is served, while a full English can be cooked to order. The main menus are based on fruit and vegetables from the market and meat from a local butcher.

Oliver Cromwell was said to have been a frequent visitor to the hotel. Records are kept of previous landlords dating back to 1620 – one of the earliest was a Roundhead.

The hotel, which has conference facilities, is just five miles from Stansted Airport and transport can be provided. The hotel is an excellent base for visiting Thaxted Mill and surrounding villages, and the tourist attractions of nearby Cambridge.

Q P

HALSTEAD

White Hart

15 High Street, CO9 2AA

▶ At A131/A1124 crossroads
T (01787) 475657
W innpubs.co.uk
Adnams Bitter; Mauldons Bitter; guest beer
One double, three twin, one family room; four rooms with en-suite facilities
£ ££ (single occupancy £40)
Snacks and lunchtime meals daily; evening meals Mon-Thu
Accepted

This classic coaching inn dating from the 15th century has been renovated with care over the years to preserve its original features. In contrast with the two traditional bars and pool room, the garden was given a modern makeover in 2003. Now summer visitors can retreat to a spacious decked and stone-flagged area with bistro-style tables and chairs to soak up the sun and enjoy an occasional barbecue.

The same juxtaposition between old and new is maintained in the guest rooms, where exposed brick and timber panels add character to the decor, but all modern essentials are provided, with television, hospitality tray and bottled water as standard. Mostly en-suite, one twin room has an adjoining shower and WC. Children are welcome.

For breakfast you can choose the full cooked English or you can have toast and cereals if you prefer. The pub offers a good snack menu and home-cooked specials supplement the regular dishes on a daily basis.

Halstead lies on the border with Suffolk, close to Long Melford which has one of the longest high streets in England - a good hunting ground for antiques. Kentwell Hall and Hedingham Castle are nearby.

P

HORNDON ON THE HILL

☆ Bell Inn

High Road, SS17 8LD

▶ Take B1007 off A13 or A128; jct 30/31 off M25
T (01375) 642463
W bell-inn.co.uk
Draught Bass; Crouch Vale Brewers Gold; Greene King IPA, Abbot; Slater's Supreme
Five suites, six double, three twin, one family room, all en-suite; four rooms are wheelchair accessible
£ £-££ room only
Lunchtime and evening meals
Accepted

The Bell dates back over 500 years. In the Middle Ages, wool merchants and pilgrims stayed here until the River Thames was low enough to cross at Higham's Causeway. A former coaching inn, it still serves business travellers as well as walkers and cyclists. The hilltop village has been relieved by a bypass and has a restored wool market.

The delightful guest rooms are well equipped and the spacious suites are ideal for a honeymoon or other special occasion. The rates here are for room only, continental breakfast is £4 for coffee, toast made with home-made bread or croissants. However, if you want to start the day with something more substantial you can choose from a full English breakfast, smoked salmon with scrambled eggs or poached eggs and bacon, all under £9. Eggs come from a local farm, sausages and bacon from the village butcher.

The Bell's restaurant is also highly recommended and has won awards for the inventive menus that change regularly. The prices are fairly high, but the finest ingredients are used. You can eat in the charming flower-filled courtyard in summer, the bar or the restaurant.
Q P

LAYER-DE-LA-HAYE

Donkey & Buskins

Layer Road, CO2 0HU

▶ On B1026, S of Colchester
T (01206) 734774
Beer range varies
One double, one twin room, both en-suite
£ ££
Snacks and meals daily, lunchtime and evening
Accepted (not Amex)

Built in 1840, this unspoilt village free house comprises two small bars, three dining areas and a large, secluded beer garden. It has no juke box, fruit machine or television. Up to four ales are served; the pub is a rare Essex outlet for Tindall Brewery and Tindall Best Bitter is often available, and the even rarer Mersea Island beers.

The Donkey and Buskins was winner of Colchester and North East Essex CAMRA's Most Improved Pub for 2005-6. One of the improvements is the newly-opened B&B accommodation - two brand new chalet rooms set apart from the pub in woodland. A full English breakfast of fruit juice and cereals followed by a plate of eggs, bacon, sausage, mushrooms and tomato is included in the price.

The Donkey is close to Mersea Island and well placed for exploring the Thames estuary and Essex coast, including Clacton and Brightlingsea, as well as nearby nature reserves. Q P

MONK STREET

Farmhouse Inn

CM6 2NR

▶ On B184, near Thaxted
T (01371) 830864
W farmhouseinn.org
Greene King IPA; Mighty Oak Oscar Wilde, Maldon Gold; guest beers
Eleven double/twin/family rooms, all en-suite
£ £ room only (single occupancy £40)
Lunchtime and evening meals
Accepted

As the name suggests, this is a converted farmhouse, set in a quiet hamlet. The 16th-century structure has been extended and outbuildings put to other uses – the rustic-style restaurant has taken over what was once a barn and stables. The menu, which always includes a selection of fish and vegetarian dishes, relies on local supplies of meat, poultry and fruit. Meals are also available in the traditional bar, which stocks a real cider in summer. The inn benefits from two spacious, well maintained gardens.

The guest rooms are simply furnished, with television and hospitality tray; a z-bed or cot can be supplied for family use. The room rate varies depending on the time of year and offers are often available; a full English breakfast is £6.75 per person, continental is available on request. Most dietary requirements can be catered for with notice.

Monk Street lies in the Chelmer Valley in open countryside. The inn, situated just a few yards from the river, enjoys good views. Historic Thaxted, with its 14th-century church, windmill and other fine old buildings is two miles away. The pub (with its ample parking) is very convenient for Stansted Airport (five miles) and the M11.

Q P

RICKLING GREEN

Cricketers' Arms

CB11 3YG

▶ Off B1383 near Quendon
T (01799) 543210
W thecricketersarms.com
Greene King IPA, Abbot; Jennings Cumberland; guest beer
Five double, two twin, two family rooms, all en-suite
£ £££-££££
Snacks lunchtime, meals lunchtime and evening
Accepted

An upmarket 18th-century country inn overlooking the famous old cricket pitch at Rickling Green, the Cricketers has beautiful, newly refurbished bedrooms with satellite TV and DVD player. Two rooms are wheelchair accessible. Room rates include breakfast - full English, continental or special requirements. A big plus is that you can pay an extra £20 to leave your car at the Cricketers for up to seven nights while you fly off from Stansted airport five miles away, the price including a shuttle service to and from the airport.

Featuring in CAMRA's Good Pub Food guide, the Cricketers offers superb dining. Two restaurants serve dishes such as wild boar and Toulouse sausages with Dijon mustard mash, crayfish risotto or smoked salmon with truffle champ potatoes, and an à la carte menu featuring Denham estate fallow venison and rack of lamb.

The beamed bar is furnished with comfortable leather settees, and the cask ales are served straight from barrels behind the bar; outside is a Japanese style garden. In a rural location on the borders of Essex and Cambridgeshire, the pub is close to Quendon Hall and Audley End House.

Q P

RIDGEWELL

White Horse Inn

Mill Road, CO9 4SG

- ▶ On A1017, midway between Colchester and Cambridge
- T (01440) 785532
- W ridgewellwh.com
- Beer range varies
- Five double, two twin, two family rooms, all en-suite
- £ ££
- Lunchtime Tue-Sun; evenings Mon-Sat
- Accepted (not Amex)

Voted 2006 Pub of the Year by Essex CAMRA, the White Horse is something of a rarity as it serves all its real ales by gravity dispense, straight from the cask. It offers three or four frequently-changing beers from breweries both local and nationwide as well as three traditional ciders. The 19th-century hostelry has a large open-plan bar and a recommended restaurant serving home-cooked fare at reasonable prices. Most dietary needs can be catered for on request. The guest accommodation is in a separate purpose-built block that has been designed to look like converted stables. The rooms are spacious enough to accommodate a wheelchair and are well equipped. They all have TV with DVD player and tea and coffee making facilities. In the morning cereals and fruit juice are followed by egg, bacon, local sausages and baked beans or you can order scrambled, poached or boiled eggs if you prefer.

Places of interest nearby include Castle Hedingham, Audley End House and Gainsborough's birthplace at Sudbury, and you can take a ride on the Colne Valley steam railway. P

Gloucs & Bristol

BLEDINGTON

☆ King's Head Inn

The Green, OX7 6XQ

▶ Off B4450
T (01608) 658365
F (01608) 658902
W kingsheadinn.net
Hook Norton Hooky Bitter; guest beers
Ten double, two twin-bedded rooms, all en-suite
£ ££-££££
Lunchtime and evening meals
Accepted

A perennial entry in CAMRA's Good Beer Guide and listed in most of CAMRA's food and accommodation guides, this classic English inn, situated just off the village green by a brook, started life as a cider house in the 16th century. Now a privately owned free house, it has maintained a reputation for high quality in all areas – ale, food and accommodation – for many years. The warm, welcoming bar, with high-backed settles and an open inglenook fireplace, is popular with locals and visitors.

The twelve guest rooms are individually decorated and well equipped (with Internet connection). Six rooms above the pub all have standard double beds, while a further six in the courtyard are more spacious, with king-sized beds. Prices vary depending on the room. Three courtyard rooms on the ground floor may suit guests with mobility problems.

The pub sources all its ingredients locally and much of it is organically produced. Aberdeen Angus beef comes from a farmer in the neighbouring village and fresh bread and cheese from Daylesford Organic. Breakfast is excellent, with a cooked meal accompanied by fresh fruit, yogurt and cereals. Kippers and salmon are also available.

P

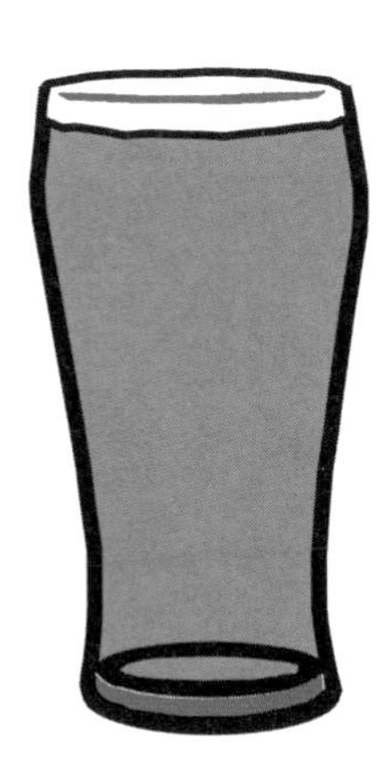

BREAM
Rising Sun
High Street, GL15 6JF

▶ At top of High Street
T (01594) 564555
W therisingsunbream.co.uk
Freeminer Speculation Ale; guest beers
Four double, one twin room (wheelchair accessible), all en-suite
£ £ (single occupancy £35)
Lunchtime and evening meals and snacks
Accepted

The Rising Sun dates back to 1765 but was gutted and extended during the 1990s and for a short while renamed the Village Inn. Now a free house, it is a favourite with local CAMRA members for its welcoming atmosphere and choice of guest beers sourced from within a 100-mile radius. The restaurant, dominated by a large stone hearth, offers a traditional menu of home-made fare based on local produce. Overnight guests can tuck into a full English breakfast, a vegetarian alternative, kippers or a continental selection.

The guest accommodation here is fairly new and includes one room with full facilities for disabled guests. All rooms have an en-suite shower. They are fairly plainly decorated and furnished but neat, with TV and hospitality tray; an iron and hair dryer are available.

At the heart of the Forest of Dean, the pub benefits from splendid views and is close to many attractions such as the narrow gauge railway (for Thomas the Tank Engine fans), Nagshead Nature Reserve, Clearwell Caves and the Puzzle Wood where paths laid down in the 1800s have been restored amid beautiful scenery.

❀ ♣ P

CHIPPING CAMPDEN
Volunteer Inn
Lower High Street, GL55 6DY

▶ Near town centre
T (01386) 840688
W thevolunteerinn.com
Hook Norton Hooky Bitter; Shepherd Neame Spitfire; Wickwar Cotswold Way
Two double, two twin, one family room, all en-suite
£ ££
Lunchtime and evening meals
Accepted

The two-bar Volunteer dates back 200 years and features much exposed Cotswold stone – even in the bedrooms. The lounge is warmed by a log fire in winter and in summer drinkers can drift out into the attractive garden.

Although the pub is located at the lower end of the High Street in a quiet spot, the owner does warn that there can be some noise from the bar in the bedrooms – not an uncommon feature of pub accommodation and something that most clients will accept for the conviviality of staying in a pub rather than an anonymous hotel. In any case, the Volunteer has not taken advantage of the more relaxed opening hours and closes at 11pm.

The bedrooms have TV and facilities for making hot drinks. A continental breakfast tray can be provided for early risers, or you can take your time over a full cooked English version. Main meals at the pub are reasonably priced, or you can explore other dining options in this lovely old town.

The pub enjoys a strong local following and also attracts walkers as it stands at the start of the Cotswold Way, a well-known route along the Cotswold Hill to Bath.

Q ❀

CIRENCESTER

Oddfellows Arms

12-14 Chester Street, GL7 1HF

- ▶ 10 mins' walk from town centre
- T (01285) 641540
- F (01285) 656034
- W oddfellowsarms.com
- Beer range varies
- Two double, one en-suite single, one single room with private bathroom
- £ ££
- Lunchtime and evening meals and snacks
- Accepted

This privately-owned pub dates back to the 1890s and is popular with locals and visitors. Recently refurbished, it retains a traditional interior of bare floorboards and solid wood furniture. The restaurant is similarly furnished, with French doors opening on to a spacious patio and garden that has an attractive children's play area. Note, however, that the pub does not accommodate children overnight.

Work has also been completed on the guest rooms which are light and bright with country-style pine furniture. They are all en-suite apart from one single, which has a private bathroom, and each room has a TV and hospitality tray. The rooms have been graded three stars by the south west tourist board. A hearty breakfast starts with cereals or porridge, followed by a full English with as much tea or coffee as you want.

The Oddfellows is a 10-minute walk from the centre of the lovely old town of Cirencester and three minutes from the National coach stop; the nearest rail station is Kemble four miles away. As well as museums and good shopping facilities in the town itself, other attractions are within easy reach, including Cotswold Wildlife Park, Chedworth Roman Villa and Westonbirt Arboretum. Q ❀

COCKLEFORD

☆ Green Dragon Inn

GL53 9NW

- ▶ Off A417 between Cirencester and Cheltenham
- T (01242) 870271
- W green-dragon-inn.co.uk
- Butcombe Bitter; Courage Directors; Hook Norton Hooky Bitter
- Five double, three twin rooms, all en-suite, plus one super king-sized suite
- £ £££ (suite ££££; single occupancy £57)
- Lunchtime and evening meals
- Accepted

At the heart of the Cotswolds, this picturesque pub in a peaceful hamlet makes an ideal base for touring the area. Its 17th-century origins have been well preserved, with stone walls, exposed beams and two log fires burning in winter. The rustic atmosphere is enhanced by wonderful hand-crafted furniture made by the famous Robert Thompson (the Mouse Man of Kilburn) whose trademark was a carved mouse.

The guest rooms are in a separate annexe where you will be assured of a quiet night's rest. They have all modern conveniences: power shower, modem connection, TV and hospitality tray, and newspapers are supplied in the morning. The St George's Suite is very spacious with comfortable sofas, wide screen TV, a desk and luxurious bathroom, perfect for a special occasion at £120 per night. Children are welcome (z-beds and cots can be supplied) and pets can be accommodated by prior arrangement.

The full English breakfast includes Gloucester Old Spot sausages and black pudding, accompanied by fresh fruit, yogurt and cereals if required. Good local produce including Cerney goats cheese and fish from Cockleford Trout Farm features on an excellent menu and home-made special dishes are chalked up every day. ❀ P

FORTHAMPTON

Lower Lode Inn

GL19 4RE

- ▶ Off A438, between M5 and M50
- T (01684) 293224
- F (01684) 291883
- Donnington BB; Hook Norton Old Hooky; Sharp's Doom Bar; guest beers
- Three family rooms (available as single or double occupancy), all en-suite
- £ £
- Lunchtime and evening meals
- Accepted

The inn, licensed since 1590, benefits from a fantastic riverside location and is set in three acres of lawned frontage on the Severn. Understandably popular with boaters, there are public moorings nearby and the pub has its own private slipway. From April until October a ferry operates from Tewkesbury to Lower Lode's picnic area, so some customers arrive that way, but drivers are warned that the approach roads to the inn are occasionally susceptible to flooding.

Two of the guest rooms have riverside views over to Tewkesbury Abbey. Generous in size, they are all designated as family rooms (children are welcome) and have TV and tea and coffee making facilities. Pets can be accommodated. The rooms are decorated in keeping with the style of the rest of the old building. A traditional full English breakfast is served, but variations can be provided if requested in advance. Full of character, the inn remains unspoilt by commercialism and has a friendly, family atmosphere.

There is a CC Club hideaway site here and day fishing is available. The pub makes a good base for touring the Malverns and the Cotswolds; the newly developed Gloucester Docks are also worth visiting.

P

FROCESTER

George Inn

Peter Street, GL10 3TQ

- ▶ (01453) 822302
- W georgeinn.co.uk
- Black Sheep Bitter; Caledonian Deuchars IPA; guest beers
- Two double, one twin, three family rooms, all en-suite
- £ ££
- Snacks and meals daily, lunchtime and evening (not Sun eve)
- Accepted

The George is a convivial village pub at the foot of Frocester Hill. It has been welcoming overnight guests since the early 18th century when it opened as a coaching inn on the route between Gloucester and Bath. Once called the Royal Gloucestershire Hussars, it was given its present name in 1998.

A traditional pub with a real log fire and a sunny courtyard garden, but no juke box or gaming machine, the George is run by four locals from the village. Usually serving three guest beers, chosen through SIBA, it hosts occasional mini beer festivals and stocks Westons Old Rosie cider.

Accommodation is in large, recently-refurbished rooms with period features, most providing both bath and shower, with a traditional English breakfast included - eggs prepared any way you like them. The George is well-known locally for good food made with as much local produce as possible, including meat from local farm Frocester Fayre.

Lots of rural footpaths, and the Cotswold Way passing within a mile, bring plenty of ramblers to the pub, which is just five minutes' drive from the M5. Local attractions include Berkeley Castle and Slimbridge Wildfowl and Wetlands Trust.

Q P

GLOUCESTER

☆ New Inn Hotel

16 Northgate Street, GL1 1SF

- ▶ City centre, by cathedral
- T (01452) 522177
- F (01452) 301054
- W newinnglos.com
- Beer range varies
- Seventeen double, eight twin, two family, three single rooms and two four-poster suites, all with en-suite facilities
- £ £££ (discount for CAMRA members)
- Lunchtime and evening meals
- Accepted

Dating from 1455, the New Inn is said to be the finest example of a medieval galleried inn in the country and it is likely that Shakespeare acted in the courtyard. Another reputed visitor is the ghost of Lady Jane Grey (the short-lived Queen of England).

The hotel comprises a coffee shop, restaurant, Regency function room (where you can get married), and a back bar that hosts night-club style entertainment at the weekend. Of more interest to real ale lovers however, is the attractive beamed main bar where you may find as many as eight beers on handpump from various breweries including RCH, Palmer and Sarah Hughes. It also stocks Westons Old Rosie cider.

The guest rooms have recently been refurbished and provide TV, hospitality tray and modern bathroom facilities. For a touch of class, book the Oak Suite with its four-poster bed and exposed oak beams. A generous cooked breakfast is served.

The inn is yards from Gloucester's splendid cathedral and also worth a visit are the historic Docks which have been renovated as a leisure and shopping complex.

KINGSCOTE

Hunters Hall Inn

GL8 8XZ

- ▶ On A4135, opposite turning to Kingscote
- T (01453) 860393
- W huntershallinn.com
- Greene King Ruddles, Abbot; Uley Bitter; guest beer
- Six double, five twin, one family room, all en-suite
- £ £££
- Snacks and meals daily, lunchtime and evening
- Accepted

A 16th-century ivy covered coaching inn close to Tetbury, the Hunters Hall has a charming interior with beamed ceilings and open fires. There are three bars plus a restaurant with a noted menu of traditional dishes. Outside is a large garden with children's play area – very popular with families in the summer months.

The 12 letting rooms are in a converted stable and blacksmith's block, all equipped with colour TV, CD player, tea and coffee making, and an iron. A two-bedroom family suite sleeps four people, and there is a lovely four-poster bedroom. One room on the ground floor has disabled facilities. Prices vary depending on the room, with breakfast included - a wide choice of fruit juice, yoghurt, cereals and fruit on the breakfast bar, followed by a traditional English of sausage, bacon, eggs fried, scrambled or poached, hash brown, fried bread, tomato and baked beans; or buttered kippers or smoked haddock.

Local attractions include Owipen Manor, Berkeley Castle, Chavenage House, Dyrham Park, hilltop village Painswick with Rococo Garden and Westonbirt Arboretum. Close by are the charming towns of Wotton-under-Edge and Stroud.

Q P

MARSHFIELD

Catherine Wheel

39 High Street, SN14 8LR

- ▶ Off A420, 5 miles from M4 jct 18
- T (01225) 892220
- W thecatherinewheel.co.uk
- Courage Directors; Bath SPA; guest beers
- Two double, one family room, all en-suite
- £ ££ (£50 single occupancy)
- Lunchtime and evening meals
- Accepted

The 16th-century Catherine Wheel served as a main stopping point for travellers between London and Bristol. Now, due to its location at the edge of the Cotswolds, its trade comes from tourists, cyclists and walkers (the Cotswold Way passes nearby). The building has been carefully restored to maintain its original character, retaining wood panelling, exposed stone walls and large open fireplaces.

The spacious main bar leads down through further rooms to a small patio garden where meals can be served. The hotel enjoys a good reputation for home-cooked food using local produce – the menu is imaginative and dishes well presented (no meals Monday lunchtime or Sunday evening).

Guest rooms are spacious and comfortable, equipped with TV and hospitality tray. Your breakfast will be cooked to order according to your requirements; a full English is provided along with cereals, juice and plenty of tea or coffee.

Marshfield is near Chippenham and close to the centre of Bath, so there is plenty to see and do nearby; sports fans can visit Castle Combe motor racing circuit or attend the Badminton Horse Trials.

Q P

MEYSEY HAMPTON

Masons Arms

28 High Street, GL7 7JF

- ▶ Between A417 and A419
- T (01283) 850164
- Bath Gem; Hook Norton Hooky Bitter; Wye Valley Hereford Pale Ale; guest beers
- Nine double/twin rooms, all en-suite; three can accommodate families
- £ ££ (single occupancy £45)
- Lunchtime and evening meals and snacks
- Accepted (not Amex)

Situated next to the green, opposite the cricket pitch in an award-winning village, the Masons enjoys an enviable location. It attracts walkers, cyclists and equestrians but is particularly popular with lovers of water sports. Two miles away is Cotswold Water Park with facilities for sailing, jet skiing, sail boarding, water skiing and all things aquatic. On the southern fringe of the Cotswolds, it makes a good base for touring, with Cirencester, Bath, Stratford and many renowned beauty spots within striking distance.

This early 18th-century Cotswold stone pub has recently changed hands and been refurbished and extended, retaining its original traditional feel. The bar area, still warmed by an open fire, is frequented by locals. A top chef is in charge of the restaurant and everything here is cooked from scratch, using plenty of local produce. The chef also cooks breakfast for overnight guests, so you can be sure that your full English will be top quality. Most special requests can be catered for.

The comfortable en-suite guest rooms have a three diamond rating from the English tourist board; children are welcome to stay and pets can be accommodated.

Q P

NORTH CERNEY

Bathurst Arms

GL7 7BZ

- ▶ On A435, 5 miles north of Cirencester
- T (01285) 831281
- F (01285) 831155
- W bathurstarms.com
- Hook Norton Hooky Bitter; Wickwar Cotswold Way; guest beer
- Four double, two twin rooms, all en-suite
- £ ££ (single occupancy £55)
- Lunchtime and evening meals
- Accepted (not Amex)

Part of the Bathurst estate, this late 17th-century pub remains a proper local while catering well for some of the thousands of tourists who visit the Cotswolds. Full of character, with flagstone floors and a stove in the inglenook, the pub combines a traditional atmosphere in the bar with a smart restaurant offering a modern menu – although old favourites such as locally-made Old Spot sausages with mash and cod and chips are not forgotten. The pub offers an excellent wine list; around 100 wines are displayed in the wine room and regular tasting events are organised. The River Churn runs though the pretty flower-filled garden, which has a boules court.

Comfortable accommodation includes some rooms with four-poster beds; all have Egyptian cotton bedlinen and hand-made Cotswold toiletries as well as tea and coffee making facilities. Free wireless Internet connection is available. Children are welcome and pets can be accommodated. An à la carte breakfast is cooked to order, with Gloucester sausages of course. Some of the produce comes from the pub's own allotment.

Places of interest nearby include the Roman villa at Chedworth, Colesbourne Gardens and the spa town of Cheltenham.

SLIMBRIDGE

Tudor Arms

Shepherds Patch, GL2 7BP

- ▶ One mile off A38, 800 yards from Wildfowl & Wetlands Trust
- T (01453) 890306
- F (01453) 890103
- E ritatudorarms@aol.com
- Uley Pig's Ear; Wadworth 6X; Wickwar BOB; guest beers
- Two double, five twin, five family rooms, all en-suite; five wheelchair accessible
- £ ££ (£45 single occupancy)
- Lunchtime and evening meals and snacks
- Accepted

The Tudor Arms lies alongside the Gloucester/Sharpness Canal, which these days is mostly used by leisure craft. The majority of the pub's customers, at least those who aren't locals, are canal users or visitors to the famous Wildfowl and Wetlands Trust that was established by Sir Peter Scott. Other local places of interest include Berkeley Castle (where Edward II was murdered) and a museum dedicated to Edward Jenner.

Built in the 1800s, the building was originally a smallholding making cider, and only became fully licensed in the 1950s. The inn was renovated in the 1990s and 12 guest rooms added in a separate purpose-built annexe. Although just five of the rooms are designated for families, all the rooms are large and can accommodate up to three people. TV, hospitality tray, hair dryer and toiletries are provided. A full English breakfast is included with eggs cooked to your preference and sausages made by the local butcher.

A snack menu is available throughout the day; main meals include pub favourites supplemented by a selection of chef's specials. Three guest beers that change weekly are mostly from local craft brewers, or you could try a pint of Moles Black Rat cider.

Hampshire

CHARTER ALLEY

White Hart

White Hart Lane, RG26 5QA

- ▶ 1 mile west of A340
- T (01256) 850048
- W whitehartcharteralley.com
- Otter Ale; Stonehenge Spire Ale; West Berkshire Maggs Mild; guest beers
- Nine double, one twin room, all en-suite
- £ £££
- Snacks and meals daily, lunchtime and evening
- Accepted

Tucked away up a remote country lane on the edge of the village, overlooking open fields, the White Hart is just five miles from Basingstoke so makes a perfect weekend retreat from London. Built in 1819 when it was run by the local wheelwright with his forge next door, the pub is the oldest in the village. It has been considerably extended since then, with open fires and oak beams. The delightful patio and garden are busy in the summer months.

The accommodation is modern and bright with en-suite shower rooms, tea and coffee making and broadband Internet access. One room is wheelchair accessible and children are welcome. The room rate includes a full English breakfast or cereals and toast.

The White Hart is known for its excellent pies – steak and kidney with real ale, chicken and smoked bacon, steak and Stilton or game of local pheasant, venison, rabbit and pigeon in beer; meals are available for residents only on Sunday and Monday evenings.

The surrounding countryside is ideal for walkers and cyclists to explore; Vyne House (NT), Milestones Museum and Old Basing House are not far away.

Q P

MILFORD-ON-SEA
Red Lion
32 High Street, SO41 0QD

- ▶ Off A337 between Christchurch and Lymington
- T (01590) 642236
- F (01590) 641787
- Fuller's London Pride; Ringwood Best Bitter; guest beers
- Two double, one twin room, all en-suite
- £ ££
- Lunchtime and evening meals
- Accepted

Midway between Bournemouth and Southampton, this seaside hotel mostly caters for locals in winter but enjoys a thriving tourist trade during the summer season. The 18th-century village pub has a friendly atmosphere; pool and darts are played here and live bands perform on occasion, but there is no juke box or television to spoil the peace.

The bar, which features photos of submarines, is linked to the dining area by a wheelchair ramp; drinkers spill over into this space when diners have finished their meals. In summer you can enjoy your pint of Hampshire's Ringwood beer or real cider outside in the large lawned garden which is away from the traffic on the High Street.

The en-suite guest rooms overlook the garden and are equipped with tea and coffee making facilities. The accommodation is not suitable for children. A full English breakfast is provided, and most of the produce used for meals is provided by suppliers in the village.

Milford lies in the New Forest and is just three miles from the popular yachting centre of Lymington, so the Red Lion makes a good base for exploring the area.

Q P

WHITCHURCH
White Hart Hotel
The Square, RG28 7DN

- ▶ Off A34, south of Newbury at B3400 crossroads
- T (01256) 892900
- W whitearthotelwhitchurch.co.uk
- Arkells 3B, Moonlight
- Six double, four single rooms, all en-suite; three twin, two family rooms with shared facilities
- £ ££
- Lunchtime and evening meals and snacks
- Accepted

This 15th-century coaching inn, 20 minutes' drive from Stonehenge, has been refurbished and updated by owners Julie and Andy and is now a refreshing blend of old features and new innovations. The bar has a modern look with comfy leather sofas and original games machines such as Pac-Man and old Space Invader tables, and you can't miss the huge clock. All around the bar and in other rooms works of art by local artists are displayed for sale. There are three dining areas: the elegant Gallery Restaurant, a large open no-smoking space and the coffee lounge where you can enjoy home-made cakes with your coffee or, in summer, a cream tea.

Some of the guest rooms are in the main hotel and others in an annexe in the grounds. Due to the age of the building the comfortable and attractive rooms are all different - some have bowed walls. The beds feature charming hand-made bed spreads. A travel cot is available. The twin and family rooms share bathroom facilities. Pets can be accommodated. A hearty breakfast includes local eggs, sausages and black pudding, or if you prefer a sausage or bacon sandwich or eggs on toast.

P

WINCHESTER
Wykeham Arms
75 Kingsgate Street, SO23 9PE

▶ By Cathedral Close and college gates
T (01962) 853834
E wykeham.arms@fullers.co.uk
Fuller's Chiswick, Gale's Butser, HSB; guest beers
Ten double, two twin, two single rooms, all en-suite
£ £££-££££
Snacks and meals daily, lunchtime and evening (not Sun eve)
Accepted

Situated in one of the country's most charming, historic cities, the 250-year-old award-winning Wykeham Arms retains its sense of history and identity as a local pub offering log fires, candles, wine, ale and good food. Filled with memorabilia – 2,000 pewter mugs at the last count - and Nelsonia, the many-roomed inn is full of interesting nooks and crannies.

Bedrooms each have an individual character and come fully equipped with everything from colour TV to tea and coffee with fresh milk, as well as their own teddy bear – so perhaps it is surprising that children cannot stay. This is a place for a luxurious, pampering get away, with prices to match, but room rates include an especially good breakfast where hot porridge is an option, followed by full English with black pudding or kippers with horseradish sauce.

The pub is known for imaginative dining and gained a star in CAMRA's Good Pub Food guide. The menu changes daily – one recent Saturday saw starters such as bang bang chicken and home-cured salmon gravadlax followed by main courses including rack of Hampshire Downs lamb, Gressingham duck with fresh plum sauce, yellow fin tuna and broad bean and asparagus risotto.

Q P

WOLVERTON TOWNSEND
George & Dragon
RG26 5ST

▶ 1 mile east of A339
T (01635) 298292
Brakspear Special; Fuller's London Pride; Ringwood Best; Wadworth IPA; guest beers
Four double rooms, all en-suite
£ £££
Snacks and meals daily, lunchtime and evening
Accepted

Oak beams festooned with hops, polished brass and two open log-burning fires all add to the charm of a pub dating back to the 16th century, under the same ownership for more than 20 years. There are two bars as well as a dining area, function room/skittle alley and large beer garden set in a delightful orchard.

Accommodation was added in 2000 in a converted dairy separate from the main building, with just four double rooms all with bath and shower, colour TV and tea and coffee making facilities. The tariff includes a full English breakfast – or anything else that you would like on request. Children are not permitted.

Main meals are quite romantic, eaten by candlelight in the restaurant. Home-cooked cuisine using meat from a local farm includes steaks and lamb; fish, curries, vegetarian dishes, daily specials and bar snacks are all available, too, accompanied by a good range of real ales. The function room is available for events catering for up to 200 people for weddings or barbecues – or 30-80 at a skittle party. Wolverton is located between Basingstoke and Newbury, so handy for the races.

Q P

Herefordshire

AYMESTREY

Riverside Inn

HR6 9ST

- ▶ On A4110, 18 miles N of Hereford
- T (01568) 708440
- W theriversideinn.org
- Wye Valley Hereford Pale Ale, Golden Ale; guest beers
- Four double, one twin, one single room, all en-suite
- £ ££-£££
- Snacks and meals daily, lunchtime and evening
- Accepted

Set in some of the most beautiful walking country in England, and midway along the 30-mile marked Mortimer Trail, the 16th-century Riverside Inn is an ideal retreat for walkers. Free transport is provided to and from the start of walks, and two or three day packages are available, including packed lunch, breakfast and dinner – June is a good time to visit, for the Herefordshire Walking Festival.

And after a tiring day, you can relax in a spacious, individually furnished double room with colour TV, and tea and coffee facilities. For a longer stay, two suites with separate bedroom and lounge area are also available overlooking the River Lugg; The Hayloft is particularly popular, opening onto the extensive gardens. Convertible sofa beds in the suites can be used for children. A full English breakfast is included, with home-made preserves.

The Riverside is well known for food, growing its own herbs, vegetables and fruit, and sourcing 90 per cent of products locally, and merits a star in CAMRA's Good Pub Food guide. Meals in the stylish bar include Cornish cod in real ale batter with home-made tartar sauce, or in the restaurant you might find haunch of Ludlow venison on spiced red cabbage. Q

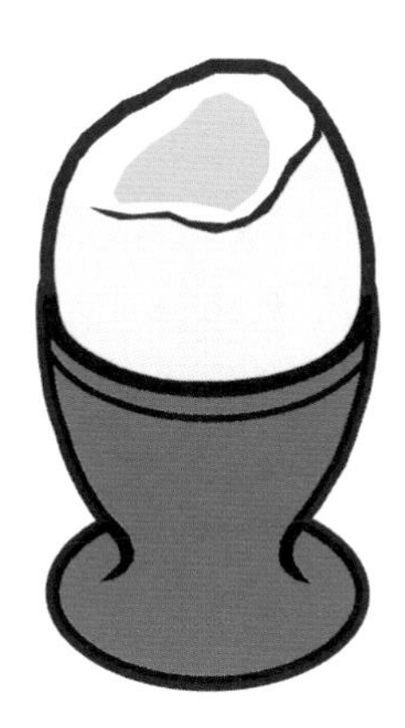

CRASWALL

Bull's Head

HR2 0PN

- ▶ Six miles from Hay-on-Wye via Forester road
- T (01981) 510616
- W thebullsheadpub.com
- Spinning Dog Hereford Organic Bitter; Wye Valley Butty Bach; guest beers
- Two double, one family room, one en-suite, two sharing bathroom
- £ ££
- Snacks and meals daily, lunchtime and evening
- Accepted (not Amex)

A delightful, 400-year-old drovers' inn set in over two acres of grounds at the foot of Black Hill, the Bull's Head was immortalised in Bruce Chatwin's book. Full of character, the three beamed bedrooms are individually designed and offer modern comforts with spectacular views over the valley and hill. A full English breakfast, with alternative choices, is included in the price. Or you can rough it at £5 per night per tent in the pub's fields.

Inside, the inn has wood-burning fires, beams, flagstone floors and two stylish dining areas serving excellent food such as Craswall pie of beef and gammon in Butty Bach gravy, local cider and apple sausages with scrumpy cider gravy, crispy sticky beef, seafood mille feuille, local Herefordshire steaks or a country game casserole with rosemary and paprika dumplings. If you just want a snack, try one of their famous huffers - doorsteps of home-baked seasoned bread with various fillings.

Attracting walkers, wildlife spotters and tourists to an area perfect for outdoor pursuits, the Bull's Head is close to the book 'capital' of Hay-on-Wye. Weston's and Gwatkin's ciders are stocked.

EWYAS HAROLD

Dog Inn

HR2 0EX

- ▶ Just off B347, in village centre
- T (01981) 240598
- W thedoginn.net
- Beer range varies
- One double, one single room, shared bathroom
- £ £
- Snacks and meals daily, lunchtime and evening
- Accepted

Built with stone from the local castle in 1509, this friendly village inn has variously been called the Well, Dog, Castle and now the Dog again. Excellent value for money, the attractive, newly refurbished bedrooms with exposed beams have colour TV and tea and coffee making facilities. For breakfast there is the full English with two eggs as well as sausage, bacon, mushrooms, tomato and toast.

The main bar has a stone floor, beams and wood burning stove, plus a games room and restaurant serving simple, home-made meals using local ingredients. Choose from pies and hot pots of the day, lamb shank in red wine sauce, and good steaks – sirloin, fillet and T-bone - all reasonably priced.

In the bar are local and regional real ales and inexpensive snacks – filled sandwiches and baguettes from prawn to hot steak, the all day breakfast, ham, egg and chips, and the 'dog's pyjamas' – double cheese burger with bacon, onion and mushrooms.

The inn is situated in walking, fishing and shooting country close to the Golden Valley and Brecon Beacons. A beer festival is held in the summer.

Q P

KENTCHURCH
Bridge Inn
HR2 0BY

- On B4347, off A465 at Pontrilas
- T (01981) 240408
- F (01981) 240213
- Beer range varies
- One family room, en-suite
- £ £
- Snacks and meals Wed-Sun, lunchtime and evening
- Accepted

Set in a delightful location on the banks of the River Monnow, close to the Welsh border, this bright red building is thought to date from the 14th century. The welcoming single front bar serves three weekly-changing ales, often including one from Wye Valley Brewery and another local micro, with beer festivals on the spring and August bank holidays.

Though accommodation is limited to just one letting room, it is a large en-suite family room overlooking the river and the garden with its petanque piste. The tariff includes a cooked breakfast of egg, bacon, sausage, tomato, mushrooms and hash brown.

Awarded a star in CAMRA's Good Pub Food guide, the restaurant offers the finest fresh food. Home-cooked by the landlords using local meat and produce from nearby markets, the menu is English style with continental flourishes. Blackboard starters might be warm Brie salad with dill vinaigrette or home-made tuna fishcakes, followed by Gloucester Old Spot gammon with local free-range eggs or Welsh Black rump steak. The three-course Sunday lunch is good value and recommended.

The Bridge's grounds have space for campers and caravanners.

Q P

ROSS-ON-WYE
King's Head
8 High Street, HR9 5HL

- T (01989) 763174
- W kingshead.co.uk
- Wye Valley Bitter; guest beers
- Ten double, four twin, one family room, all en-suite
- £ £££
- Snacks and meals daily, lunchtime and evening
- Accepted

This handsome 14th-century family-run coaching inn is set on the picturesque main street of the small town of Ross-on-Wye, where a street market is held every Thursday and Saturday. The King's Head is ideally situated for exploring the Forest of Dean, Brecon Beacons and the Cotswolds, with Tintern Abbey and Symonds Yat within easy reach.

During Georgian times the inn was extended by a second storey – hence the change in façade. The interior features oak beams, stone fireplaces, a busy bar popular with locals and visitors, and a restaurant with 73-foot well.

Comfortable bedrooms offer colour TV, direct dial phone, tea and coffee trays and a trouser press. The price includes breakfast starting with cereals, juice or fresh fruit followed by traditional English with back bacon and local sausages, scrambled eggs with local smoked salmon or kipper fillets.

Meals, served in the bar or restaurant, are tempting after a day's sight-seeing – cod in fresh beer batter, steak and Wye Valley ale pie, confit of Madgetts Farm duck, rib eye of Herefordshire beef, and daily specials such as local pork in Canon Pyon apple brandy.

The hotel's secure car park is opposite Palace Pound in the High Street. **Q P**

SYMONDS YAT
Old Court Hotel
HR9 6DA

▶ Just off A40 south, between Ross-on-Wye and Monmouth
T (01600) 890367
F (01600) 890964
W oldcourthotel.co.uk
Brains Rev James; Wye Valley Bitter; guest beer
Ten double, three twin, two family rooms, all en-suite
£ £££
Snacks and meals daily, lunchtime and evening
Accepted

The Old Court Hotel is the splendid grade II listed ancestral manor house of the Gwillim family – Elizabeth Gwillim Simcoe was the doughty wife of John Graves Simcoe, founding father and first governor of Upper Canada. Set in the main building or west wing, the themed bedrooms (including three with four-posters) are individually dedicated to the family and their adventures. The tariff per double room per night includes fruit and cereals followed by full English with local sausage and black pudding, or smoked haddock with poached egg.

The family-run hotel features an unusual cabinet bar carved in 1681, opening outwards and inwards, where real ales from regional and local breweries are served to guests including walkers, bird watchers and tourists. There is a swimming pool in the spacious gardens.

A la carte and table d'hôte menus are served in the restaurant, the former Great Hall, and bar snacks and teas are available in the bars, lounges, conservatory, patio and gardens. Food is a real treat with local suppliers listed on the menu – Risby Court Farm Hereford beef or Madgetts Farm free-range duck and turkey. The smoked salmon comes from a family-run smokehouse in the Scottish Highlands. Sharing dishes include meat charcuterie or home-made nachos, to follow you could try Madgetts Farm duck leg confit or traditional Herefordshire beef steak and kidney pie.

P

TARRINGTON
Tarrington Arms
Ledbury Road, HR1 4HX

▶ On A438 in village
T (01432) 890796
F (01432) 890678
W tarringtonarms.co.uk
Wood Shropshire Lad; Wye Valley Bitter; guest beer
Two double, one twin, one family room, all en-suite
£ £
Snacks and meals daily, lunchtime and evening (not Sun eve)
Accepted

Surrounded by hop fields, this classic, red brick Georgian pub with impressive colonnade entrance has a public bar and lounge bar featuring old photos of hop pickers, a bistro-style restaurant, open fire and outside patio area and garden.
The family-run inn has a comfortable, friendly and welcoming feel, offering simply furnished en-suite rooms with TV, tea and coffee at value for money prices including a full English breakfast. Children are welcome but pets are not permitted.

The bistro restaurant is renowned for its seafood and steaks. A fish night on the third Wednesday of the month features choices from lobster to sea bream, tuna and oysters – though you might find chef's specials such as muntjak with juniper and port. Traditional Sunday roasts, including Hereford beef, are popular too, and there is an excellent vegetarian choice. Prices are reasonable but the quality is high. The guest beer is from a small regional or micro brewery.

An ideal base for walkers who tramp the nearby Malvern Hills, the inn is also popular with tourists who enjoy visits to Eastnor Castle, Ross-on-Wye, Ledbury and Hereford. Q P

TITLEY
Stagg Inn
HR5 3RL

▶ On B4355 between Kington and Presteigne
T (01544) 230221
W thestagg.co.uk
Hobsons Best Bitter, Town Crier; guest beers
Three double rooms, all en-suite
£ £££
Snacks and meals daily, lunchtime and evening
Accepted

As well as three rooms in the pub itself, the owners let three further rooms in the Old Vicarage, a short walk away in the village, where guests also have a sitting room and large garden with croquet. The room tariff includes a full English breakfast with local bacon and sausage, scrambled eggs with smoked salmon, or poached kipper, as well as toast with home-made jam and marmalade.

Much added to over the years, the family-run medieval inn has a rustic atmosphere, especially in the bar which is also popular with locals. A busy gastro-pub which has won many awards, the Stagg serves innovative dishes made with local meat and produce. All meals are freshly prepared and special diets can be catered for.

After a day spent walking part of the nearby 30-mile Mortimer Trail through lovely countryside, you will have worked up an appetite for pigeon breast on celeriac purée, seared scallops with mint oil, free-range chicken baked with ratatouille, rack of lamb with sweetbreads, sea bass or Herefordshire beef with field mushrooms.

This inn is just a half hour drive from Hay-on-Wye and Ludlow.
Q P

Stagg inn, Titley, Herefordshire

Hertfordshire

ALDBURY

Greyhound

19 Stocks Road, HP23 5RT

▶ Opposite pond in village centre
T (01442) 851228
F (01442) 851495
W greyhoundaldbury.co.uk
Badger First Gold, Tanglefoot
Five double, two twin, one family room, all en-suite
£ ££-£££
Snacks and meals daily, lunchtime and evening
Accepted (not Amex)

A family-run former coaching inn overlooking the ancient stocks and duck pond in one of the prettiest villages in England, once used for filming the Shillingford Tales. The Greyhound bar has olde-world charm with beams, open fire and wooden settles.

The eight letting rooms are newly furnished and decorated down to new beds and linen, all with colour TV, tea and coffee making equipment and mineral water. The full English breakfast includes bacon, egg, sausage, tomato, black pudding, mushrooms and baked beans, or any of these items with eggs as you like them.

The Greyhound restaurant is well know for good food including quite spectacular Yorkshire puddings served with roast rib of beef or legs of lamb and rosemary gravy on Sundays, honey and soya-glazed duck, chicken stuffed with tarragon and garlic, or light bites such as baby mozzarella with roast peppers, an oriental platter or salmon and dill fishcakes, and fine ploughman's. Dishes are good value, mainly below £10.

The pub is close to Tring with its fascinating offshoot of the Natural History Museum, Whipsnade Zoo, and NT Ashridge Park.

Q

BISHOP'S STORTFORD
Jolly Brewers
170 South Street, CM23 3BQ

- ▶ Near town centre
- T (01279) 836055
- F (01279) 501305
- W jollybrewers.co.uk
- Everards Tiger; Greene King IPA; Taylord Landlord; guest beers
- Six twin rooms, all en-suite
- £ £
- Snacks and meals daily, lunchtime and evening (not Fri-Sun eves)
- Accepted

Built in 1862 on the edge of the town centre in this old market town, the Jolly Brewers lives up to its name by taking full advantage of the changes in the licensing laws, staying open from noon to midnight at weekends. Originally named the Teetotallers, it proved an unpopular name that was soon changed. Two bars and a games room with pool and darts make this a typical town centre pub, decorated in traditional style. Outside is a beer garden.

A 'travel lodge' style accommodation block was built last year accessed by a covered external walkway, with the convenience of a car space in front of each bedroom.

Accommodation prices include a continental breakfast in your room, though a full English breakfast can be provided by arrangement. Children, but not pets, are welcome and one room is wheelchair accessible.

Handy for Stansted Airport, Bishops' Stortford is also in travelling distance of Cambridge, Saffron Walden and Thaxted, with walks on the River Stort, a windmill and castle to visit nearby. The pub is within walking distance of the station.

Q ❀ P

GREAT OFFLEY
Red Lion
Kings Walden Road, SG5 3DZ

- ▶ Off A505
- T (01462) 768281
- E redlionoffley@supanet.com
- Thwaites Lancaster Bomber; Young's Bitter; guest beers
- One double, four twin rooms, all en-suite
- £ £
- Snacks and meals daily, lunchtime and evening
- Accepted

Set in glorious countryside, the Red Lion is a traditional country pub built around 1700 with beams and large open fire in the welcoming main bar, attractive back garden and large TV screen. The five bedrooms are in a small converted cottage in the back garden, all en-suite, four with showers and one with a bath. Two of the rooms are joined by a door, and can be linked up to make a family room. Accommodation is excellent value; no cooked breakfast is provided but each room is equipped with a fridge and with cereal, tea, coffee and orange juice. All the rooms have TV, hairdryer and alarm clock. No pets are permitted.

The inn has a reputation for good food using local produce, including meat from the local butcher, local vegetables and potatoes from a nearby farmer. These are used to make the splendid chips served with fresh fish on Wednesdays. Another treat on the varied menu is the speciality Red Lion pancake. Food is served in both the top bar/dining area and conservatory.

The pub attracts a wide clientele, including walkers, cyclists and people using Offley flying club close by. An annual beer festival is held in spring.

Q ❀ P

NUTHAMPSTEAD

Woodman Inn

Stocking Lane, SG8 8NB

- ▶ Signed off A10
- T (01763) 848328
- F (01763) 848328
- W thewoodman-inn.co.uk
- Adnams Bitter; Nethergate IPA; guest beers
- One double, two twin, one single room, all en-suite or with private bathroom
- £ ££
- Snacks and meals daily, lunchtime and evening (not Sun eve)
- Accepted

A pretty, thatched 17th-century free house with an L-shaped bar, splendid open fires and plenty of character set in a rural environment with an attractive large garden and car park. The new barn-style restaurant and function room offers an à la carte menu with house specials and snacks, featuring meat from the local butcher and nearby farms.

The bedrooms are in the oldest part of the inn, with a TV lounge – though the rooms have TV as well. All are either en-suite or with a private bathroom; the tariff includes breakfast with good choice of cereals, a full English of bacon, sausage, egg, tomato, mushrooms and sauté potato, or scrambled eggs on toast.

Popular with walkers, cyclists, motorbike and vintage car enthusiasts, as well as business folk and locals, the pub is ideally placed for visiting Duxford Imperial War Museum – during WWII the USAF 398th Bomber Group was based nearby and much memorabilia is displayed. Other local attractions include an international standard Olympic clay shooting ground, golf course, and city of Cambridge.

Q P

RADLETT

Red Lion Hotel

78-80 Watling Street, WD7 7NP

- ▶ On main road, opposite railway station
- T (01923) 855341
- F (01923) 853438
- W redlionradlett.co.uk
- Young's Bitter, Special, seasonal beers
- Seven double, three twin, two single, one family room, all en-suite
- £ ££-£££
- Snacks and meals daily, lunchtime and evening
- Accepted

On the old Roman road into London, the Red Lion is an ideal place to stay if you want to visit the capital. With its own car park, this Victorian hotel is directly opposite the station, with Kings Cross station just 20 minutes away – or Luton airport in the other direction. The modern, air conditioned bedrooms are all en-suite with trouser press, hair dryer, ironing, modem point and satellite TV. The price includes a full English breakfast, or continental if preferred. Reduced rates are available for a two or three night stay at the weekend.

Built in 1906, the Red Lion was originally a temperance house but is now a Young's pub with a large, split-level bar and 60-seater restaurant serving home-cooked meals. The dining room offers traditional British food as well as more modern cuisine. Starters include asparagus with honey mustard dressing, goat's cheese and butternut squash tartlet, or moules marinière. Main meals might be roast Shetland salmon with sorrel sauce, Cumberland sausages with mash and onion gravy, roast rump of new season lamb or a choice of steaks including fillet steak with brandy and peppercorn sauce.

Q P

Isle of Wight

BEMBRIDGE

Crab & Lobster Inn

32 Forelands Field Road, PO35 5TR

- ▶ From Bembridge follow signs to lifeboat station, then pick up pub signs
- T (01983) 872244
- F (01983) 873495
- W crabandlobsterinn.co.uk
- Goddards Fuggle-Dee-Dum; Greene King IPA; guest beers
- Four double/twin and one family room, all en-suite
- £ £££
- Lunchtime and evening meals and snacks
- Accepted (not Amex)

Given its name, its no surprise that seafood is a speciality here. The menu at the island's Dining Pub of the Year 2006 offers locally-caught lobster, home-made crab cakes and a crab and lobster platter for two, as well as plenty of other seafood options, served all year round.

A friendly pub popular with both locals and visitors, you can dine in the newly refurbished restaurant or the friendly bar, where you will find the award-winning Goddards beer, brewed on the island. Or take your pint out onto the attractive patio and enjoy the fresh sea air and stunning view – the pub is right by the sea, overlooking the Bembridge Ledge.

The guest rooms offer modern facilities, television and hospitality tray. They are spacious, light and airy with pleasing decor; some have spectacular sea views. Children are welcome to stay. The breakfast menu caters for all tastes: continental, full English, eggs cooked as you like them or fish – smoked haddock or kippers are available on request.

Q P

COWES

Duke of York

Mill Hill Road, PO31 7BT

- T (01983) 295171
- F (01983) 295047
- Beer range varies
- Four double, seven twin, two single, two family rooms, all en-suite except one shared bathroom
- ££
- Snacks and meals daily, lunchtime and evening
- Accepted

Close to the centre of Cowes just a few minutes from the harbour, high street, marina and yacht clubs, the Duke of York could not be more convenient for ferries to Southampton and has a large car park. A family hotel run by Barry Cass for nearly 40 years, the front of the building dates from 1780 while the rest was added in the 1900s. An open bar and restaurant on a nautical theme contains the original 55-foot gaff spar from the Britannia.

All rooms are en-suite apart from two that share a bathroom, with colour TV and tea and coffee making facilities, and are recently refurbished. The price includes a hearty full English or smoked haddock, and newspaper. Group and long stay rates are also available, plus fully inclusive packages, and special rates for both Cowes and Power Boat Weeks. One ground floor room is wheelchair accessible.

Though the beer range varies, Goddards Fuggle-Dee-Dum and Ringwood ales are regulars. Sally Cass dishes up home-cooked daily specials using seasonal produce. The inn is popular with yachtsmen, walkers, cyclists and business folk.

Q P

GURNARD

Woodvale

1 Prince's Esplanade, PO31 8LE

- Along coast road, 2 miles from West Cowes
- T (01983) 292037
- W the-woodvale.co.uk
- Badger Tanglefoot; Fuller's London Pride; Ringwood Fortyniner; guest beers
- Four double, one single, all en-suite
- £££
- Lunchtime and evening meals; food served all day Sunday
- Accepted

The Woodvale enjoys a privileged position on the Esplanade with superb views across the Solent – the four double rooms all benefit from sea views and the sunsets can be quite stunning. Formerly the Mew Langton Hotel, the inn has been recently renovated and now offers excellent amenities including a function room with a private bar and balcony overlooking the Solent.

The bar is popular with locals and visitors alike, with a good beer range and an extensive menu of freshly-cooked food, supplemented by a specials board.

The spacious bedrooms have sitting areas, tea and coffee making facilities, television and hairdryer. Children are not permitted. A varied breakfast menu kicks off with cereals or porridge, followed by a full English breakfast with choice of scrambled, fried or poached egg. Normally taken in the dining room, breakfast can be served out on the balcony in good weather.

The island's top tourist attractions are all within a 10-15 mile radius, but when the sun is shining you may prefer to just relax in the pub garden and watch a yachting regatta or power boat race, or enjoy a game of petanque on the pub's own court.

SHANKLIN

Glenbrook Hotel (King Harry's Bar)

6 Church Road, PO37 6NU

- ▶ On main Shanklin road
- T (01983) 863119
- E nicola.ottley@btinternet.com
- Fuller's ESB; Young's Bitter; guest beers
- Four double, one single room, all en-suite
- £ ££
- Lunchtime and evening meals and snacks
- Accepted

Although dating from the mid-19th century this is not a typical Victorian pub. Under a thatched roof is a mix of mock-Tudor bars, Henry VIII's Kitchen – an intimate restaurant specialising in steaks and grills – the elegant Squires dining room and the Will Somers Room – a function room with private bar that opens onto the garden. Live music is performed in the larger of the two bars on Friday evenings.

The relaxing en-suite accommodation continues the Tudor theme with four-poster beds, though there are modern comforts such as a television and hospitality tray. The large garden overlooking Chine Waters, floodlit at night, is a delight. It is very natural, with a stream, wild flowers and ferns.

At breakfast time you can choose between a full English – generous enough to set you up for the day – or a lighter option of poached or scrambled egg, or hot smoked mackerel. Main meals aim to satisfy Tudor appetites – steaks weighing a full 16oz or a whole roasted chicken are the specialities on the Tower menu – presumably for those who think this meal might be their last. The Court menu offers more modest portions.

Q ❀ ⊞ ● P ⊓ ⇌ ⊟

TOTLAND BAY

Highdown Inn

Highdown Lane, PO38 0HY

- T (01983) 752450
- F (01983) 752450
- W highdowninn.com
- Brakspear Bitter; Ringwood Best Bitter; Wadworth 6X; Wychwood Hobgoblin
- Two double, one twin, one single room; one en-suite, the others with shared facilities
- £ £-££
- Lunchtime and evening meals
- Accepted

In the west of the island, lying at the foot of Tennyson Downs, not far from the Needles, this rural pub is served by the island's open top bus route and is ideally situated for walkers and cyclists. In an area of outstanding natural beauty, the pub is welcoming to families with children and their dogs. There is a large garden – in good weather meals can be taken on the pretty patio.

The guest rooms all benefit from views over the surrounding countryside and are comfortably furnished with TV, fresh towels and bathrobe, and facilities for making hot drinks. At breakfast you can enjoy award-winning sausages and smoked bacon from the local butcher with fresh farm eggs. The tomatoes and mushrooms are grown locally. Smoked fish is also available as well as fruit, yogurt and cereals.

Fresh local ingredients, including locally-caught fish, also feature on the main menu, served in the cosy bars or the restaurant. In summer the most popular dish is the speciality seafood platter, while in winter there is usually a good choice of game.

⛰ Q ❀ ⊞ ♣ ● P ⊓ ⊟

Kent

BENENDEN
Bull
The Street, TN17 4DE

T (01580) 240054
W thebullatbenenden.co.uk
Harveys Sussex Best Bitter; Larkins Traditional; Westerham Special Bitter; Young's Bitter; guest beers
Two double, one twin, one family room, all en-suite
£ ££
Snacks and meals daily lunchtime and evening
Accepted

Mid Kent CAMRA Pub of the Year 2006 makes a splendid retreat for the weekend. Built in 1601, the Bull is a sizeable country inn set in a central position on the famous village green overlooking the cricket pitch – in summer you can enjoy a quintessentially English afternoon watching the match with a pint of ale.

The Bull's welcoming interior has a roaring fire, oak beams, wooden floors and large inglenook, with live music staged on a Sunday afternoon. Outside there is a popular beer garden.

The four rooms, all en-suite, overlook the green and are light and airy, furnished to a high standard with antiques, broadband, DVD player, complimentary toiletries and tea and coffee making facilities. A full English breakfast is included in the room tariff.

Meals can be taken in both the bar and 49-seater dining room, including dishes such as wild rabbit casserole, fish pie, home-cooked ham with free range egg and chips, Rye Bay dressed crab in season, fresh sea bass or wild mushroom and chicken terrine, plus a Sunday lunch carvery.

The pub attracts a mix of tourists, walkers, business folk and locals. Real cider is served.

P

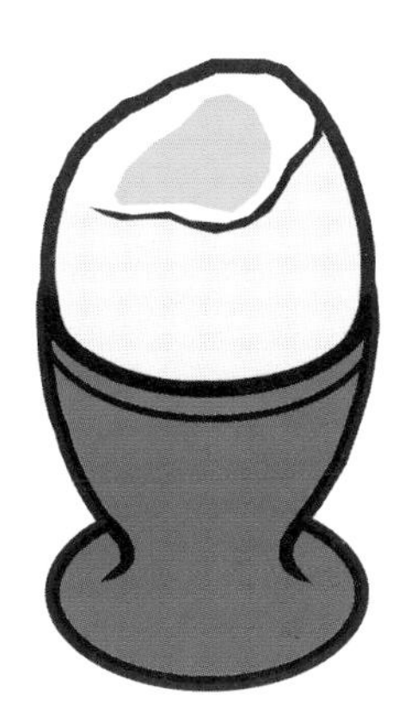

BRENCHLEY

☆ Halfway House

Horsmonden Road, TN12 7AX

- ▶ Just outside Brenchley heading towards Horsemonden
- T (01892) 722526
- W halfway-house-brenchley.co.uk
- Goacher's Fine Light; Harveys Sussex Best Bitter; Larkins Chiddingstone; Rother Valley Smild; Wychwood Hobgoblin; guest beers
- Three twin-bedded rooms, all en-suite; one wheelchair accessible
- £ ££ (£35 single occupancy)
- Lunchtime and evening meals (not Sun eve)
- Accepted

The Halfway House was brought back to life a few years ago by a new owner who rearranged the layout to make room for casks at the back of the bar. Dedicated to real ale (all the beers are served by gravity dispense), he stocks a changing range and hosts two beer festivals a year; mild ale and Chiddingstone cider are also usually available.

During the renovations more of the building was opened up and the interior now comprises six charming rooms with timber floors, exposed beams and old agricultural implements. In contrast, the twin-bedded rooms in an annexe with their own entrance are quite modern. Simply but comfortably furnished, they have TV and hospitality trays. Overnight guests can tuck into a full English breakfast or something simpler on request. Children are welcome to stay.

The award-winning pub enjoys a delightful setting in a two-acre garden with petanque pitches and a children's play area. Brenchley is a lovely old village with an ancient church at its centre. Bedgebury Pinetum, Royal Tunbridge Wells and the wonderful garden created at Sissinghurst by Vita Sackville-West number among the tourist highlights.

Q

CANTERBURY

King's Head

204 Wincheap, CT1 3RY

- ▶ On A28 towards Ashford
- T (01227) 462885
- F (01227) 462885
- W smoothhound.co.uk/hotels/thekingshead.html
- Fuller's London Pride; Greene King IPA; guest beer
- Two double, one twin room, all en-suite
- £ ££
- Lunchtime and evening meals
- Accepted

A typical Kentish pub, this grade II listed building, with exposed beams, decorative hops and much bric-a-brac, has a real country feel despite its location just 10 minutes' walk from the centre of Kent's county town. The pub serves its local clientele well - bar billiards, chess and crib are played in the bar, while the attractive garden has a pitch where teams gather in summer to play the Kent game of bat and trap (also known as 'lazy man's cricket'). Fans of the more active version of the game have only to travel a mile and a half to reach the Kent County Cricket ground.

The English Tourist Council has graded the guest rooms three star and children and pets are welcome. The charming beamed rooms (just nudging into our second price range) are equipped with tea and coffee making facilities, TV, hair dryer and a small selection of toiletries. A good choice is offered at breakfast, with a variety of cereals, fruit or porridge, followed by a full English with sausages made by a local butcher, kippers or eggs with toast. That should set you up for a day exploring Canterbury's historic centre, magnificent cathedral and delightful shops.

Q P

DOVER
Blake's of Dover
52 Castle Street, CT16 1PJ

▶ Off A20 Marine Parade
T (01304) 202194
W blakesofdover.com
Beer range varies
Two double, two family rooms, all en-suite
£ £-££ (room only)
Snacks and meals daily, lunchtime and evening (not Sun)
Accepted

Handy not just for the sights of Dover but for those catching early Channel ferry or Euro Tunnel crossings, this excellent real ale house also offers four-diamond rated accommodation. Attractively decorated en-suite rooms sleep two to four people, with colour TV, tea, coffee and biscuits, internet access and hair dryer. The higher spec rooms have a king size bed, and there is a self-contained suite at the top of the building – 'stairs not for the faint hearted' - with lounge, kitchen and bathroom. The full English breakfast costs £5.95, with home-smoked salmon an option.

Originally a late Georgian terraced house, the bar serves four or more real ales, all from micro-breweries, always including one from the Kent area. The ground floor restaurant specialises in fresh fish, offering locally-caught Dover and lemon sole, plaice, sea bream, bass, cod baked with lemon and garlic, Charlie Jenkins' naturally-smoked haddock, traditional fish and chips, prices around £10-15, and meat dishes from Moroccan lamb to plain steaks or beef and ale pie.

Those not crossing the Channel can visit the White Cliffs, Dover Castle, museum and a Bronze Age boat.

Q

FAVERSHAM
Sun Inn
10 West Street, ME13 7JE

▶ Town centre
T (01795) 535098
F (01795) 535322
W sunfaversham.co.uk
Shepherd Neame Master Brew Bitter, Spitfire
Seven double, one twin, three family rooms, all en-suite
£ ££
Lunchtime and evening meals
Accepted

The beer does not have to travel far to reach the Sun Inn. Shepherd Neame, probably the oldest continuous brewer in the country (since 1698), is in nearby Court Street. Its visitor centre is in a restored medieval hall and brewery tours can be arranged. The Sun, too, is ancient - it was built in 1396 and has been licensed for almost 400 years. It has had an interesting history, including being severely damaged when the local gunpowder factory blew up in 1781.

The pub is full of olde-worlde character, retaining exposed beams and a huge inglenook, but it has been refurbished, so the light, spacious guest rooms are well equipped with Sky TV, hospitality tray, hair dryer and ironing board, while Wifi Internet connection has truly brought it into the 21st century. The pub offers cereals, yogurt and fruit for breakfast, along with a full cooked meal, choice of eggs or smoked haddock. Main meals, based on local produce, can be taken in the restaurant or bar. The pub also has a pleasant patio garden.

Faversham is just a few miles from Whitstable, famous for its oysters, and historic Canterbury with its World Heritage site.

LADDINGFORD

Chequers Inn

Lees Road, ME18 6BP

- ▶ East of A228
- T (01622) 871266
- Adnams Bitter; Fuller's London Pride; guest beers
- One en-suite double
- £ ££
- Snacks and meals daily, lunchtime and evening
- Accepted

National village pub of the year, this friendly 15th-century village inn is as pretty as a picture in summer with award-winning hanging baskets and window boxes. The entrance opens into the main bar with a dining area to the left and cosier room on the right; in winter there is a roaring log fire. Children are welcome - the huge garden has animals and a play area.

Accommodation is in just one high-quality four diamond rated double room with TV, tea and coffee and ironing board. A generous full English breakfast is included, or alternatives from 'Danish-style' cold ham and cheese, boiled or scrambled eggs to pastries and croissants.

A noted main menu offers cod in Adnams batter, lemon-dressed salmon, local lamb chops with fresh vegetables, spicy chilli pancakes, Cumberland toad-in-the-hole, a real Spanish omelette or the chef's special sizzling fajitas. Thursday night is speciality sausage night and there are pie nights and paella cooked at table.

With easy access to the M20 and A21, the inn is well-placed for all Kent attractions: Leeds Castle and the Hop Farm Country Park are nearby. The Chequers holds a beer festival with 30 ales in April.

Q P

LENHAM

Dog & Bear

The Square, ME17 2PG

- Follow signs from A20, close to M20 jct 8
- T (01622) 858219
- W dogandbearlenham.co.uk
- Shepherd Neame Master Brew Bitter, Spitfire, seasonal beer
- Thirteen double, five twin, three family, three single rooms, all en-suite
- £ ££
- Snacks and meals daily, lunchtime and evening
- Accepted

Wake up to an enticing breakfast choice at this Shepherd Neame house. Grapefruit, prunes and cereals are followed by the full English with fresh tomatoes and button mushrooms, free-range farm eggs cooked as you like them, grilled kippers, a continental platter with croissant and home-cooked ham, and decaf coffee or speciality teas.

All bedrooms have been refurbished to a high standard providing TV with Sky, radio alarm, beverage tray and modem point; some are wheelchair accessible. Breakfast is included in the price.

The pub itself was built in 1602 and visited by Queen Anne a century later – her coat of arms decorates the entrance. With wooden beams and log fire, this is a traditional hostelry in a quintessentially English square. It has a function room and restaurant serving locally-sourced produce such as pan-fried mackerel with mango dressing, home-made pork and herb meatballs, roast topside of Kentish beef, Whitstable Bay haddock in beer batter, home-made salmon and spring onion fishcakes, main meals priced around £8.

Visitors can enjoy guided tours of Sheps' brewery. Maidstone and Canterbury are both within easy reach.

OLD ROMNEY

Rose & Crown

Swamp Road, TN29 9SQ

- Just off A259
- T (01797) 367500
- W roseandcrown-oldromney.co.uk
- Greene King IPA, Abbot, Taylor Landlord; guest beer
- Five twin, two double/family, two single rooms; five rooms en-suite, four with shared bathroom
- £ £
- Lunchtime and evening meals
- Accepted

Romney Marsh can be a wild and windswept place but has its own charm and, with numerous sporting facilities in the area, attracts walkers, cyclists and birdwatchers in particular. The Rose and Crown was built as two cottages, knocked together in 1689 to become an inn.

The pub retains two traditionally-furnished bars where old-fashioned pub games such as cribbage and shove-ha'penny are played. Guest beers are usually from local micro-breweries and Kentish cider from Biddenden is sold in summer. Food is served in the conservatory and the pub has a lovely garden with a play area. Children are very welcome; they will also enjoy a visit to the Romney, Hythe and Dymchurch light railway that runs nearby.

The guest rooms, in a purpose-built annexe on the ground floor, were refurbished in 2005. Suitable for disabled use, they have TV and tea and coffee making facilities, and the patio doors open out onto the garden with views over the fields. Five rooms including the family rooms have en-suite facilities, while two twins and two singles share two bathrooms between them. Pets can stay if you bring their own bed. A full English breakfast is provided.

The pub is convenient for Dover ferries, the Channel Tunnel and the Eurostar services stopping at Ashford. P

RUSTHALL

☆ Beacon

Tea Garden Lane, TN3 9JH

▶ On A264, a mile from Tunbridge Wells towards East Grinstead
T (01892) 524252
F (01892) 534288
W the-beacon.co.uk
Harveys Sussex Best Bitter; Larkins Traditional; Taylor Landlord
Two double, one single room, all en-suite
£ £££
Lunchtime and evening meals
Accepted

The Beacon - perched on a sandstone outcrop with far-reaching views - stands in 17 acres of grounds. You can wander through woodland walks, spot wildlife, sit by the lake, go fishing or search for the genuine Tunbridge Wells chalybeate spring. Built in 1895 as a private house for Sir Walter Harris, it was converted to a small hotel in the 1950s. Original architectural features have been retained, including stained glass windows and ornate ceiling plasterwork in what is now the bar.

The recently reopened guest rooms have been decorated in contrasting individual styles. The Georgian is a cosy double room with a feature fireplace and roll topped bath, the Colonial, also a double, has warm colour tones, African fabrics and a large shower room, while the single is dubbed Contemporary - light and airy with a subtle colour scheme.

A varied menu is offered for breakfast; the usual full English or alternatively kippers or smoked salmon and scrambled egg. The award-winning pub is a member of Kentish Fayre and uses as much local produce as possible, including lamb and beef, and fish supplied by a boat owner in Rye.

Q P

STANSTED
Black Horse
Tumblefield Road, TN15 7PR

▶ One mile north of A20, jct 2
T (01732) 822355
E blackhorsekent@tiscali.co.uk
Larkins Traditional; guest beers
Three double/twin rooms, all en-suite
£ ££
Lunchtime and evening meals
Accepted

The Black Horse is an ideal base for exploring the Garden of England, situated within striking distance of many major tourist sites including Leeds Castle, Chartwell and Ightham Mote. A few minutes' drive from the M25 and M20 motorways, the racing circuit at Brands Hatch is close by.

The pub specialises in Kentish ales, with a changing range including Larkins, Westerham and Millis, and stocks Biddenden cider. It hosts a Kent week in July when all the produce it offers is from the county, but local ingredients are always used in the home-cooked meals as far as possible, including meat from a nearby farm and locally grown vegetables.

Set in a downland village, this large Victorian pub stands in two acres of private grounds including a garden and children's play area. The South Downs is covered by a network of footpaths, so the pub attracts walkers, but it is also a focus for the local community.

The guest accommodation here is flexible - the three rooms are suitable for couples, singletons or families and children are welcome. An excellent full English breakfast includes local eggs and sausages, but a vegetarian version or a lighter continental meal are also available.

Q P

WATERINGBURY
Wateringbury
103 Tonbridge Road, ME18 5NS

T (01622) 812632
E wateringbury@spiritgroup.com
Beer range varies
Thirty double, six twin, four family rooms, all en-suite
£ £
Snacks and meals daily, lunchtime and evening
Accepted

Forty modern hotel rooms are incorporated into a traditional pub originally known as the King's Head after Edward III, with licensees traced back to 1855. Now a Chef and Brewer operation, it carries the corporate promise of a full refund if room or service are not up to scratch.

All the rooms have Internet and queen-sized bed; one is adapted for disabled use. Room rates are cheaper over the weekend; breakfast is extra at £7.50 for the full English or £5.25 for the continental.

The village dates back to the Saxons. It was home to Sir Oliver Style, High Sheriff of London, who retired there in 1660 after dealing with the Gunpowder Plot. The pub itself has beamed ceilings, an open fire, beer garden, and is candlelit at night. The choice of real ales changes weekly.

The comprehensive food menu offers starters such as duck and porcini ravioli or mushroom Stilton rarebit, followed by main courses including outdoor reared pork sausages, beef and Old Speckled Hen pie, halibut with horseradish and herb crust, and fillet steak.

The pub is close to the Hop and Lavender Farm at Shoreham, and Kent showground.

Q P

Lancashire & Merseyside

BASHALL EAVES

☆ Red Pump Inn

Clitheroe Road, BB7 3DA

- ▶ Three miles north of Clitheroe, follow signs for Edisford Bridge
- T (01254) 826227
- F (01254) 826750
- W theredpumpinn.co.uk
- Beer range varies
- One double room with private bathroom; two twin en-suite rooms
- £ £££
- Lunchtime and evening meals
- Accepted

Built in the mid-18th century, the Red Pump is one of the oldest pubs in the Ribble Valley, an area of outstanding natural beauty. During 2006 new owners breathed new life into the place by restoring it to the traditional country inn it once was.

Relaxed and informal, the inn now has a great bar and snug with a roaring fire where you can find a good selection of real ales, always including one from the local Bowland Brewery. The owners aim to match beers to dishes on an enticing menu. Thursday is steak night, while Friday is devoted to fish and seafood. Local and seasonal produce including game is used as much as possible.

Breakfasts are good, too. There's the 'Lancashire Hit' of Bowland bacon, sausages made to the inn's own recipe, local free-range eggs, tomatoes, mushrooms and fried bread, or you can choose kedgeree with smoked haddock and basmati rice, or smoked salmon and scrambled eggs. Follow with toast and home-made jams and preserves.

The bedrooms, opened in autumn 2006, are well appointed and designed with comfort in mind. The twin rooms have en-suite facilities, the double has a king-sized bed and private bathroom. The Inn has recently been given a four-star 'Quality in Tourism' rating for its accommodation.

Q ♣ P

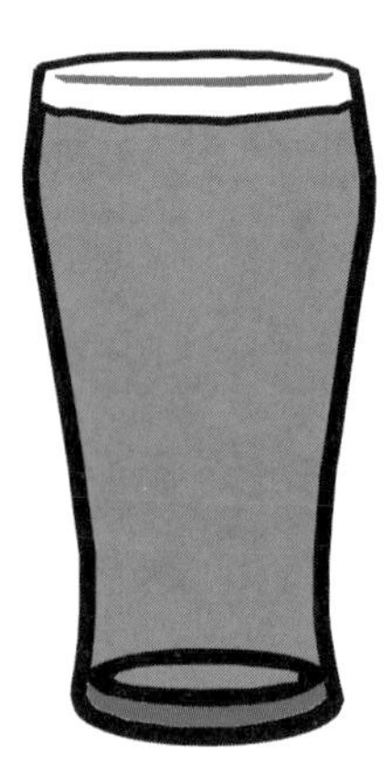

BLACKPOOL

Highlands

206 Queens Promenade, Bispham, FY2 9JS

- ▶ On the seafront
- T (01253) 354877
- E thehighlandslm@aol.com
- Thwaites Original, Lancaster Bomber
- Five double, one family room, all en-suite
- £ ££
- Lunchtime and evening meals and snacks
- Accepted

Away from the hustle and bustle of central Blackpool, Bispham lies at the northern edge of the town. The Highlands enjoys a pleasant location on the promenade, within walking distance of many amenities including North Shore golf course, a bowling green and shops and restaurants. You can hop on a tram to explore Blackpool Pleasure Beach and other attractions.

A family-run hotel, it offers modern en-suite guest accommodation. All the rooms have television, tea and coffee making facilities and wireless Internet connection. In the morning you can enjoy a full English breakfast – egg, two sausages, bacon, beans, mushrooms, hash brown and fresh tomato, which should see you through until lunchtime when you can try something from the hotel's award-winning snack menu.

The main menu is good for those on a budget as many items are on a 'two for one' deal including vegetarian dishes. Bispham and Blackpool offer plenty of other options for dining if you prefer to go out. The hotel bar stocks beers from Lancashire's Thwaites Brewery, which celebrates its 200th anniversary in 2007 and is still owned by descendants of the founder, Daniel Thwaites.

♣ P

BURNLEY

Sparrow Hawk Hotel

Church Street, BB11 2DN

- ▶ Close to Burnley Cricket and FC grounds
- T (01282) 421551
- W sparrowhawkhotel.co.uk
- Moorhouses Premier, Blond Witch, Pendle Witches; guests
- Ten double, nine twin, one family, thirteen single rooms
- £ £-££
- Snacks and meals daily lunchtime and evening
- Accepted

Providing high quality, budget rooms in an independently owned Victorian hotel close to the centre of Burnley, the Sparrow Hawk is within easy reach of the M65, close to both bus station and central train station, and just round the corner from the cricket and football grounds.

The modern bedrooms, all en-suite, have TV, radio and tea and coffee facilities. The tariff varies depending on whether you want to visit at the weekend or during the week, but includes full English breakfast of sausage, bacon, egg, tomato, mushrooms, beans, fried bread and hash browns.

The Sparrow Hawk bar offers Moorhouses ales, and provides entertainment at night from Wednesday to Saturday, and on Sunday lunchtime. The Farrier's Loft is a bistro-style restaurant, with bar food served in the Smithies.

Bar meals include freshly-made sandwiches from home roast ham to peppered beef. Main meals range from beer battered cod and chips, home-made sausages with mash and onion gravy, steak and ale pie, or lamb's liver and bacon with bubble and squeak in red onion gravy, to hand-made burgers and chicken and bacon salad bowl. ♣ P

ECCLESTON
Original Farmers Arms
Towngate, PR7 5QS

- ▶ On B5250, 1 mile from M6
- T (01257) 451594
- F (01257) 453329
- Phoenix Arizona; Taylor Landlord; guests
- Two double, two twin rooms, one en-suite and three shared bathrooms
- £ £ (room only)
- Snacks and meals daily, lunchtime and evening
- Accepted

A traditional, white painted English village pub built in 1700, owned by the same family for the past 20 years. More recently it has extended into adjoining cottages to provide a substantial dining area serving award-winning food.

Excellent value for money, the room rate for the country-style bedrooms does not include breakfast, but £4 buys the full English with locally-made sausages, £2 the continental. All rooms have wash basin, shaver point, colour TV, radio alarm, tea and coffee, hairdryer and dressing gown.

The main menu ranges from prize-winning black pudding with onion and mustard sauce to chicken with asparagus and Lancashire cheese, rack of lamb, and a giant mixed grill. But an ever-changing specials board might provide delights such as roast, stuffed suckling pig, roast whole baby loin of lamb with Cumberland sausage in redcurrant sauce, half a duck with orange and strawberries, or venison steak with venison sausages in plum and port sauce, mains £9-£14.

Local attractions include Botany Bay, Marton Mere wild bird sanctuary, Chorley market and Blackpool.
P

HESKIN
Farmers Arms
Wood Lane, PR7 5NP

- ▶ On B5250, 2 miles from M6 jct 27
- T (01257) 451276
- F (01257) 453958
- W farmersarms.co.uk
- Boddingtons Bitter; Castle Eden; Flowers IPA; Taylor Landlord; guest beers
- Two double, two twin, one single room, all en-suite
- £ £
- Snacks and meals daily, lunchtime and evening
- Accepted

This family-run 17th-century inn was once called the Pleasant Retreat, but was renamed the Farmers Arms in 1902 and the country-style bedrooms all have farming names: hayrick, barn, ploughmans, herdsman... All rooms have en-suite facilities, TV and tea and coffee making.

The price of accommodation at the Farmers Arms includes either breakfast or an evening meal. The breakfast is full English, large or small, or any combination including poached or scrambled eggs on toast. If you're leaving too early for breakfast and opt for an evening meal, the menu includes fresh local salads of ham or beef cooked by the local butcher, steak pie, roast chicken, steak and onions on a barm cake with chips or chicken curry. For a supplement is a range of grilled steaks or the mixed grill of lamb chop, steak, gammon, black pudding, egg, onion rings, mushrooms and chips, plus home-made garlic dip.

Enjoyed by a mix of folk from families to walkers and sports enthusiasts, the inn is adorned with flowers and hanging baskets. The attractive beer garden with a play area for children is popular throughout the summer. P

LATHOM

Briars Hall Hotel

Briars Lane, L40 5TH

- ▶ Next to M6 jct 27
- T (01704) 892368
- F (01704) 892772
- W briarshallhotel.co.uk
- Tetley Bitter; Thwaites Original; guest beers
- 23 rooms, all en-suite
- £ ££
- Snacks and meals daily, lunchtime and evening
- Accepted

Built in 1745, the hall has been used for processing corn, then as a stud farm, as well as a family home before becoming a hotel in 1970. It is reputed to be haunted by a lady and a gentleman. The main bar is constructed from wood reclaimed from an old church. The hotel has a beauty salon and water garden among its facilities. Bedrooms are all recently refurbished with flat-screen TVs. A full English breakfast, with meat from the local butcher, is included in the price.

An extensive menu offers light bites in the daytime from hot ciabatta sandwiches, deep-fried black pudding and jacket potatoes to home-made beef lasagne, Cumberland sausage with mash, fish 'n' chips or chicken korma. Evening meals in the à la carte restaurant might start with a plate of seafood or smoked duck breast with raspberries and cashews, followed by whole rainbow trout, lamb Henry, pork fillet with home-cured ham in mustard cream, or half a roast Barbary duck with black cherry and brandy sauce, all around £10.

Briars Hall is popular with cyclists who can pedal to the Viking town of Ormskirk, Lathom Chapel, Rivington Pike and Parbold Hill for the view.

Q ❀ ⊞ ♿ ♣ P ≥

LONGRIDGE

Corporation Arms

Lower Road, PR3 2YJ

- ▶ Near B6243/B6243 jct
- T (01772) 782644
- W corporationarms.co.uk
- Beer range varies
- Four double, one family room (single and twin available), all en-suite
- £ ££
- Snacks and meals daily, lunchtime and evening
- Accepted

Today's handsome building is on the site of an earlier farm and pub built in 1750, and was once owned by Blackburn Grammar School, later sold to Preston Corporation (hence its name); the town's coat of arms is above the entrance. It is said that Oliver Cromwell brought his steed to drink from the horse trough on the way to the Battle of Preston.

The en-suite guest rooms at this family-run inn are all air conditioned and equipped with TV and digi boxes, tea and coffee facilities, hairdryer, trouser press, radio alarm clock plus ironing board on request. The tariff includes a generous cooked breakfast with scrambled, poached or fried egg; alternatively, choose porridge followed by Manx kippers.

The main menu offers a choice of grilled steaks, Cumberland sausage, home-made steak and ale pie, grilled cod with pancetta, pork with sweet onions and Lancashire cheese and, of course, Lancashire hotpot; most dishes are also available as half portions. The inn stocks a good range of changing ales, often from local breweries.

The garden has wonderful views across the Ribble Valley. Nearby is Beacon Fell, with the bright lights of Blackpool a 20-minute drive away. ♨ ❀ ⊞ ♿ P ⊡

SOUTHPORT

☆ Berkeley Arms

19 Queens Road, PR9 9HN

T (01704) 500811
W berkeley-arms.com
Adnams Bitter; Banks's Bitter; Hawkshead Bitter; Marston's Pedigree; Moorhouses Black Cat, Pendle Witches; guest beer
Four double, four twin, one family, two single rooms, all en-suite
£ £
Evening meals daily
Accepted

The Berkeley is a late Victorian house converted to a small hotel and bar before World War II, retaining its original character and period features. You will always find at least eight cask ales on offer – and the range of ales is probably as perfect a beer list as you will find anywhere. The only pub in the area serving one of my favourites, Hawkshead Bitter, on my last visit I found the quality of every beer I tried outstanding.

Modern and comfortable with Sky TV, tea and coffee making, hair dryer, ironing facilities and even a travel cot if needed, the en-suite rooms are excellent value. The tariff includes a full English breakfast, or continental if preferred. You can breakfast alfresco, weather permitting.

Main meals are regular pub grub – steak and ale pie, giant Yorky with sausage and mash - but the kitchen is known locally for a wide choice of fabulous big pizzas, home-made down to the yeast crust.

The sea front is a bracing short walk away. And with four top golf courses near Southport, it is an ideal location for a golfing holiday.

❀ ⊟ ♣ P ⇌

SOUTHPORT

Scarisbrick Hotel

Lord Street, PR8 1NZ

T (01704) 543000
F (01704) 533335
W scarisbrickhotel.co.uk
Moorhouses Pride of Pendle; Tetley Bitter; guest beers
Fifty-one double, twenty-eight twin, five single, four family rooms, all en-suite; some rooms wheelchair accessible
£ ££££
Lunchtime and evening meals
Accepted

This large hotel stands on the tree-lined main boulevard in Southport, close to the town hall, library and art gallery and convenient for the shops. The Scarisbrick offers a wonderful array of leisure facilities, including a swimming pool, gym, sauna, steam room and beauty/aromatherapy studio, making it the ideal venue for a

relaxing break. Southport is well known for its high quality golf courses (12 within the town's boundaries) and the hotel offers golfing breaks with dinner, bed and breakfast.

The spacious guest rooms are kept in very good order, decorated in somewhat flamboyant style in keeping with the building's high Victorian origins. Some rooms have king-sized beds, one has a four-poster and a Jacuzzi; they all have hospitality tray, hair dryer, ironing facilities, television and Internet connection. Children are welcome to stay. In the morning a continental buffet and full cooked breakfast are available.

The hotel has a choice of restaurants with cuisine to suit all tastes and its bars offer a good range of real ales, including five guests and a house beer, Flag and Turret, brewed for them by Tetley.

WORSTON
Calf's Head
BB7 1DA

- ▶ 100 yards from A59, Clitheroe bypass
- T (01200) 441218
- F (01200) 441510
- W calfshead.co.uk
- Jennings Bitter, Cumberland Ale; guest beers
- Eight double/twin, one family, two single rooms, all en-suite
- £ £
- Lunchtime and evening meals and snacks
- Accepted

This country house hotel is 100 years old, built on the site of a farm alehouse that was established 400 years ago. The Calf's Head enjoys a good reputation locally with regular customers coming from near and far. There are several dining areas, a comfortable bar and a large garden with a stream that is home to ducks.

Meals here are good value and the menus, on boards around the premises, are varied. The hotel holds a wedding licence and with 11 guest rooms can cater for parties. The deluxe bedroom with views over Pendle serves as the bridal suite for the occasion and the newly married couple can relax in the double jacuzzi.

All the bedrooms have recently been modernised in individual style and equipped with hospitality trays and television. Two rooms are on the ground floor. Accommodation here is good value; at breakfast there is a choice of the full cooked English or a lighter alternative with fresh fruit salad, yogurt and cereals.

Situated at the foot of the Pendle with its Witches Trail, the surrounding countryside provides for a gentle stroll or more severe fell climb. Cycle routes and horse riding are nearby. The castle town of Clitheroe is just two miles away. Q P

WREA GREEN
Villa Country House Hotel
Moss Side Lane, PR4 2PE

- ▶ Off B5259
- T (01772) 684347
- F (01772) 687647
- W villahotel-wreagreen.co.uk
- Copper Dragon Scotts 1816; Jennings Cumberland Ale; guest beers
- Twenty-five double en-suite rooms; cots available and children welcome, some rooms wheelchair accessible
- £ ££££
- Lunchtime and evening meals and snacks
- Accepted (not Diners Club)

Built in the 1800s as an impressive residence for a wealthy gentleman, the Villa, approached by a sweeping private drive, stands in rolling parkland in the delightful village of Wrea Green. In keeping with its origins, the cosy bar has oak panelling and deep, comfortable leather armchairs and sofas where you can warm yourself by a roaring fire in winter. The elegant, award-winning restaurant specialises in seasonal dishes, so in July pigeon and asparagus might feature, in August hare and rhubarb. The hotel also has a year round schedule of themed events, and special rates are available for weekend breaks.

The Villa is popular for wedding receptions and family parties and has conference facilities. Its spacious, stylish guest rooms are air-conditioned and equipped to a high standard. The breakfast bar offers fruit, cheeses, yogurt, continental meats, preserves and pastries, and you can order a full English breakfast, or eggs with smoked salmon or smoked haddock.

Wrea Green and the surrounding countryside is worth exploring, while nearby are the historic towns of Lytham and St Anne's, offering good shopping facilities and, of course, golf. P

Leicestershire

LUTTERWORTH

Greyhound Coaching Inn

9 Market Street, LE17 4EJ

T (01455) 553307
F (01455) 554558
W greyhoundinn.co.uk
Greene King IPA, Old Speckled Hen; guest beers
Twenty four double, six twin, four family rooms, all en-suite
£ ££
Snacks and meals daily, lunchtime and evening
Accepted

The Greyhound, a traditional coaching inn built around a cobbled courtyard, has been hosting overnight guests for almost three hundred years. Just half a mile from junction 20 of the M1, today's guests reach it more easily than the coaches did – though travellers from yesteryear would still have found a decent pint on arrival.

All the rooms are designed with their own individual character, with five on the ground floor wheelchair accessible. They are equipped with broadband and satellite flat screen TV, trouser press, hair dryer and tea and coffee making. The room tariff includes a comprehensive breakfast, from Lincolnshire sausages to home-cooked ham and eggs or grilled kipper.

The family-owned hostelry is now a grade II listed building, situated opposite the market place where a market is held every Thursday. It has an à la carte restaurant and Sunday carvery. The lounge bar serves superb sandwiches, char-grilled steaks, freshly-made omelettes, lamb shanks and deep fried haddock as well as fine real ale.

In striking distance of Warwick Castle and Coventry Cathedral, Foxton Locks and Stratford-upon-Avon are also nearby.

Q ❀ P

MARKET BOSWORTH
Ye Olde Red Lion Hotel
1 Park Street, CV13 0LL

- T (01455) 291713
- W yeolderedlionmarketbosworth.com
- Banks's Original, Bitter; Greene King Abbot; Marston's Pedigree; Theakston Old Peculier; guest beers
- Three double, one twin, one single room, all en-suite
- £ ££
- Snacks and meals daily lunchtime and Tue-Sat evening
- Accepted

Situated near the old market square, Ye Olde Red Lion is a 400-year-old pub with an open-plan layout, crackling log fire in the dining area in winter, and a large, beamed bar. A varied menu offering good food at reasonable prices, an excellent selection of real ales, live music and a monthly quiz make it a popular meeting place for all ages, locals as well as visitors, walkers and cyclists. Outside, there is a beer patio.

The accommodation is in individually decorated rooms, some with four poster beds, all providing TV and tea and coffee facilities. A full English breakfast with local sausages and farm eggs is included. Main meals are good - expect simple bar snacks and meals at lunchtime, in the evening a fuller menu with pasta, vegetarian and steak dishes as well as boeuf bourguignonne, braised lamb shoulder or fisherman's crumble.

The Olde Red Lion is well placed for visiting a variety of attractions from Market Bosworth itself, recorded in the Domesday Book, to the site of the famous Battle of Bosworth which ended the Wars of the Roses in 1485, Bosworth Country Park, Bosworth Water Trust and Twycross Zoo.

P

MEDBOURNE
Nevill Arms
12 Waterfall Way, LE16 8EE

- ▶ On B664
- T (01858) 565288
- Adnams Bitter; Greene King Abbot Ale; guest beers
- Five double, three twin rooms, all en-suite
- £ ££
- Snacks and meals daily, lunchtime and evening
- Accepted

The initials MGN above the main door of the Nevill Arms are those of Captain Nevill, who was heir to the nearby Holt estate when this former coaching inn was rebuilt in 1863. The original hostelry was destroyed by fire in 1856 – legend suggests that a spark caused the fire after the village blacksmith wagered that he could support an anvil on his chest while a horseshoe was forged on it.

Bedrooms at the pub are converted from a house adjacent to the building; breakfast is served in the conservatory overlooking the garden where you can choose from fresh fruit and cereals, followed by a full English cooked breakfast and toast, preserves, tea or coffee. One room is wheelchair accessible, and children are welcome, but not pets.

Set between Market Harborough and Uppingham, the pub attracts walkers, cyclists and family groups who can be sure of a warm welcome. The attractive stone building has a heavily beamed bar with a large inglenook fireplace where a real fire burns in winter.

♣

SOMERBY

Stilton Cheese

High Street, LE14 2QB

- ▶ Signed from A606 between Melton Mowbray and Oakham
- T (01664) 454394
- Grainstore Ten Fifty; Marston's Pedigree; Tetley Bitter; guest beers
- Two double, one twin room, shared bathroom
- £ £
- Snacks and meals daily, lunchtime and evening
- Accepted (not Amex or Diners)

Built of the local ironstone, this hop-festooned late 16th-century village pub has hunting prints on the walls, copper and brass pots hanging from the ceiling and real fires in winter. Hundreds of pump clips from the guest ales (two on at any one time) decorate the low beams, and a real cider is always available, as well as 20 malt whiskies.

The Stilton Cheese is renowned for its food and features in CAMRA's Good Pub Food guide. Tempting specials include home-made Stilton and cranberry parcels, duck liver and raisin pâté, stuffed pork en-croute with sherry sauce, wild boar and apple sausages or game pie, plus lots of veggie options and irresistible puds such as ginger and walnut treacle tart.

Simple, value-for-money accommodation is in three bedrooms above the bar, sharing a bathroom. The room rate includes a full English breakfast with a choice of poached or scrambled eggs.

The pub is close to a good equestrian centre and attracts horse riders as well as hikers enjoying good walking in the surrounding countryside. Nearby is Burrough Hill Roman Fort.

Q P

Lincolnshire

COLEBY
Bell Inn
Far Lane, LN5 0AH

- ▶ Off A607
- T (01522) 810240
- F (01522) 811800
- W thebellinncoleby.co.uk
- Beer range varies
- Two double en-suite rooms, one twin with private bathroom
- £ £ (room only)
- Lunchtime and evening meals
- Accepted (not American Express)

On its website the Bell is described as a restaurant, although the low beamed ceilings and the decor in the olde-worlde bar and lounge are typical of many a traditional country pub. And the real ale is good enough to earn it a place in CAMRA's Good Beer Guide, which says, 'The pub, although undoubtedly food led serving excellent meals, actively welcomes drinkers'. It stocks beers from the more interesting breweries on Carlsberg-Tetley's finest cask list.

The restaurant offers an 'early bird' menu with half a bottle of wine for around £17; there is a separate fish and seafood menu and the scrumptious desserts are all home made. There is also a private dining room for parties, overlooking the terrace. The low-priced accommodation includes three rooms with TV and coffee and tea making facilities. Children are welcome.

Prices here are just for the room. A continental breakfast costs £3.95 or you can choose the full English, good value at under £6: egg, bacon, sausage, black pudding, fried bread, tomato, mushrooms and beans.

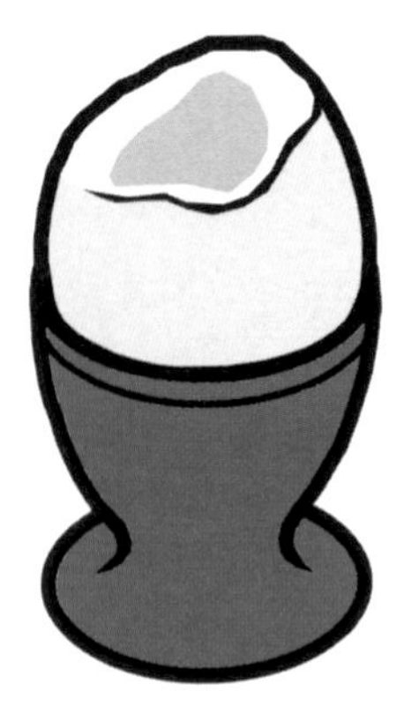

GRANTHAM
Angel & Royal Hotel
4-5 High Street, NG31 6PN

▶ Centre of town
T (01476) 565816
F (01476) 567149
W angelandroyal.co.uk
Beer range varies
Twenty-one double, three twin, four family and one single room, all en-suite
£ ££££
Lunchtime and evening meals
Accepted

When in Grantham you should take time to visit this splendid building which has recently undergone a £2 million refurbishment programme. The Angel Bar, with its magnificent 9ft x 6ft inglenook fireplace, has been a famous watering hole for 600 years.

Reputedly the oldest of all England's inns (circa 1203), the Angel & Royal is certainly one of the most historic – it was here that Richard III signed the death warrant for his cousin, the Duke of Buckingham. The King's Room, where the event was said to have taken place, is now a splendid dining room and the venue for a re-enactment with costumes and food of the 15th century. An all-in package for the occasion includes overnight accommodation in one of the hotel's en-suite rooms. Individually styled, the rooms combine period charm with modern equipment such as satellite TV, CD/DVD players, trouser press and butler's hospitality tray. Luxurious fluffy towels and toiletries are provided. All the rooms overlook the main courtyard, one is on the ground floor.

Weekend breaks are a good option: for £210 per couple you can stay for two nights, with a three-course evening meal on Friday in the King's Restaurant and Saturday dinner in Bertie's Bistro.

Q P

LINCOLN
Pyewipe Inn
Fossebank, Saxilby Road, LN1 2BG

▶ Off A57, by jct with A46 Lincoln bypass
T (01522) 528708
F (01522) 525009
W pyewipeinn.co.uk
Greene King Abbot; Taylor Landlord; Wells Bombardier; guest beer
One suite, twelve double, seven twin/family rooms all en-suite; one room is suitable for disabled visitors
£ ££-£££
Lunchtime and evening meals
Accepted

Many of the Pyewipe's customers arrive by water. The Fossedyke Navigation runs for 11 miles from Torksey on the River Trent to Brayford Pool in Lincoln. Boats tie up here all year round, while guests staying at the Pyewipe can walk beside the Fossedyke into the centre of Lincoln in under 20 minutes. The pub stands in four acres of riverside grounds, with plenty of space to land a helicopter. The inn enjoys clear country views across to Lincoln Cathedral.

The same panorama is offered from the Lodge, purpose-built in 2001 among mature trees in the grounds. Here 20 guest rooms are individually styled and fairly simply furnished to provide comfortable accommodation in either a king-sized or two queen-sized beds. Children are welcome and one room is equipped for disabled guests. Pets can be accommodated. The room rates include full English breakfast.

The pub itself was licensed in 1778 and has a lounge bar and a further lounge and restaurant. Several clubs and societies are based here, including amateur radio, car clubs and a historic boat restoration project.

P

LITTLE BYTHAM

Willoughby Arms

Station Road, NG33 4RA

T (01780) 410276
F (01780) 411248
Beer range varies
One double, one family, one single room, all en-suite
£ £
Snacks and meals Tues-Sun, lunchtime and evening
Accepted

This grade II listed building dating back 200 years was once the old private railway waiting rooms of the local lord. It is sited in a village famous among train buffs for the grand Victorian viaduct carrying the main line between London and Scotland. Lincolnshire CAMRA Pub of the Year 2004, the Willoughby Arms itself is renowned by local beer buffs for the award-winning Newby Wyke brewery to the rear, which usually supplies three of the pub's six real ales.

It offers inexpensive accommodation: three bedrooms, two large and a smaller single, recently tastefully refurbished, with TV and tea and coffee making facilities. The tariff includes an excellent breakfast with a choice of 10 items including eggs cooked three ways, sausage, black pudding and fried bread – not counting porridge or fresh grapefruit to start.

The Willoughby has a games room, lounge bar and dining room with traditional high ceilings. Wednesday is curry night, food is served in the bar and dining room. Westons Old Rosie cider is always available and there is a monthly quiz night plus occasional beer festivals.

The pub attracts a varied clientele of walkers, cyclists, real ale drinkers, locals and what it terms 'the five o'clock crowd'.

Q P

LOUTH

Masons Arms Hotel

Cornmarket, LN11 9PY

Town centre
T (01507) 609525
F (08707) 066450
W themasons.co.uk
Bateman XB, XXXB; Marston's Pedigree; Taylor Landlord; guest beers
Five double, two twin, three single rooms; five en-suite, five with shared facilities
£ £
Lunchtime and evening meals and snacks
Accepted

A former posting inn built in 1725, this grade II listed building can be picked out in the town centre by its wrought iron balcony and bay windows. Originally the Bricklayers Arms, its named changed in the late 19th-century as it became the meeting place for the Louth Masonic Lodge until 1908 – Masonic symbols remain around the pub.

The pub offers good value accommodation in its ten guest rooms, all with TV and radio, plus facilities for making hot drinks. Children are welcome and you can even bring your dog to stay. In the morning you can choose your own hot breakfast including eggs cooked as you like them.

The restaurant 'Upstairs at the Masons' offers a tempting menu based on local produce including fresh fish from Grimsby. The 'Downstairs' bar is known for the excellence of its cellar and the quality real ale.

Voted local CAMRA Pub of the Year in 2006, the pub features regularly in the Good Beer Guide. Editor Roger Protz praises its beer from Lincolnshire brewery Bateman, particularly the Dark Mild (now rarely seen) which he described as, 'kept in a succulent condition at the Masons Arms'.

ABOVE: Masons Arms Hotel, Louth. BELOW: Houblon Inn, Oasby

OASBY
Houblon Inn
NG32 3NB

▶ Off A52/A15, south of Lincoln
T (01529) 455215
W houblon-inn.co.uk
Everards Tiger; guest beers
Four double/twin en-suite rooms also available as singles
£ ££ (£40 single occupancy)
Lunchtime and evening meals
Accepted (not Amex)

When new licensees took over the pretty Houblon Arms it had suffered from years of neglect. They sensitively restored the inn, retaining its original features such as stone floors, exposed beams and brickwork and open hearths. So successful were they that in 2006 local CAMRA members voted it their Country Pub of the Year – no doubt partly influenced by the four excellent guest ales from local craft brewers.

The attention to detail extends to the garden, now attractively laid out with old-fashioned benches and flowerbeds, and the converted barn now used for overnight accommodation. The four spacious, comfortable guest rooms have their own front doors and individual decor, one with a four-poster bed. They are provided with fluffy towels, hair dryer, TV, hospitality tray and easy chairs. Children are welcome.

Breakfast, served in the pub, starts with cereal and fruit salad followed by a full English or smoked salmon with scrambled egg. The kitchen uses local produce, freshly cooked, and organic pork. Hand-written menus, inventive and varied enough to suit all tastes, change daily; dishes can be adapted to suit dietary requirements.
Q ♣ P

THORNTON CURTIS
Thornton Hunt Inn
DN39 6XW

▶ On A1077 between Wooton and Barton
T (01469) 531252
W thornton-inn.co.uk
Taylor Landlord; Tetley Bitter; Highwood Tom Wood seasonal beers
Five double, one single room, all en-suite
£ £
Snacks and meals daily, lunchtime and evening
Accepted (not Amex or Diners)

A mile from the ruins of Thornton Abbey, this well appointed local opposite a picturesque church is a family-run grade II listed building with rustic decor, exposed beams, brasses and rural pictures and, in the beer garden, an extensive children's fun trail.

Inexpensive accommodation is available in six en-suite rooms with a separate entrance; one room on the ground floor is designed for disabled access. They provide TV, tea and coffee making and the tariff includes a fine breakfast of fruit followed by cereal then a full traditional breakfast including middle cut bacon and Lincolnshire sausages. Children are welcome, but no pets.

The pub is best known for its excellent food. A former winner of Lincolnshire Taste of Excellence, local produce is used for good old-fashioned pub food such as home-made steak and real ale pie, cottage pie with leek and cheese topping and home-made vegetable Cumberland pie.

Places to visit include Palm Farm, Normanby country park, North Lincolnshire Museum and Wrawby Post Mill. The pub is also convenient for Humberside airport and the Humber Bridge. P

London

KING'S CROSS

Harrison

28 Harrison Street, WC1H 8JF

- ▶ Off Gray's Inn Road, between King's Cross and Russell Sq stations
- T (0207) 278 3966
- F (0207) 278 3966
- W harrisonbar.co.uk
- Taylor Landlord; guest beers
- Three double, one twin room, all en-suite
- £ £££
- Lunchtime and evening meals
- Accepted

King's Cross has been a pretty run-down part of London for some time now, so it is good to see work being carried out to restore the St Pancras station and hotel to its former glory. The Harrison, a freehouse and hotel slightly away from the hustle and bustle of Gray's Inn Road in a leafy residential area, will no doubt benefit from the regeneration of this whole area.

Itself the subject of a recent refurbishment, the Art Deco pub has been furnished in keeping with its origins and two fireplaces have been restored. Light and airy, the bar has attractive wood and leather seating. Independently run, it stocks a good range of foreign bottled beers and offers an enticing gastro-pub menu based on fresh locally-sourced produce.

The guest rooms have been given a three diamond rating by the English Tourist Board. Attractively designed with a pale palette, they have modern furnishings, including high quality beds and bed linen. Ideal for business travellers, they are equipped with Wifi Internet connection, TV and DVD player. The full English breakfast includes Cumberland sausage and home-made potato rösti accompanied by crusty bread; a vegetarian alternative is also available.

STOKE NEWINGTON

Rose & Crown

199 Church Street, N16 9ES

- T (020) 7254 7497
- Adnams Bitter; Marston's Pedigree; guest beers
- Four double rooms, all en-suite
- £ ££
- Snacks and meals lunchtime only
- Accepted

Originally built in 1806 as a stopover inn on the way out of London, this traditional pub was rebuilt in 1934 as a Truman's house. It retains many period features including the original window and wood-panelled walls, an Art Deco ceiling, two fires and a stone floor. The pub offers four weekly guest beers from a variety of breweries as well as the regular Adnams and Marston's.

One of the few real ale pubs in North London providing reasonably-priced accommodation, the en-suite rooms, two double and two twin, also available for single use, are equipped with TV and tea and coffee making; the tariff includes a continental breakfast of fruit juice, yoghurts, cereal, toast and unlimited tea or coffee. Home-made food including vegetarian and vegan options is also available every lunchtime. Children and dogs are welcome.

Close to historic Clissold House and Park, this is the gateway to Stoke Newington's nightlife, but is also ideal for lazy Sunday afternoons – or you can use it as a base for sightseeing in central London. There is a weekly quiz.

ST JOHN'S WOOD

New Inn

2 Allitsen Road, NW8 6LA

- ▶ Off St John's Wood High Street
- T (0207) 722 0726
- W newinnlondon.co.uk
- Greene King IPA, Abbot
- Three double, two twin rooms, all en-suite
- £ ££ (room only)
- Lunchtime and evening meals
- Accepted

Dating from 1810, this attractive corner pub stands in a quiet, leafy area of St John's Wood and offers excellent value accommodation: rooms at £70 per night must represent one of the better deals in the capital. Breakfast is charged separately, a continental is £5 per person or full English £8.

Just five minutes' walk from the underground, the inn is ideally situated for visiting central London attractions, and the vibrant Camden Market nearby. The pub is also convenient for cricket fans, as Lords ground is a mere five minutes' walk, while London Zoo, Regent's Park and Madame Tussauds are all close by.

The rooms are furnished in unfussy style with dark wood furnishings and matching duvet covers and curtains. The doubles have king-sized beds; all rooms have television, hairdryer, tea and coffee making facilities and Wifi Internet access. Children are welcome to stay.

The open-plan bar, again featuring dark wood and plain furnishings, is partially divided to provide drinking and dining areas where traditional English or Thai dishes are served.

New Inn, St John's Wood

CHISLEHURST
Bull's Head Hotel
Royal Parade, BR7 6NR

- ▶ Off A222 Bromley road
- T (0208) 467 1727
- F (0208) 467 5931
- W thebullsheadhotel.co.uk
- Wells Bombardier; Young's Bitter, Special, Winter Warmer; guest beers
- Four double, one twin room, all en-suite
- £ £££ (£77 single occupancy)
- Lunchtime and evening meals and snacks
- Accepted

In leafy, affluent Chislehurst, this fine hotel dates from 1753 and may have been visited by Napoleon during his exile from France. One certain visitor was boxer Henry Cooper who stayed here while in training in the 1960s, when the late Young's chairman John Young presented him with a silver horseshoe for luck.

The pub gets busy on a Friday evening, but there is plenty of space in the bar, lounge and TV bar. Bar meals and snacks are available or you can dine in the attractive restaurant, which serves a three-course menu for around £23. The hotel also holds a wedding licence, has conference facilities and a delightful patio garden that hosts barbecues in summer.

Children are welcome in the lounge bar and to stay overnight – a cot is provided free of charge, or a z-bed for £10. The pleasant guest rooms all have television, hospitality tray, trouser press, hairdryer and Wifi Internet connection. A varied breakfast menu, served in the restaurant, caters for all tastes and appetites.

Chislehurst is surrounded by countryside with famous caves and Scadbury Nature Reserve nearby, yet central London is just 30 minutes away by train. Brands Hatch motor racing circuit is a 15-minute drive.

Q P

CLAPHAM
Windmill Hotel
Clapham Common South Side, SW4 9DE

- ▶ Near Clapham Common and Clapham South tube stations
- T (0208) 673 4578
- F (0208) 675 1486
- W windmillclapham.co.uk
- Wells Bombardier; Young's Bitter, Special, Winter Warmer
- Twenty double, nine single rooms, all en-suite; one room wheelchair accessible
- £ ££££ (Sun-Thu) £££ (Fri-Sat)
- Meals and snacks served all day
- Accepted

The Windmill has stood on Clapham Common since at least 1665, when the local miller was also registered as an alehouse keeper. It came under the Young's fold way back in 1848, and the hotel was added 100 years later. The pub has recently been completely refurbished to cater for its 21st-century customers. Locals relax on comfy sofas in the bar, while the neat, modern guest rooms have all the facilities demanded by today's business visitors and tourists. The air-conditioned bedrooms have Wifi Internet access, satellite television, trouser press and hair dryer. Children are welcome to stay.

A varied breakfast menu is served from 7am (8am Sat and Sun) right through until midday, and is available for all customers, not just residents. A full cooked meal, with eggs any style, can be substituted for the vegetarian version, or there is a continental breakfast, salmon and scrambled egg muffin, free range eggs on toast, egg and bacon bap, grilled kippers or mushrooms on toast with hollandaise. Fruit, pancakes and cereals are also available. Main meals and snacks are served from midday until 10pm, with afternoon teas until 6pm.

P

WESTMINSTER
Sanctuary House Hotel
33 Tothill Street, SW1H 9LA

- ▶ Near St James's Park tube, turn right out of Broadway exit
- T (020) 7799 4044
- W sanctuaryhousehotel.com
- Fuller's Chiswick, Discovery, London Pride, ESB, seasonal
- Thirty-four double/twin rooms, all en-suite
- £ ££££
- Snacks and meals daily
- Accepted

It's location, location, location at this Fuller's pub with 34 en-suite rooms above. Staying here puts you right in the heart of the capital, two minutes' walk from the Houses of Parliament, London Eye and Westminster Abbey, close to Buckingham Palace and St James's Park, and within easy reach of the West End and London's major tourist attractions by bus and tube.

A traditional Victorian-style pub, it has a modern mural on the back wall depicting the sometimes harrowing history of this former sanctuary for monks, though there are also jollier prints of monks supping pints of ale.

Excellent home-cooked pub food is served in the Ale & Pie House on the ground floor until 9pm including cod in Fuller's beer batter, steak, mushroom and ale pie, home-cooked ham, egg and chips, pork and leek bangers, char-grilled rump steak, chicken and spinach pie and a good range of snacks and sandwiches.

Luxury rooms are in a beautifully refurbished townhouse, all with air conditioning, Internet access, TV, and some with four poster bed. Two rooms are wheelchair accessible. Breakfast is £10.50 for the full English. ♿ ⇌ 🚌

WIMBLEDON
Rose & Crown
55 Wimbledon High Street, SW19 5BA

- T (0208) 947 471
- W roseandcrownwimbledon.co.uk
- Young's Bitter, Special; guest beers
- Nine double, four twin, one family room, all en-suite; one room adapted for disabled guests
- £ ££££
- Lunchtime and evening meals; sandwiches available in the afternoon
- Accepted

The Rose & Crown is at the heart of Wimbledon village, a few minutes' walk from the most famous club in the world. Fans of the game can visit the Tennis Museum, and Wimbledon Common and Theatre are also close by.

The hotel is owned by Young's; in 2006 brewing ceased in Wandsworth after more than 400 years and the brewery moved out of its London home where it had been based since 1831. However, Young's is looking forward rather than back and has invested in the refurbishment of several of its premises to provide modern, comfortable overnight accommodation.

Rooms at the Rose & Crown are not large, but offer air-conditioned comfort and modern facilities such as wireless Internet connection, Sky TV, hairdryer, iron and hospitality tray. In the morning a full English breakfast is provided with a choice of scrambled, fried or poached egg.

You can have lunch or an evening meal at the pub; on summer weekends a barbecue menu is on offer in the sunny courtyard and an outside bar is set up during Wimbledon fortnight. The Hand in Hand, another Young's pub, is a Wimbledon institution that is also well worth a visit.
Q ❀ ♿ 🚌

HAMMERSMITH

Brook Green Hotel

170 Shepherd's Bush Road, W6 7PB

- ▶ On A219
- T (020) 7603 2516
- W brookgreenhotel.co.uk
- Young's Bitter, Special
- Fourteen double/twin rooms, all en-suite
- £ ££££ (£££ Fri & Sat)
- Lunchtime and evening meals and snacks
- Accepted

This Young's hotel stands on the busy main road opposite Brook Green, a leafy oasis between Hammersmith and Shepherd's Bush. Built in the 1880s, Brook Green functioned as a hotel until the 1930s. Now, after refurbishment by Young's in 2000, it again provides overnight accommodation. High, elaborately decorated ceilings and carefully restored wood and glasswork characterise the main bar on the ground floor where you can enjoy Young's ales, including seasonal offerings, and a meal or snack – food is served all day at weekends.

Beneath the bar is a function room and entertainment venue where regular live music – jazz and blues – is staged, as well as comedy nights and swing dancing. Upstairs the air-conditioned guest rooms are classically styled with dark wood furnishings, Sky TV, ironing facilities, hospitality tray and modem connection. Children under 12 sharing a parent's room are charged £20. In the morning you can have fruit, cereal or yogurt as well as a cooked breakfast or whatever items you choose from the full English.

The hotel is an ideal choice for visitors to Earls Court, Olympia, the Hammersmith Apollo and, just five minutes from Hammersmith tube, central London.

HAMPTON HILL

Roebuck

72 Hampton Road, TW12 1JN

- T (0208) 255 8133
- Badger First Gold, Tanglefoot; Young's Bitter; guest beers
- Three single, one twin room, all en-suite
- £ ££
- Lunchtime meals weekdays
- Accepted

The Roebuck has enjoyed a change of fortune due to new licensees who have transformed it from being a rather dismal pub into a friendly, welcoming haven. On the outside this 200-year-old hostelry remains somewhat uninspiring but the interior sports a diverse collection of bric-a-brac and ephemera, from a life-sized carving of an Indian chief and fishing rods on the ceiling to transport memorabilia, including working traffic lights that are used to signal last orders and closing time. The pub now also benefits from an award-winning garden, with a summerhouse for cooler evenings.

Popular with real ale fans, the two monthly changing guest beers generally come from small breweries such as Itchen Valley, Hepworth and – closer to home – Twickenham.

The guest rooms have en-suite showers, television and tea and coffee making facilities and represent good value for the capital. They are often booked by walkers at the weekend, but the pub is also handy for Hampton Court Palace, Kew Gardens and the rugby at Twickenham. A very full English breakfast is complemented by toast made with locally baked bread, plus cereals, yogurt and fruit on request. The pub does not serve evening meals but the lunches are recommended.

HAMPTON WICK
White Hart Hotel
High Street, KT1 4DA

T (0208) 977 1786
W whiteharthoteluk.com
Fuller's London Pride, ESB; guest beers
Twenty-five double, six twin, six family rooms, all en-suite; two rooms wheelchair accessible
£ £££-££££
Lunchtime and evening meals and snacks
Accepted

A familiar landmark in the Kingston area, this handsome mock-Tudor building owned by West London's Fuller's Brewery is just a stone's throw from the River Thames. The hotel is fronted by an attractive patio, separated by railings from the street, which gets very busy in summer.

Guest accommodation is in a courtyard behind the hotel. The rooms are well appointed and air conditioned, with Sky TV, trouser press and ironing facilities, and hospitality tray. Four of the double rooms are designated 'superior' and feature four-poster beds, while two rooms are adapted for disabled visitors. Children are welcome and pets may be accepted.

The generous breakfast starts with a selection of fruit, yogurts and cereals and is followed by two of everything – eggs, sausages, bacon rashers, plus tomatoes, mushrooms and hash browns. A varied Fuller's menu with a good snack selection is served at other times.

Weekend visitors can take advantage of a special deal, staying Friday and Saturday nights and receiving a free ticket for a riverboat cruise on the Thames to either Richmond or Hampton Court Palace. Kingston, excellent for shopping, is a short stroll from the hotel. Q P

ISLEWORTH
Bridge Inn
457 London Road, TW7 5AA

On A315, next to Isleworth rail station
T (0208) 568 0088
F (0208) 568 0088
W mclean-inns.com
Fuller's London Pride; Greene King Ruddles Best Bitter, Abbot; guest beers
Eight twin (three en-suite), two single rooms; four rooms wheelchair accessible
£ £
Lunchtime and evening meals
Accepted (not Amex or Diners)

If you are looking for inexpensive accommodation within easy reach of Heathrow Airport, the Bridge is ideal. The pub stands on a corner site on the A315, which links directly to the M4, five miles from Heathrow and next to Isleworth rail station. Twickenham Rugby Stadium is just a mile away, so this is an obvious stopover for fans.

The rooms represent good value for the capital and, if you are happy to share bathroom facilities, you can get away with paying as little as £25 for a night's B&B. Rates are slightly higher during the week than at the weekend, when a full English breakfast is not available. The rooms are basic but they do include TV, hair dryer and tea and coffee making facilities. Discounts are available for longer stays.

The friendly, family-run pub attracts a varied clientele and has a bar, games room and popular Thai restaurant that has been run by a Thai family for twelve years. English dishes also feature on the menu.

KEW
Coach & Horses Hotel
8 Kew Green, TW9 3BH

▶ On Kew Green, off A205
T (020) 8940 1208
F (020) 8948 8787
W coachhotelkew.co.uk
Young's Bitter, Special
Thirty-one double/twin rooms, all en-suite; some wheelchair accessible
£ ££££ (£££ Fri & Sat)
Meals and snacks served all day
Accepted

The Coach and Horses enjoys a wonderful position opposite the Royal Botanic Gardens, easily accessible from the M4 and 20 minutes' drive from Heathrow Airport. Just a few minutes' walk from the tube and mainline stations, it is also convenient for central London.

As its name suggests, this Young's hotel was a former coaching house and dates back to the 17th century. The brewery undertook a sensitive renovation of the property in 2001. The traditional bar, with its open fire, is a relaxing place to enjoy a pint of Young's ale and a bar snack, while the oak-panelled restaurant also serves food all day. Its atrium is licensed for civil weddings and adjoins a function room that can accommodate 80 guests.

The bedrooms are modern in style, with en-suite bath and shower, and benefit from air conditioning; some rooms have been adapted to cater for disabled guests and all have TV, trouser press and hair dryer. Rates are lower at the weekend when guests can also take advantage of special deals for two or three night stays. Children under 12 sharing a parent's room are charged at £15 per night. A full English breakfast is served. Q ❀ ♿ P ⇌ 🚌

TWICKENHAM
Pope's Grotto
Cross Deep, TW1 4RB

▶ Off A305, by the River Thames
T (0208) 892 3050
W popesgrotto.co.uk
Young's Bitter, Special
Thirty-two double or twin rooms, all en-suite; two rooms wheelchair accessible
£ £££ (Fri-Sun) ££££ (Mon-Thu)
Lunchtime and evening meals and snacks
Accepted

This Young's hotel occupies a fairly large plot, a rugby throw from the River Thames. It gets wholeheartedly involved with the sport throughout the season, offering prizes and giveaways during the games. The traditional bar sports plasma-screen TVs for sports fans of all types. A third Young's beer is usually available here.

The hotel has a function room with its own patio ideal for family gatherings or business meetings. The guest accommodation is popular with business people, local visitors and tourists (weekend rates are considerably lower). The comfortable rooms have modern fixtures and fittings including Sky TV, ironing centre, hair dryer and hospitality tray. Some rooms have balconies overlooking the Thames. Children are welcome and families can normally be accommodated in adjoining rooms (children sharing a parent's room are charged at £20). Two double rooms have been adapted to suit disabled guests.

A good choice is offered in the morning from a full English breakfast with eggs as you like them or continental (with cheese and ham) to eggs Benedict, grilled kippers with tomato or scrambled eggs and smoked salmon on a toasted muffin. Meals in the restaurant are freshly prepared and include daily chef's specials. Q ❀ ♿ P ⇌ 🚌

Greater Manchester

CHEADLE HULME
Governor's House
43 Ravenoak Road, SK8 7EQ

▶ Ravenoak Road is a continuation of Station Road in town centre
T (0161) 488 4222
Hardys and Hansons Olde Trip; guest beers
Ten double en-suite rooms
£ £
Meals and snacks are served all day
Accepted

This substantial, traditional pub is part of the Hardys and Hansons estate – the independent Nottinghamshire brewer that was taken over by the expanding Greene King in 2006. Sadly, by the end of the year all brewing had been transferred to Suffolk and the fate of the H&H brand remains uncertain – hopefully you will continue to be able to sample Olde Trip here.

The pub is a busy, lively venue catering for all ages including children, who are welcome to stay overnight. The bar has games machines and regular live music; discos, quizzes and other events are staged. An ATM is available. Standard pub food is served at all times and prices are reasonable. The accommodation is good value, too. Each room is equipped with Sky TV, fridge, iron and kettle. At the time of writing only a light breakfast is offered – fruit, yogurt and cereals – but cooked meals are planned.

The Governor's House is convenient for business travellers and those using public transport, as it is within walking distance of the station, with fast trains to Manchester taking around 20 minutes. For tourists Bramhall Hall, the splendid black and white timber framed manor house, is well worth a visit.

Q ❀ ♿ P ⇌ 🚌

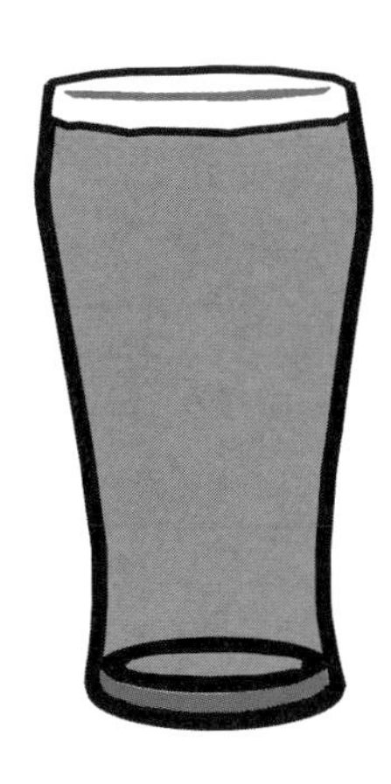

GREENFIELD
Railway
Shawhall Bank Road, OL3 7JZ

- ▶ Opposite station
- T (01457) 872307
- W railway-greenfield.co.uk
- Caledonian Deuchars IPA; John Smith's Bitter; Taylor Landlord; Wells Bombardier; guest beer
- One double, three twin rooms (also available as singles), shared bathroom
- £ £
- Evening meals if booked
- Not accepted

The Railway is a hidden gem surrounded by beautiful hills and pleasant valleys. Built around 1845 to accommodate the new railway line, it is little changed with beams and a tap room with a log fire and old Saddleworth photos, plus marvellous views across the Chew Valley. Two minutes from the canal traversed by narrow boats, it is close to endless moorland, walking, climbing and bouldering, and a Roman fort.

Accommodation here is in spotlessly clean bedrooms, two rooms looking out over the valley, the other two over the village and station. The bathroom is shared. Rooms are kitted out with biscuits as well as tea and coffee, colour Sky TV with teletext, and you are welcome to borrow an iron or hairdryer. A hearty breakfast is included, with potato cakes and black pudding; packed lunches and evening meals can be provided for guests if booked in advance. Note that you cannot pay by credit card – 'still 1950 here' – says the landlord.

The hostelry is a renowned local venue for live music – Cajun and R&B, jazz and pop – on Thursday, Friday (unplugged) and Sunday, enjoyed by 'a good happy mix from 18 to 80'.

P

HAWKSHAW
Red Lion
81 Ramsbottom Road, BL8 4JS

- ▶ On A676, 5 miles from the centre of Bolton
- T (01204) 856600
- Bank Top Flat Cap; Jennings Bitter, Cumberland Ale; guest beer
- Two double, three twin rooms, all en-suite
- £ ££
- Lunchtime and evening meals and snacks
- Accepted

This attractive stone pub was rebuilt in 1990 in traditional style. Its single large bar enjoys a good local following of mostly middle-aged customers who enjoy the food here as well as the real ale.

The accommodation attracts a varied clientele from business clients to football supporters attending games at Old Trafford or the Reebok Stadium as well as walkers. The comfortable rooms have TV and tea and coffee making facilities; the Red Lion suite boasts a four-poster bed. A hearty breakfast is cooked to order with a choice of fried, poached or scrambled eggs.

Meals can be taken in the bar or the award-winning restaurant. A varied menu is based on local produce delivered daily. Particularly recommended are the braised shoulder of lamb in red wine sauce and the roast goosnargh duckling with green peppercorn sauce. If you want a snack a good selection of sandwiches can be ordered with or without a bowl of soup. Children are welcome.

Hawkshaw is a picturesque village in the Irwell Valley, with plenty to offer visitors. You can enjoy the scenery from a steam train on the East Lancashire Railway or visit nearby Jumbles Country Park for walks, sailing and fishing. P

LITTLEBOROUGH
Moorcock
Halifax Road, OL15 0LD

- ▶ On A58
- T (01706) 378156
- E moorcock@btinternet.com
- Jennings Cumberland Ale; Taylor Landlord; guest beers
- Two double, three twin, one family, one single room, all en-suite
- £ £-££ (room only)
- Snacks and meals daily, lunchtime and evening
- Accepted

Described as 'a gem nestling in the Pennine foothills' by local CAMRA members, visitors can admire glorious panoramic views of the surrounding countryside. Built as a farmhouse in 1641 and first licensed two centuries later, the Moorcock has a popular restaurant and bar where drinkers can enjoy five real ales, the guests from local brewers.

Bedrooms are designed in country style with wooden floors, large luxurious shower, hospitality tray, hair dryer and room service. The price varies depending on the room and does not include breakfast which costs £6 for a full English, £4 for continental. If you are celebrating, an extra £50 per room buys a bouquet of flowers, bottle of champagne, fresh fruit and hand-made chocolates. Special rates are available for weekend breaks including dinner.

Food is very popular at the Moorcock, from the two-course Sunday lunch at around £10 to the local dish rag pudding (minced steak and onions steamed in suet pastry) – with main courses around £8-£13.

Close to the Pennine Way and Hollingworth Lake in good walking country, the inn is also convenient for Manchester City centre just 15 minutes away by train.

Q P

LYDGATE
☆ White Hart
51 Stockport Road, OL4 4JJ

- ▶ At A669/A6050 jct
- T (01457) 872566
- W thewhitehart.co.uk
- Lees Bitter; Taylor Landlord; Tetley Bitter; guest beers
- Twelve double/twin rooms (also available as singles or family occupancy), all en-suite
- £ ££££ (£105 single occupancy)
- Lunchtime and evening meals
- Accepted

If you are celebrating a special occasion or just feel like pushing the boat out, this is the place to stay in Greater Manchester. Not only did owner and chef John Rudden win national Chef of the Year in 2006, he also coached his youngest team member to take Young Pub Chef of the Year at the same time. Dining here is a marvellous experience and the reason why customers come from miles around. Oh, and the beer's good, too. The main bar boasts no fewer than eight handpumps and the small snug has its own servery.

This old stone free house adjoins the village church and school. A popular local since 1788, three of its regulars were the inspiration for the characters Compo, Clegg and Blamire in Last of the Summer Wine.

By the time John Rudden and his partner bought the property in 1994 it was semi-derelict. They quickly turned the pub around, immediately winning plaudits for the cuisine, and in 1997 opened the first guest rooms. Individually designed, the rooms offer absolute comfort with office services available to guests. Five rooms can accommodate families (maximum three children, room rate £184). Breakfast, as you would expect, is terrific, too, with home-made sausages and preserves. P

ROCHDALE
Flying Horse Hotel
37 Packer Street, OL16 1NJ

▶ Town centre, beside Town Hall
T (01706) 646412
F (01706) 712649
W theflyinghorsehotel.co.uk
Lees Bitter; Phoenix Arizona, Pale Moonlight; Taylor Best Bitter, Landlord; guest beers
One double, three twin, one family, five single rooms, all en-suite
£ £
Evening meals for residents
Accepted

An imposing building, the Flying Horse stands next to the equally impressive town hall; this town-centre venue attracts customers of all ages, although its adjoining sister bar/night club (Mystique) admits over-21s only at the weekend. The hotel is a haunt for regulars, but also caters well for travellers. The guest rooms, decorated in traditional style, have TV and tea and coffee making facilities. Children are welcome to stay. In the morning guests can help themselves to hot drinks before tucking into a full English breakfast.

This purpose-built hotel, dating back to the early 20th century, has a spacious, open-plan lounge bar that stocks everything from local ales to champagne. Bar snacks are available and evening meals.

Ideal for those travelling by public transport, it is within walking distance of the rail station and town-centre bus routes and convenient for all the town's amenities. The hotel does not have its own car park but there is a large pay and display facility opposite.

Rochdale is on the edge of the Pennines so you are not far from open country; Healey Dell Nature Reserve is nearby, while hikers can set out on the 50-mile circular Rochdale Way.

UPPERMILL
Waggon Inn
32-34 High Street, OL3 6HR

▶ Town centre, off M62 jct 19 or 21
T (01457) 872376
F (01457) 875085
W thewaggoninn.co.uk
Robinson's Unicorn, seasonal beers; guest beers from Robinson's range
One double, one twin/double, two family rooms, all en-suite
£ ££
Lunchtime daily, evening meals Tue-Sat
Accepted

The Waggon opened as a beer house in 1860 and stands opposite the Saddleworth Museum at the centre of this old woollen mill town. The renovated Huddersfield Canal runs through the town; canal boat trips start from behind the museum. Saddleworth is renowned for its numerous festivals - during the Rushcart weekend in August morris dancers from all over the world gather to dance outside the pub and there is a parade when morris dancers pull the rushcart through the villages.

If you want to stay here during any of the town's annual events you will need to book early. The pub's guest rooms were created three years ago and have modern decor and facilities. All have power showers and three also have bathtubs. At breakfast, fresh orange juice and cereals are followed by a full English affair or a simpler alternative such as scrambled egg on toast. Good, home-cooked food includes a Sunday roast, and the popular 'chip shop special' from 5pm-7pm on Friday.

The pub is a 15-minute walk from Greenfield Station on the mainline route from Manchester Victoria and 40 minutes' drive from Manchester Airport.
Q P

WORTHINGTON

Crown Hotel

Platt Lane, WN1 2XF

▶ North of Wigan, between the A49 and A106

T (08000) 686678

F (01257) 428981

W thecrownatworthington.co.uk

Beer range varies

Five double, one double/twin, four single rooms, all en-suite

£ £ (room only)

Lunchtime and evening meals

Accepted

The Crown has recently become a favourite of local CAMRA members and now has a policy of offering at least five cask ales, often showcasing independent brewers such as Bank Top and Moorhouses. It is a rare outlet for the local Mayflower Brewery in Wigan. It held its first beer festival in the upstairs function room in 2006 and was voted local CAMRA Pub of the Year. The friendly, sometimes lively, bar attracts both locals and visitors.

The Crown has much more to offer than just good beer. It has 10 newly redesigned bedrooms, where soft colours and upmarket fittings ensure a comfortable night's rest. TV, trouser press and tea and coffee making facilities are provided. In the morning you can enjoy a traditional breakfast (an optional extra at around £5 a head) in the hotel's smart and spacious conservatory restaurant.

The food here is good, with the regular menu augmented by chalkboard specials and children's dishes. On Sunday a traditional carvery is served all day until 8.30pm. The hotel's large decked sun terrace has patio heaters so you can sit out and admire the views of open farmland late into the evening.

P

Norfolk

BEACHAMWELL
Great Danes Country Inn
Old Hall Lane, PE37 8BG

▶ Off A1122 between Downham Market and Swaffham
T (01366) 328443
F (01366) 328443
E carole@gtdanes.fsnet.co.uk
Greene King Old Speckled Hen; Marston's Pedigree; Woodforde's Wherry, Norfolk Nog; guest beers
Five double/twin en-suite rooms, two with wheelchair access
£ ££
Lunchtime and evening meals
Accepted

The Great Danes caters for both 'locals' from a wide radius and tourists from afar. It enjoys a peaceful setting by the green opposite the church. The old village inn offers a friendly, homely atmosphere in the cosy bar. Its country style is carried through to the guest accommodation which is simply, but comfortably furnished. Two of the rooms are in a converted barn on the ground floor, so are suitable for guests with mobility problems, but check first with the inn to ensure their suitability. Two rooms can accommodate families.

A continental breakfast is included in the price – cereals, croissant, fruit juice, toast and home-made preserves - or, for £5 extra, you can choose the full cooked English. The kitchen makes use of local produce as much as possible – Swaffham 'sizzler sausages' are featured in the breakfast – and the restaurant majors on 'home-style' cooking.

Near the market town of Swaffham, the pub is close to tourist spots such as the NT's Oxborough Hall, Gooderstone Water Gardens and the Sandringham estate.
Q ♣ P

BRANCASTER STAITHE

☆ White Horse

PE31 8BY

- ▶ On the north Norfolk coast, off A149, on Coast Hopper bus route
- T (01485) 210262
- F (01485) 210930
- W whitehorsebrancaster.co.uk
- Adnams Bitter; Fuller's London Pride; Woodforde's Wherry; guest beers
- Eight double, seven twin rooms; five can be used as family rooms, two have wheelchair access; all are en-suite
- £ £££-££££
- Lunchtime and evening meals
- Accepted

In a magical setting overlooking the salt marshes, the White Horse's charming seaside ambience makes it a popular destination for locals, families, walkers, sailors and city weekenders. The lovely bright bar, full of scrubbed pine and works by local artists, should be your first port of call for a pint of local ale. Then head out to the dining area and conservatory restaurant with its sun deck that gives stunning panoramic views of the tidal marshes over to Scolt Head Island. Time it right and you will be rewarded with a fantastic sunset. In winter you might catch sight of the pinkfoot geese that fly over in their thousands.

Avid birdwatchers should book the 'room at the top' that boasts a viewing telescope to the tidal marsh. All the rooms are spacious and modern, decorated in seascape colours. Seven are situated above the pub and eight rooms are in a curved annexe that follows the contours of the land, each with a private terrace overlooking the marsh, giving access to the Norfolk Coastal Path at the foot of the garden. Dogs are welcome in these rooms. An extensive spread is offered at breakfast and the award-winning restaurant specialises in seafood and local seasonal produce.

Q ♣ P

CLEY NEXT THE SEA

Three Swallows

Newgate Green, NR27 7TT

T (01263) 740526
Adnams Bitter; Greene King IPA, Abbot
Four en-suite double, one family and one twin room with private shower; two wheelchair accessible
£ ££ (single occupancy £40)
Lunchtime and evening meals, all day Sat and Sun until 9pm
Accepted

Set by the village green and flanked by the parish church, this traditional rural pub overlooks the picturesque Glaven Valley. Three main areas warmed by open coal fires feature wood floors and panelling, enlivened by an interesting collection of ancient photographs. Outside, the pub's award-winning garden features an aviary, ornamental pond and children's play area. Cley's saltwater marshes are famous for birds, making the pub popular with wildlife watchers.

Children are welcome to stay (a family room is £90 for three or four occupants), and pets too. The family and twin room are in the main building, the four en-suite double rooms, also available as singles, are in a converted barn. TV, tea and coffee making facilities and hair dryer are provided in all rooms.

The breakfast menu is divided into 'ploughmans' for those with hearty appetites and 'ploughboys' - a smaller version including bacon, local sausage or tomato and fried egg. Alternatively you can have eggs done as you like them with thick toast or freshly-grilled local-cured kippers topped with a poached egg. An extensive menu is offered at other meal times.

Q

DEOPHAM

Victoria Inn

Church Road, NR18 9DT

▶ Half mile north of church
T (01953) 850783
Spectrum 42; Woodforde Wherry; guest beers
One double, two twin rooms, all en-suite
£ £
Snacks and meals daily lunchtime, evening Tue-Sat
Accepted

Some parts of the Victoria date back to 1684, with the pub later extended to include accommodation and a restaurant. Slightly tucked away, the inn has beamed ceilings and lots of character, chairs grouped around a real fire in winter, while outside the pretty garden has a petanque pitch. A free house, it offers real cider and interesting guest beers – 'real ale enthusiasts seek us out, they never know what beer they're going to find and they love it'.

Accommodation is welcoming and comfortable, with guests commenting that they feel it's a home away from home. Facilities include tea and coffee making, and the full English breakfast uses free-range eggs and sausages from the local butcher. Meals include vegetarian options and mid-week specials, using local produce and fish from local fisheries as much as possible – this year they have started to grow their own vegetables.

The Victoria supports pool and darts teams, and hosts monthly live music or karaoke. Close to Wymondham historic market town and Abbey, there are walks and cycle routes nearby.

Q P

DEREHAM
George Hotel
Swaffham Road, NR19 2AZ

- Town centre, near the war memorial, 15 miles from Norwich
- T (01362) 696801
- W lottiesrestaurant.co.uk
- Adnams Bitter; Fuller's London Pride; Greene King Old Speckled Hen; Woodforde's Wherry; guest beers
- Five double, two twin, one family room, all en-suite
- £ ££ (£50 single occupancy)
- Lunchtime and evening meals
- Accepted

This old coaching inn occupies a large site at the centre of this market town not far from Norwich. The public rooms include a wood-panelled bar warmed by local fires where you can sample any one of six mostly East Anglian ales and good bar meals. There is also a colonial-style lounge furnished with big leather sofas and tub chairs and a new air-conditioned conservatory for dining, leading out to the patio. For a special occasion you may wish to eat in the elegant Victorian-style dining room where excellent meals from locally-produced ingredients are cooked to order.

The recently-refurbished guest rooms, with country-style pine furnishings, are large enough to contain a coffee table and easy chair, they also have TV, Internet connection, trouser press and hospitality tray. Duvets rather than traditional bedding are used. Children are welcome. Your breakfast will be cooked to order, according to your preference. Kippers and kedgeree make interesting alternatives to the full English or you can opt for a continental breakfast.

The hotel is just a short stroll from Dereham golf course, and packages including green fees and accommodation are available. The hotel holds a wedding licence. P

DOWNHAM MARKET
Crown Hotel
Bridge Street, PE38 9DH

- Town centre, off A10
- T (01366) 382322
- F (01366) 386554
- W crowncoachinginn.co.uk
- Adnams Bitter; Greene King IPA, Abbot; guest beers
- Six double, five twin, three family rooms, most en-suite
- £ £ (room only)
- Lunchtime and evening meals and snacks
- Accepted

Downham was once the scene of bread riots, when in 1816 hungry agricultural workers kept the justices of the peace prisoners until the militia arrived. No fear of going hungry if you stay at the Crown, however, where the breakfast alone would keep most people going for a good while, but just in case there is a super snack list and a main menu of pub favourites, supplemented by daily specials. Much of the produce is purchased in the local market from an organic grower. The room rate does not include breakfast; the full English including local sausages is around £6. Ask at the bar for other options, they will always try to oblige, and to cater for special dietery needs, too.

This 17th-century former coaching inn stands at the heart of a traditional market town centre. Locals and visitors alike appreciate its well-preserved, beamed interior, open fires and good choice of real ales from independent breweries. The guest rooms, most of which are en-suite, have all been recently refurbished. The new king-sized room has a spacious bathroom with shower and bathtub; all have TV with Freeview channels and hospitality tray.
Q P

GREAT BIRCHAM

☆ King's Head Hotel

Lynn Road, PE31 6RJ

▶ Off A148, between King's Lynn and Fakeham on B1153
T (01485) 578265
W the-kings-head-bircham.co.uk
Adnams Bitter; Fuller's London Pride; Woodforde's Wherry; guest beer
Twelve double en-suite rooms
£ ££££
Lunchtime and evening meals
Accepted

High standards and a touch of sophistication are the keynotes at this grade II listed Victorian hotel, refurbished in a modern style with stainless steel, pale wood and abstract artworks.

The guest rooms are individually designed, with king-sized beds, luxurious bathrooms with hand-made toiletries, Internet connection, games console, CD and DVD player. The King's Head is expensive – the cheapest double room is £125 per night including breakfast – however there is a dinner, bed and breakfast rate at off peak times (Sun-Thu, Oct-Easter, excluding school holidays) which offers excellent value, given the quality of the food served in the award-winning restaurant.

As you might expect, they take a little extra effort with the breakfast here. The continental version includes croissants, yogurt, home-made muesli, fresh or poached fruit. Or there's porridge, boiled eggs, smoked salmon with scrambled egg, locally smoked haddock with spinach and poached egg, a full English or breakfast sandwiches.

For all its classy trimmings, the King's Head features in CAMRA's Good Beer Guide as a proper pub, with excellent beer, a friendly welcome in the bar and even a quiz night. Q P

INGHAM

Swan Inn

Swan Corner, NR12 9AB

▶ On B1151, 1 mile north-east of Stalham towards Sea Palling
T (01692) 581099
E info@theinghamswan.co.uk
Woodforde's beers
Four double, one twin room, all en-suite
£ ££-£££
Lunchtime and evening meals
Accepted

This lovely flint and thatch pub is in a 14th-century terrace that originally formed part of Ingham Priory. It stands next to an imposing church in a village a few miles from the coast and the Broads in an unspoilt area of Norfolk, 17 miles from Norwich.

Now owned by the Norfolk brewery, Woodforde's, you will always find a good selection of its ales here. You can sup in one of the spacious bars, where exposed beams, flint walls and inglenook fireplaces combine to give a truly rustic atmosphere. In the summer you can enjoy your pint and a home-cooked meal out in the secluded courtyard.

The guest accommodation is in a converted barn, where again the original features of bare brick walls and solid beams have been preserved. Furnished in country style, rooms have TV, tea and coffee making facilities and hair dryer; one is a four-poster suite (the most expensive room at £90 for the night). Children and pets are welcome by arrangement. In the morning a full English breakfast is served; for main meals an excellent menu is available in the bar and restaurant. Quiz nights and themed evenings are regular events.
Q P

KENNINGHALL

Red Lion

East Church Street, NR16 2EP

- ▶ Opposite the village church
- T (01953) 887849
- Greene King IPA, Morland Original, Abbot, Old Speckled Hen; Woodforde's Wherry; guest beers
- Two double, two twin rooms, all en-suite
- £ ££
- Lunchtime and evening meals
- Accepted

The Red Lion has been licensed since 1722 but the main building is believed to date back some 400 years. It was closed for several years during the 1990s, then a refurbishment uncovered some wonderful original features, including the original fireplaces and the delightful snug which is one of just two of its kind in East Anglia. The work also revealed the building's origins as three cottages, one of which was an ale house.

The inn reopened in 1997 and some time later the stables and an adjacent butcher's shop were converted to provide guest accommodation, offering all necessary modern accoutrements including en-suite showers and WC, television and facilities for making hot drinks. Children and pets are welcome.

The kitchen relies on locally-sourced produce for the full English breakfast and for its food served in the restaurant. Meals, including char-grilled steaks, fresh fish and specials, are all cooked to order. Special dietary needs can be met by prior arrangement.

The pub has its own bowling green which is always busy – you can watch a game from the patio. Live music is performed here occasionally. Snetterton race track, Banham Zoo and Bressingham Steam Museum are all nearby.

Q P

KING'S LYNN

Stuart House Hotel

35 Goodwins Road, PE30 5QX

- T (01553) 772169
- F (01553) 774788
- W stuarthousehotel.co.uk
- Adnams Bitter; Oakham JHB; guest beers
- Four double, four twin, three family, three single rooms, all en-suite
- £ £££-££££
- Evening meals daily
- Accepted

A charming and cosy family-run hotel close to the centre of King's Lynn, the building dates back to 1860 when it was the private home of a local businessman, and decorations are in keeping with its era. There are always three real ales to choose from in the cosy Victorian bar and an annual beer festival is hosted the last weekend in July.

Guest rooms offer a high standard of comfort, all individually furnished, with prices rising to £140 for the Sandringham four-poster room complete with jacuzzi. A full English breakfast is included.

The relaxed and friendly restaurant provides a varied menu complemented by specials using local produce as far as possible, and there are themed events throughout the year, such as gourmet and murder mystery dinners. Regular Friday night entertainment sometimes features jazz and blues bands.

There is plenty of interest in King's Lynn itself, such as the Town House and Lynn Museum, Tuesday's medieval market and Saturday's market place where Trinity Guildhall houses an old gaol exhibition.

Q P

LARLING
Angel Inn
NR16 2QU

- ▶ Off A11 between Thetford and Norwich
- T (01953) 717963
- F (01953) 718561
- Adnams Bitter; guest beers
- One double, four twin rooms, all en-suite
- £ ££
- Snacks and meals daily, lunchtime and evening
- Accepted

A detour well worth taking, says the local CAMRA branch – for the Angel serves five lovingly kept real ales from micro-breweries all over the UK, always including a mild, as well as over 100 whiskies. This heavily beamed, atmospheric watering hole serves the local community as well as visitors to the area and football fans on their way to watch Norwich play.

The 17th-century coaching inn has been run by three generations of the same family. The delicious full English breakfast is a highlight of an overnight stay here. In fact the food at the Angel is almost as renowned as the beer, with local produce used to create such specials as fresh cod in Adnams batter or smoked haddock mornay. A separate oriental section includes Thai green chicken curry, hot and spicy pork stir fry, chicken korma and prawn madras, all around £8.

Less than 20 miles from Norwich, on the edge of Thetford Forest, the inn is close to several country parks. The surrounding countryside is ideal for walking, bird watching and cycling. The inn will provide packed lunches and picnics on request. Every August a beer festival is held featuring over 70 real ales and ciders with live music and a barbecue. A caravan and camping site is open in the grounds in summer.

P

OLD BUCKENHAM
Gamekeeper
The Green, NR17 1RE

- ▶ B1105, 2 miles from Attleborough towards Diss
- T (01953) 860397
- W thegamekeeperfreehouse.com
- Adnams Bitter, Broadside; Wolf Golden Jackal; Woodforde Wherry; guest beer
- Three double rooms with shared bathroom
- £ ££
- Snacks and meals daily, lunchtime and evening
- Accepted (not Amex or Diners)

This 17th-century, grade II listed free house on the village green has a real rustic feel with pamment-floored bar area, exposed beams and a hop-bedecked brick inglenook with roaring fire in winter. A Cask Marque accredited establishment, one area is dedicated to drinking – the house beer is brewed by Wolf. A framed history of the pub lists all the previous landlords.

Two separate dining rooms offer a tempting menu made with fresh local ingredients. Sunday lunch is recommended. Outside is a beer garden and a large function room housing a skittle alley.

Accommodation is in three individually designed rooms providing TV, tea and coffee making facilities and hand basin – the rooms are not en-suite. The room rate includes a hearty English breakfast of sausage, bacon, egg, mushrooms, tomatoes, beans and toast.

Close to Old Buckenham airfield, Snetterton race track and Banham Zoo, the Gamekeeper snares sky divers and racing drivers among its clientele, as well as farmers and locals. Norwich, with its many tourist attractions and fine choice of real ale pubs, is an easy drive along the A11, and on a bus route, too.

P

SMALLBURGH

Crown Inn

NR12 9AD

▶ On A149 between Stalham and North Walsham
T (01692) 536314
Adnams Bitter; Greene King IPA, Abbot; guest beers
One double, one twin room, both en-suite
£ ££ (£40 single occupancy)
Lunchtime and evening meals and bar snacks
Accepted

A regular entry in CAMRA's Good Beer Guide, this traditional thatched village inn dating back to the 15th century not only stocks good ale – with two guest beers always on handpump – but more unusually keeps a range of premium rums. It caters mostly for the over-30s and no under-14s are admitted; this applies to the accommodation, too. The guest rooms, which are separate from the owners' quarters, have recently been refurbished and have tea and coffee making facilities. A TV is provided in the beamed lounge.

For breakfast you can tuck into a full English, or if you order it the night before, fish is available as an alternative. All meat and vegetables served in the dining room are sourced locally, with dishes cooked to order so special dietary needs can be accommodated; snacks are available in the bar. The pub has a games room and a peaceful garden.

The pub's location is close enough to the Broads and the North Norfolk coast to provide a useful base for visitors, but far enough away not to be disturbed by the hustle and bustle of the tourist season, making it popular with walkers, cyclists and anglers.

P

SWAFFHAM

Lydney House

Norwich Road, PE37 7QS

▶ On the old Norwich road, just out of town
T (01760) 723355
F (01760) 721410
W lydney-house.demon.co.uk
Woodforde's Wherry, Nelson's Revenge; guest beers
Five double, one twin, two single, one family room, all en-suite
£ £££
Evening meals
Accepted

Built as a private home for a Georgian merchant, the hotel stands in its own grounds, set back from the road, a five-minute walk from the centre of Swaffham. The extensive garden is home to ducks, rabbits, bats and other wildlife and features some wonderful specimen trees; it is a lovely tranquil spot for an early evening drink in summer.

The traditional hotel bar still sells the local ales straight from the barrel and keeps a stock of old-fashioned but entertaining pub games. The guest rooms, too, are furnished in traditional country fashion; two feature four-poster beds. They are equipped with TV, hospitality tray, hair dryer and trouser press.

The breakfast menu offers plenty of choice – smoked haddock, kippers or a full English breakfast with local bacon, sausages and eggs. The elegant restaurant offers evening meals based on local produce as far as possible – the kitchen staff do not have far to go for their ingredients as Swaffham has a good market each Saturday.

The historic town also boasts a beautiful medieval church and, in contrast, the Ecotech Centre with its wind turbine with a viewing platform at the top. P

THORNHAM
Lifeboat Inn
Ship Lane, PE36 6LT

- ▶ Signed off A149 coast road, on Coast Hopper bus route
- T (01485) 512236
- W lifeboatinn.co.uk
- Adnams Bitter; Greene King IPA, Abbot; Woodforde's Wherry; guest beers
- Fourteen double/twin rooms, all en-suite
- £ £££-££££
- Lunchtime and evening meals
- Accepted (not Amex)

This 16th-century former haunt of smugglers stands on the edge of the salt marshes in a quiet part of north-west Norfolk. Care has been taken over the years to preserve the character throughout this wonderful old hostelry, with hanging oil lanterns adding to the atmosphere. The charming Smugglers Bar leads to an attractive conservatory shaded by an ancient vine (watered by Abbot Ale), and onto the walled patio garden.

The guest rooms are decorated with an inventive use of colour and fabrics and decorated in country style with pine furnishings. TV, tea and coffee making facilities and hair dryers are provided. Children and pets can be accommodated.

The breakfast bar offers yogurt, prunes, grapefruit, cereals or 'mix your own muesli', then you can choose from a good cooked selection: a (very) full English with egg cooked to your liking, or something fishy – smoked haddock with scrambled egg, grilled oak-smoked kipper with parsley butter or smoked haddock with poached eggs. Alternatively, you can opt for a continental breakfast of home-cooked honey baked ham with tomato and croissants or toast. Main meals here are also excellent – the seafood, particularly the Brancaster mussels, is particularly recommended. Q P

WARHAM
Three Horseshoes
Bridge Street, NR23 1NL

- ▶ Half a mile from A149 coast road
- T (01328) 710547
- W www.warham.biz
- Greene King IPA; Woodforde's Wherry; guest beer
- Three double, two single rooms; one double is en-suite the others share a bathroom
- £ ££
- Lunchtime and evening meals
- Not accepted

This archetypal village pub, dating back to 1725, is the only one in Norfolk to be listed in CAMRA's National Inventory of pubs with interiors of historic interest. The pub has remained largely unchanged since World War II. With its stone floors, open fires and gas lighting, sturdy old furniture, assorted antiques and knick-knacks in its rambling set of rooms, entering the Three Horseshoes is like taking a step back in time. Of particular note are the 1930s one-armed bandit and the green and red dial on the ceiling for playing the ancient roulette game of 'Norfolk Twister'.

The guest accommodation is not in the pub itself but in the Old Post Office Cottage next door. Exposed beams, period furnishings and an inglenook fireplace in the lounge give the cottage a homely appearance. Downstairs is a double room with en-suite shower and WC; the upstairs rooms share a bathroom. The cottage is unsuitable for small children, so only those over 14 can stay, but dogs are welcome.

Breakfast is served in the cottage dining room – from cereals to full English. In the pub, good home-cooked food is served in generous portions (a no-chips policy is upheld).

Q P

Northamptonshire

ARTHINGWORTH

Bull's Head

Kelmarsh Road, LE16 8JZ

- ▶ Off A14 jct 2
- T (01858) 525637
- W thebullsheadonline.co.uk
- Everards Tiger, Original; Wells Bombardier; guest beers
- Two double, three twin, two family, one single room, all en-suite
- £ ££
- Snacks and meals daily, lunchtime and evening
- Accepted (not Amex)

The Bull's Head is a large, 19th-century, family-run village pub converted from a farmhouse, offering modern accommodation in a newly-built eight-room annexe. The spacious en-suite rooms all provide TV/DVD, complimentary beverages and toiletries, a hair dryer and laundry facilities. One of the family rooms has disabled access. Included in the price is a hearty full English breakfast, with local farm eggs, though you can opt for a continental on request.

Threatened with closure, the Bull was taken over by enterprising new owners who refurbished it in 2006. A former CAMRA Pub of the Season, three good guest ales are available in the traditional beamed bar with log fires. A beer garden with heaters for colder evenings is always popular. Also featuring in CAMRA's Good Pub Food guide, the dining room offers an eclectic, fresh-cooked menu with such unusual delights as goose Wellington.

Arthingworth is a charming village with local attractions including stately homes Kelmarsh Hall and Althorp, plus Harrington Aviation Museum, Pitsford Reservoir, Jurassic Walkway and Rockingham Castle. Visitors include ramblers and cyclists from the nearby Brampton Valley Way.

Q P

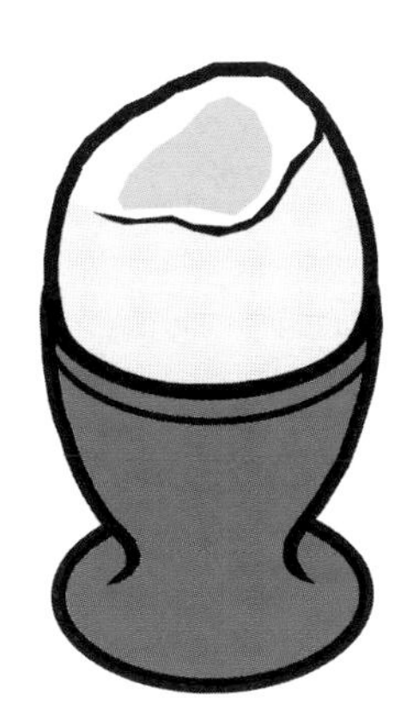

OUNDLE

Ship Inn

18 West Street, PE8 4EF

- ▶ Off A605 between Wellingborough and Peterborough
- T (01832) 273918
- W theshipinn-oundle.co.uk
- Digfield Barnwell Bitter; Oakham JHB; guest beers
- Four double, four twin, six single rooms, eleven rooms have en-suite facilities
- £ £-££ (room only)
- Lunchtime and evening meals
- Accepted

The Ship is an attractive, grade II listed stone pub in the main street, near the centre of this pleasant market town in the Nene Valley. The town is characterised by its mix of medieval, Elizabethan and Stuart architecture and some of the most attractive buildings belong to its famous public school.

The 16th-century pub, replete with low beams and a fine inglenook, is divided into several cosy drinking areas where you can sup local beers and enjoy home-made food. A lively local meeting place, it is often busy, especially when musicians play live (which is most weekends); jazz is featured on the last Sunday of the month and a quiz is held on Tuesday evening.

The en-suite accommodation is in two separate stone-built annexes that have been modernised to a high standard, with attractive decor and furnishings; one room has a four-poster bed. Three more rooms with a shared bathroom are in a cottage next to the pub. All the rooms have TV, tea and coffee making facilities, hair dryer and trouser press. The rates are for room only; breakfast is only served on Sunday for £6.50 a head.

Q P

Northumberland

ALNMOUTH

Red Lion Inn

22 Northumberland Street, NE66 2RJ

- ▶ Off A1068, 10 mins from A1
- T (01665) 830584
- F (01665) 830584
- W redlionalnmouth.co.uk
- Black Sheep Best Bitter; guest beers
- Two double, one twin/family, one single room, all en-suite
- £ £££
- Lunchtime and evening meals
- Accepted

The Red Lion has one of the best recommendations of all – many visitors return year after year – and it is easy to see why. This former coaching inn stands opposite the ancient church at the centre of Alnmouth. The cosy, wood-panelled bar serves local ales (Hadrian & Border is often on the guest pump), hearty snacks and lunches, while the restaurant, which features a couple of red lions in the windows, offers a seasonal menu in the evening. You can also lunch outside, taking in the wonderful view of the estuary afforded by the raised decking in the garden. Men can also admire the unusual mural in the Gents depicting the castles of Northumbria.

The attractive guest rooms are decorated in pale colours, maximising the natural light; they have tea and coffee making facilities and TV. Children are welcome to stay and pets are permitted by arrangement. The pub offers safe storage for cycles and golf bags – the town's golf course is nearby, as are some of the best sandy beaches in the county. Not to be missed are the fabulous gardens at Alnwick Castle that have been lovingly restored by the Duchess of Northumberland; the Grand Cascade is particularly spectacular.

Q ❀ ♣ P

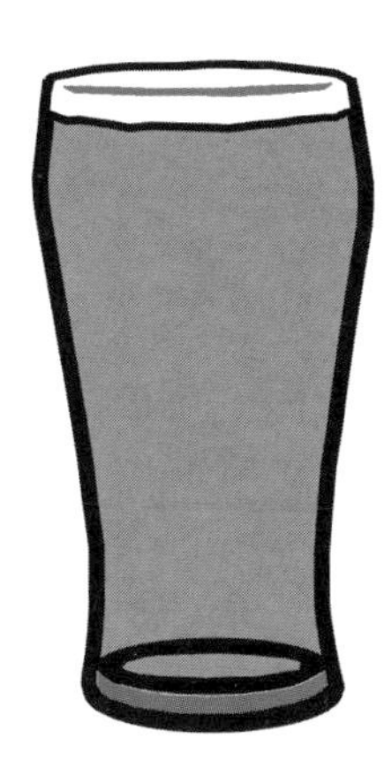

BERWICK-UPON-TWEED
Pilot Inn
31 Low Greens, TD15 1LZ

T (01289) 304214
Beer range varies
One double, one twin, one family room, two en-suite
£ £-££
Meals lunchtime only March-November
Not accepted

In Berwick-upon-Tweed, the gateway to the Borders, the Pilot Inn claims to be the only real ale B&B in town. It is a stone built, double fronted, terraced local dating back to the 19th century – note the 1916 photograph inside. A central drinking passageway with an attractive mosaic floor and service hatch leads to three further rooms. The wood-panelled public bar features brass nautical artefacts, old wooden beams and an open coal fire.

Room prices include a hearty English breakfast of sausage, bacon, egg, hash brown, baked beans, tomato and toast. Other home-cooked bar meals, featuring local seafood and meat including a Sunday roast, are served at lunchtime from the beginning of March until the end of November.

This friendly, welcoming establishment, with beer garden and quoits teams, has live music on Saturday, a guitar club on Tuesday, fiddlers' folk music night on Thursday – not forgetting Santa on the roof on Christmas Eve!

The two guest beers are often from North East micros, plus a good range of malt whiskies. Local sights include the Elizabethan Walls, Bamburgh Castle and Holy Island. The inn is next door to an 18-hole golf course.

Q

CORBRIDGE
Angel of Corbridge
Main Street, NE45 5LA

Town centre, off A68
T (01434) 632119
Beer range varies
Four double, one family room, all en-suite
£ £££ (£60 single occupancy)
Lunchtime and evening meals
Accepted

At the centre of the delightful Northumbrian town of Corbridge, the Angel is just the type of old coaching inn you would hope to find here. The building, dating from 1726, houses a refurbished bar with pale walls and natural wood fittings and furniture. The bar stocks a constantly changing range of real ales, showcasing local breweries such as Durham, Allendale and High House Farm. Morning coffee and afternoon tea are served in the inviting wood-panelled lounge, furnished with comfortable sofas, which leads through to the intimate restaurant.

The attractive guest rooms are furnished and equipped to a high standard – you can ask for a room with a four-poster bed, or a view over the valley. Some rooms overlook the pub's secluded garden. All have television and hospitality tray. The breakfast menu offers a full English meal, complete with Cumberland sausage and black pudding and a choice of free-range eggs, or you can opt for scrambled eggs with smoked salmon or a continental with rustic bread and croissants. Cereals, natural yogurt and fruit are provided.

Corbridge Station lies on the Carlisle to Newcastle line and the hotel is an ideal base for exploring Hadrian's Wall.

P

ONCE BREWED

Twice Brewed Inn

Military Road, Bardon Mill, NE47 7AN

▶ On B6318 midway between Newcastle upon Tyne and Carlisle
T (01434) 344534
W twicebrewedinn.co.uk
Beer range varies
Five double, six twin, one family, two single rooms, five en-suite, nine with shared facilities
£ £-££
Snacks and meals daily, lunchtime and evening
Accepted

Dubbing itself 'the only sign to look for on Hadrian's Wall', the Twice Brewed at Once Brewed is set among some of the most breathtaking scenery in England on the old Military Road, just half a mile from one of the most dramatic stretches of the wall, in the shadows of Steel Rigg. It is close to some of the most fascinating remains of the Roman occupation – Vindolanda, Housesteads Roman fort, Chesters and Corbridge Roman sites.

The pub itself dates back to the 17th century and was once a coaching inn but now provides modern facilities including an IT suite. Prices reflect whether the bedroom is en-suite or not, but all have basins and shaving sockets; breakfast, full English, vegetarian or continental, is included.

The family-run pub has a separate restaurant, and serves home-cooked food all day as well as 'a stonking good pint' says the landlord; beers come from an endless list of independents and micro-breweries including adjoining Bardon Mill. Very busy in the tourist season, the inn provides bicycle stands and secure cycle storage; staff are trained in sign language.

Q ❀ ♣ P

SEAHOUSES

Olde Ship Hotel

Main Street, NE68 7RD

T (01665) 720200
W seahouses.co.uk
Draught Bass; Black Sheep Best Bitter; Courage Directors; Greene King Ruddles County, Old Speckled Hen; guest beers
Thirteen double, four twin, one single room, all en-suite
£ £££-££££
Lunchtime and evening meals and snacks
Accepted (not Amex)

Set above the tiny harbour, the Olde Ship is packed full of nautical memorabilia, including the name plate from the Forefarshire, commemorating the Victorian heroine Grace Darling. The saloon bar is full of character, with a notable stained glass window, complemented by the smaller Cabin Bar where locals gather for a game of dominoes. The hotel, which started out as a farmhouse in 1745 and was licensed in 1812, has been in the present family ownership for more than 90 years. The guest rooms are closed from late November until mid-January but the pub is open all year round.

The hotel has a range of recently modernised accommodation, from single rooms to four-poster executive suites, all well equipped. Children over 10 years old are welcome to stay. The kitchen can cater for various dietary requirements with advance notice. Breakfast here covers most tastes and appetites, ranging from a full English, Craster kippers or eggs cooked to your liking, to cereals, prunes and grapefruit. The hotel also has a self-catering cottage overlooking the harbour.

Boat trips can be taken from Seahouses across to the Farne Islands, while Bamburgh Castle, Lindisfarne and Alnwick Castle with its splendid gardens are all close by.

Q ❀ ♣ P

SLALEY
Travellers Rest
NE46 1TT

▶ On B6306, 1 mile north of Slaley village and 4 miles south of Hexham
T (01434) 673231
W 1travellersrest.com
Black Sheep Best Bitter; Wylam Gold Tankard; guest beers
One double, one twin room, both en-suite
£ £
Lunchtime and evening meals and snacks
Accepted

Providing a warm welcome, good food and comfortable rooms highly rated by the ETB, the inn has been looking after travellers for more than 150 years, although the building itself is over 400 years old. Open all day for refreshments including tea and coffee, the large bar has retained its stone walls, flagged floor and big hearth. Several cosy areas have comfortable furniture where you can settle down and enjoy the excellent selection of guest beers.

Meals can be takenin the bar or restaurant. The extensive menu caters for all tastes; beef and dairy products are supplied by a local farm. The full English breakfast provided for overnight guests includes sausage, bacon, black pudding and eggs cooked as you like them.

The guest accommodation is in bright country-style bedrooms with pine furnishings. They are equipped with tea and coffee making facilities and a writing table. Children are welcome to stay and will no doubt enjoy the wooden play area in the pub's lovely natural garden. The good value B&B attracts walkers and cyclists who can take advantage of the pub's drying room for their outdoor gear. Hadrian's Wall, Kielder Forest and Derwent Water are all within easy reach. Q P

WARDEN
Boatside Inn
NE46 4SQ

▶ Just off A69 near Hexham
T (01434) 602233
W boatsideinn.co.uk
Beer range varies
One double, two twin rooms all available as singles, all en-suite and wheelchair accessible, plus two self-catering cottages
£ ££ (single occupancy £45)
Lunchtime and evening meals and snacks
Accepted

Between the River South Tyne and Warden Hill, the inn lies by an old ferry crossing that was replaced by a bridge in 1826. This lovely old pub had to be refurbished recently after the river flooded. 'Warden' comes from the old English word for 'watch hill' and was the site of an Iron Age hill fort, then a medieval village; recently vestiges of a Roman camp were found here, too. The pub is close to the World Heritage site of Hadrian's Wall and the Coast-to-Coast walking and cycling route.

Three-star guest accommodation is provided in separate modern buildings that have been built out of stone in keeping with the pub. There are three rooms for bed and breakfast and two cottages with self-catering facilities (but meals can be taken at the pub); North Tyne cottage has one double and one twin-bedded room, while South Tyne has one double en-suite. Children and pets are welcome.

In the pub you have a choice of continental or full English breakfast (included in the price for B&B guests), while the main menus are regularly changed to provide a variety of home-cooked fare from soup, traditional steak n' ale pie, fresh seafood, or something exotic from the Far East or India. Q P

Nottinghamshire

EDINGLEY
Old Reindeer
Main Street, NG22 8BE

- ▶ Off A614, between Farnsfield and Southwell
- T (01623) 882253
- W oldreindeer.co.uk
- Beer range varies
- Two double, one twin, one family room, all en-suite; two rooms wheelchair accessible
- £ ££
- Lunchtime and evening meals
- Accepted

This lovely village pub dating from the mid-17th century has evolved to keep pace with the demands of today's customers, yet managed to maintain its traditional atmosphere. While a new extension houses a smart restaurant serving excellent food – the fish and chips are particularly recommended – the bar continues to offer six well-kept ales and informal meals. Other modern additions include a disabled WC and baby-changing facilities. The pub has a games room and a garden that hosts regular barbecues in summer.

The overnight accommodation is in four en-suite rooms in a cottage attached to the pub. It has a separate entrance and guests have their own key. The family room can sleep four or five people and a cot is available on request. The rooms can be let as singles and pets are welcome to stay. A generous breakfast includes two of everything: eggs, sausages, bacon rashers, plus black pudding, mushrooms, beans, tomatoes and fried bread.

Around Edingley you will find the historic Southwell Minster, Southwell Workhouse (National Trust), Southwell Racecourse and Sherwood Forest, or you can take a walk on the nearby Southwell Trail, a former railway line. Q P

EVERTON
Blacksmith's Arms
Church Street, DN10 5BQ

- ▶ Two miles from Bawtry on A631 towards Gainsborough
- T (01777) 817281
- F (01777) 817281
- W blacksmiths-everton.co.uk
- Marston's Pedigree; John Smith's Bitter; Theakston Old Peculier; guest beers
- Four double, one twin, two single, one family room, all en-suite; one room wheelchair accessible
- £ £
- Lunchtime and evening meals
- Accepted

Everton is a conservation village that straddles the A631, the old Roman road between Lincoln and York. It is surrounded by open countryside, making the pub popular with walkers. Nearby, the Barrow Hills have a site of Special Scientific Interest that is home to rare plants and wildlife.

The 300-year-old pub was once the village smithy – the former workshop is now the games room. The bar, where the locals gather to sample the regularly changing guest ales, has retained the original tiled floor. There is also a comfortable lounge and restaurant that serves a varied menu with home-cooked dishes.

The bedrooms are in converted outbuildings, so guests can come and go as they please, even if the pub is closed. Furnished in a modern country style, they have television, tea and coffee making facilities, a mini-fridge and hairdryer. A continental breakfast is served. Children are welcome.

The pub is a 10-minute drive from the region's new regional airport (Robin Hood); Clumber Park and Sherwood Forest are also within easy reach. A few miles away is Scrooby, the former home of William Brewster, from where the Pilgrim Fathers set out on their historic voyage. Q P

FLINTHAM
Boot & Shoe
Main Street, NG23 5LA

- ▶ Off A46
- T (01636) 525246
- W bootandshoe.net
- Banks's Bitter; Brewster's Marquis; Marston's Pedigree; guest beer
- Two double, one twin, one family, one single room, all en-suite
- £ £-££
- Snacks and meals daily lunchtime and evening
- Accepted

An attractive 17th-century village inn with roaring log fire in winter, the Boot & Shoe has a bank of four handpumps in the bar, one for a weekly-changing guest ale. The guest rooms (the family room can also be booked as a twin) all have a cottage-style decor with pine furniture and matching curtains and bedspreads, equipped with colour TV, radio alarm clock, hair dryer or iron on request. The tariff includes a full English breakfast featuring local produce such as sausages from a nearby butcher, free-range eggs and fresh mushrooms.

Local produce can be found on the main menu too, including locally-raised beef – fillet, sirloin and rump steaks – with main dishes including home-cooked pies, sweet and sour chicken, poached salmon and meat balls with tagliatelle. At lunchtime a two-course meal for £5.95 is a bargain.

The rural style extends to the bar which has exposed beams, pool and darts – and a large-screen TV hidden to one side of the bar, showing major sporting events. The lawned garden, with attractive planted borders, benches and tables, is popular with families in summer.

The Boot & Shoe is a short journey from Nottingham, Newark-on-Trent and Southwell Minster.
P

KIMBERLEY

Nelson & Railway

Station Road, NG16 2NR

- One mile from M1 jct 26
- T (0115) 938 2177
- Hardys & Hansons Mild, Bitter, Olde Trip, seasonal beers
- One double, five twin, two single rooms, all en-suite
- £ ££
- Lunchtime and evening meals and snacks
- Accepted

A regular fixture in CAMRA's Good Beer Guide, the Nelson stands within sight of Hardys & Hansons Brewery which was taken over by Greene King in 2006 and now faces an uncertain future – certainly the beer range, if nothing else, may change; the worst outcome would be the eventual closure of yet another small brewery.

Run by the same family for 35 years, this traditional hostelry dates back some four centuries. New guest accommodation is being completed as we go to press in an attached building that is as old as the pub. Of the eight rooms at least some should be suitable for wheelchair users but you will need to check when booking. Breakfast is provided according to individual requirements, from cereal or toast to full English.

The pub has also earned a place in CAMRA's Good Pub Food guide for its honest, simple pub grub at extremely reasonable prices. The set menu is supplemented by daily specials, or you can have a snack for around £2. The food is nearly all home made. Meals are served in the dining area adjoining the cosy lounge. The pub benefits from a large front garden that is popular in summer.

P

LOWDHAM

Old Ship Inn

Main Street, NG14 7BE

- At the village centre, 400 yds north of A612
- T (0115) 966 3049
- W oldshipinn.co.uk
- Courage Directors; John Smith's Bitter; Wells Bombardier; guest beers
- Two double, two single, one twin or family room, all en-suite
- £ ££
- Meals and snacks available all day
- Accepted

The Old Ship, which changed hands recently, offers the best of both worlds – a traditional country pub that is close enough to the centre of Nottingham to provide a pleasant alternative for business people to a chain hotel for the night; the train from Lowdham to Nottingham takes just 15 minutes. It is also convenient for Lincoln and the tourist attractions of Robin Hood country.

The Old Ship is a proper pub: the split-level public bar has a dartboard, pool table and juke box and serves a good choice of real ales – the guest beers usually come from local micro-breweries. The beamed lounge has two distinct areas, one leads through to the restaurant where good, home-cooked food is served at any time of day. Special events such as Burns Night, St Patrick's and St George's are usually celebrated here.

The guest rooms are bright and modern and all have television and tea and coffee making facilities. Children are welcome to stay and pets can be accommodated. A very full English breakfast is served, including black pudding and baked beans if desired; kippers are also available. Meals are recommended here, all food is freshly prepared to order. P

Oxfordshire

ABINGDON

Brewery Tap

40-42 Ock Street, OX14 5BZ

- (01235) 521655
- brewerytap.net
- Greene King IPA, Morland Original; St Austell Tribute; guest beers
- Three double rooms, all en-suite
- £££
- Snacks and meals daily, lunchtime and evening
- Accepted (not Amex)

Set in the grounds of what used to be the Morland Brewery, the Brewery Tap is a grade II listed award-winning conversion of three town houses. The Morland served in the bar is now brewed by Greene King.

Accommodation is in three newly renovated and extremely comfortable large double bedrooms. All are furnished to a high standard with en-suite bathroom, TV and broadband. The room rate includes a full cooked English on request but visitors or business folk who need to make an early start may prefer the pre-packaged bloomers and baguettes with fresh fruit, juice, coffee and bottled water.

The pub has been run by the same family since 1993. Retaining many original features, it has attractive panelled walls, stone floors and an open fire. The 30-seater dining room offers an innovative menu using local produce in good home-cooked fare.

Located on the main east-west route through this historic market town, the Brewery Tap is handy for the River Thames, Market Square, town hall built by Christopher Wren, and old Abbey buildings. Oxford is a short drive away. At least four guest ales are always available. Q P

BLOXHAM
Elephant & Castle
Humber Street, OX15 4LZ

- ▶ Take jct 11 Banbury exit off M40 then A361 towards Chipping Norton
- T (01295) 720383
- F (01295) 722712
- Hook Norton Hooky Bitter, seasonal beers; guest beers
- One double, one single room, both en-suite
- £ £
- Lunchtime meals and snacks, Mon-Sat
- Accepted (not Amex or Diners)

Although the Elephant was built in the middle of the 16th-century as a coaching inn – you pass through the wide carriage entrance to reach the front door, garden and car park – guest accommodation here is a fairly new venture for the landlord of some 34 years' standing. The two bedrooms, with their own private entrance, have good quality fittings and equipment; the twin room has two extra-large beds. Both rooms benefit from views of the village church. The breakfast, which is served in the rooms, is described as 'super continental'.

Home-cooked lunches are served in the dining room where you can see the original bread oven. Snacks are available in the bar, which is frequented by locals and members of various clubs, such as motorcyclists, horse riders and morris dancers.

Places to visit nearby include Broughton Castle and Wiggington Wildfowl Centre. Beer lovers might like to book a guided tour of Hook Norton Brewery in Banbury (tel 01608 730384), which has one of the finest examples of a Victorian tower brewery. There are buses to Banbury Station, four miles away. Blenheim Palace and Stratford-upon-Avon are also both within striking distance.

Q P

CHISELHAMPTON
Coach & Horses
Watlington Road, OX44 7UX

- ▶ On B480
- T (01865) 890255
- F (01865) 891995
- W coachhorsesinn.co.uk
- Hook Norton Hooky Bitter, Old Hooky
- Seven double, two twin rooms, all en-suite
- £ ££
- Snacks and meals daily, lunch and evening
- Accepted

A picturesque 16th-century inn with nine bedrooms, plenty of beams, decorative brasses, log fires in winter, a landscaped patio for summer, fine dining in the restaurant, and bar meals too.

The chalet-style bedrooms are in converted stables around a courtyard overlooking open countryside, all providing comfortable accommodation with shower (some with bath as well), TV and tea and coffee making. One room has a four-poster. A full English breakfast is included, or you can choose kippers or continental if preferred.

The inn is renowned for good food, using local produce where possible. A sample selection from the menu tempts with starters such as brace of pancakes filled with creamy smoked chicken, followed by fresh seafood listed on the chalkboard – sea bass in crayfish sauce, whole grilled lemon sole with chive butter, lobster and mussels. Meat dishes include Devon duckling or chicken Chiselhampton with asparagus and tarragon.

There is fishing on the Thames, and places to explore include the Vale of the White Horse, Oxford, Blenheim Palace, Woodstock and the Great Western railway museum at Didcot. Q P

GREAT TEW
Falkland Arms
The Green, OX7 4DB

- ▶ Off A361 and B4022
- T (01608) 683653
- F (01608) 683653
- W falklandarms.org.uk
- Wadworth IPA, 6X, seasonal beer; guest beers
- Five double, one single room, all en-suite
- £ £££-££££
- Lunch and meals daily lunchtime and evening (not Sun eve)
- Accepted (not Diners)

An award-winning, 500-year-old picture-postcard pub in a picturesque, unspoilt, thatched village, the Falkland Arms provides the definitive secluded and peaceful weekend retreat within easy reach of London. A place where time has stood still, it is popular with 'those who don't like mobile phones, juke boxes or TVs', says the landlord.

The bar has the original oak beams, flagstone floor and inglenook fireplaces, while an incredible collection of mugs and jugs hangs from the ceiling. The range of up to seven real ales includes three from Wadworth, the rest guests; there is also real cider and a choice of English country wines. Clay pipes and snuff are on sale.

Accommodation is six beautiful bedrooms reached by the original stone spiral staircase. Two have four-poster beds, all are furnished with antiques and provide a fridge and DVD player as well as tea and coffee. The room rate includes a full English breakfast; accommodation is not available to under 14s.

Booking for evening meals in the small dining room is essential, even for B&B guests. Places of interest include Blenheim Palace and dreaming Cotswold villages.

HENLEY-ON-THAMES
Catherine Wheel Hotel
7-15 Hart Street, RG9 2AR

- ▶ Off A4130, over Henley Bridge just past the church
- T (01491) 848484
- E henleylodge@jdwetherspoon.co.uk
- Brakspear Bitter; Fuller's London Pride; Greene King IPA; Shepherd Neame Spitfire; guest beers
- Sixteen double, six twin, four family, four single rooms, all en-suite; some adapted for disabled guests
- £ ££ (room only)
- Food served all day in the Lloyds No.1 Bar below the hotel
- Accepted

Wetherspoons is a well-established pub chain that majors on regional ales and all-day food. It also owns the Lloyds No. 1 chain. Wetherlodges providing accommodation are a more recent innovation and the Catherine Wheel is a fine example.

The hotel dates back to 1499 and the company has retained many original features of the grade II building in its refurbishment. The comfortable rooms all have facilities for hot drinks, TV, hair dryer, ironing board and trouser press, plus a computer modem point. The company always makes an effort to be accessible to all, and some rooms can accommodate wheelchairs.

Breakfast is served in the Lloyds Bar below where you can order from an extensive menu. A traditional breakfast or a vegetarian version is just £3 (£2.25 for children), a bigger 'farmhouse' breakfast is £5 or you can have an 8oz steak and eggs for £6. Other alternatives are a breakfast bloomer filled with sausage, bacon and fried egg for £2.75 or simply croissants or toast and preserves. A healthy option of organic yogurt with fresh fruit or granola is also available. Organic milk and free range eggs are used.

HOOK NORTON
Sun Inn
High Street, OX15 5NH

- ▶ Signed from A361 at Milcombe
- T (01608) 737570
- W the-sun-inn.com
- Hook Norton Best Bitter, Old Hooky, seasonal beer; guest beers
- Five double, one family room, all en-suite
- £ ££
- Snacks and meals daily lunchtime and evening
- Accepted (not Amex)

A bustling village hostelry with flagstoned bar, small snug, cosy dining room, pretty patio garden and recently-refurbished function room, the Sun is an unashamedly old-fashioned country inn proudly serving the full range of the splendid Hook Norton ales brewed close by.

The accommodation offers spacious, individual bedrooms above the pub, overlooking the church at the front, the village to the rear. All are equipped with bath or shower, TV, tea and coffee making and hair dryer. The splendid full English breakfast includes local free-range eggs.

The food is one of the big attractions at the Sun, which also features in CAMRA's Good Pub Food guide, with fresh fish a speciality. Depending on availability you could enjoy Dover sole, John Dory, langoustines, a whole lobster, sea bass or bream, skate wing, halibut, brill, turbot or large Scottish scallops. There is a choice of bar snacks, too, and meat dishes such as pork fillet with bubble and squeak or marinated rib-eye steak with asparagus.

On the edge of the Cotswolds, the Sun is convenient for Cheltenham, Stratford-upon-Avon, Warwick and Oxford.

Q P

KINGWOOD COMMON
Unicorn
Colmore Lane, RG9 5LX

- ▶ Off B481 towards Stoke Row
- T (01491) 628452
- W the-unicorn.co.uk
- Brakspear Bitter, seasonal beer; Hook Norton Hooky Dark
- One double suite
- £ £££
- Snacks and meals daily, lunchtime and evening
- Accepted (not Amex)

Accommodation is rather special at the Unicorn, perfect for a romantic weekend. The delightful double suite has its own private garden, TV and DVD, multi-gym, wireless and broadband connection. A splendid breakfast is included starting with cereals and fresh fruit, warm croissants with apple jam, Canadian cured bacon, chipolatas, local barn eggs, grilled tomato,

NEXT PAGE: Unicorn, Kingwood Common

OPEN

THE
UNICORN
BRAKSPEAR

flat mushrooms and fried bread as well as good coffee and interesting teas.

The pub itself was once a blacksmith's and converted into a pub around 150 years ago, with a very warm welcome and lots of friendly regulars, as well as visitors including walkers, cyclists and those simply wanting a quiet weekend away within easy reach of London. While not setting out to be a gastro pub it does offer tasty and sometimes adventurous food.

With an open fire, traditional pub games, garden and flowers, the Unicorn keeps fine pints of two famous local ales, Brakspear and Hook Norton. It is on the bus route to Reading and close to Henley-on Thames and some delightful local walks.

⛰ Q ❀ ⊟ ♿ ♣ P 🚌

OXFORD

Head of the River

Folly Bridge, St Aldates, OX1 4LB

T (01865) 721600
F (01865) 726158
E headoftheriver@fullers.co.uk
🍺 Fuller's Discovery, London Pride, ESB, Gale's HSB; guest beers
🛏 Ten double, two family rooms, all en-suite
£ £££
🍴 Snacks and meals daily, lunchtime and evening
💳 Accepted

You couldn't wish for a better setting – a substantial real ale pub right on the River Thames close to the centre of one of England's most historic tourist cities, with a huge riverside beer garden with big umbrellas (heated at night), and a long balcony above the river. The site was originally used for boat building and was also the launching point for lifeboats when the Thames was a major arterial route during the 19th century. This large open-plan one-bar Fuller's house serves food all day, and guest ales alongside the Fuller's range, attracting both tourists and students. Some of the dozen bedrooms overlook the river; all are en-suite with bath and shower, TV and telephone, and tea and coffee making facilities. A full English or continental breakfast is included in the room rate.

Popular with tourists, the pub is an excellent base for visiting the 'dreaming spires' and Oxford's famous colleges and buildings, as well as several other fine real ale hostelries around the city. Within driving distance are Blenheim Palace and the pretty villages and market towns of Oxfordshire. A car park is provided for hotel guests.

⛰ Q ❀ ⊟ ♿ ⇌ 🚌

SWALCLIFFE

Stag's Head

The Green, OX15 5EJ

▶ On B4035, 6 miles west of Banbury
T (01295) 780232
Adnams Bitter; Hook Norton Hooky Bitter; guest beers
One en-suite twin room
£ ££
Snacks and meals daily, lunchtime and evening
Accepted (not Amex)

This picturesque 15th-century thatched village inn has wooden floors, beams and inglenook fireplace, wooden pews and tables, terraced gardens and a children's play area to the rear. Guest beers change frequently, often featuring ales from northern brewers.

It has just one letting room, converted from an old post office, with its own separate access, with en-suite shower, fridge and television. The tariff includes a fine breakfast featuring jams and marmalade home-made by Lizzie 'the jam lady' at Swalcliffe Manor Cottage Preserves nearby, using recipes dating back to the 16th century. The full English includes local sausages or eggs from the village, or you can choose a continental breakfast with croissants.

Main meals also incorporate local produce such as beef and pork from a neighbouring farm, salads from the pub garden, not forgetting pickles and preserves from the jam lady.

Swalcliffe Barn, one of the finest tithe barns in the country, is nearby, and the inn makes a good base for visiting Warwick and Boughton castles and the Cotswolds.

Q

WOOTTON

Killingworth Castle

Glympton Road, OX20 1EJ

▶ On B4027
T (01993) 811401
F (01993) 811401
W killingworthcastle.co.uk
Greene King IPA, Abbot, Morland Original; guest beers
Three double rooms, one twin, one family, all en-suite
£ £££
Snacks and meals daily, lunchtime and evening
Accepted

The Killingworth Castle was built in 1637 as a coaching inn on what was the main London-Worcester-Aberystwyth route – now a small back lane. It is still accommodating weary travellers – eight years ago an old barn was converted to four modern, welcoming rooms, all individually designed with beams, pine furniture and en-suite bathroom; one adapted for wheelchair users. A full English breakfast is included in the price; alternatives are available on request.

The pub retains many original features including the long beamed bar with log burning stove, and a smaller rear bar with games and bar billiards. Country-style pine furniture, timber and flagstone floors are complemented by book cases and farming artefacts. There is a large garden and the pub is a long-standing music venue with live entertainment every Friday.

The main menu offers a reasonably priced selection including a classic paella, beef and ale pie, trout stuffed with celeriac and fennel and lamb shank with rosemary, spinach and wild rice risotto.

Well situated for visiting Woodstock, Blenheim Palace and the Cotswolds, the Killingworth is popular with tourists, walkers and locals alike. Q P

Shropshire

BRIDGNORTH
Fox Inn
46 Hospital Street, WV15 5AR

- ▶ On A442 in town centre
- T (01746) 769611
- W thefoxinnbridgnorth.co.uk
- Hook Norton Hooky Bitter, Old Hooky; guest beers
- Four double, one twin room, all en-suite
- £ ££
- Lunchtime and evening meals and lunchtime snacks
- Accepted

This is one of those happy, albeit rare occasions, when the restyling of the interior of an old, traditional coaching inn into a contemporary, stylish bar, blending 16th-century exposed beams with cool modern furnishings, has been a triumph. The same effect has been pulled off in the five smart guest rooms, where the neutral colours and luxurious en-suite shower rooms are very attractive. In all the renovation work great care has been taken with the use of high quality fittings and furniture. The bedrooms have free wireless Internet connection, TV, trouser press and iron, and facilities for making hot drinks.

An adventurous menu offers light lunch for around a fiver - Moroccan style potato cakes with grilled halloumi, goat's cheese fritter with raspberry coulis or rarebit of Shropshire blue ciabatta – or main dishes including fresh cod in beer and black pepper batter, or sausage trio of the week, for under £10.The full evening menu is just as interesting – but at breakfast, traditionalists can rest assured that a proper full English cooked meal is served.

Bridgnorth has an abundance of real ale pubs, so a stroll through town will be rewarded. P

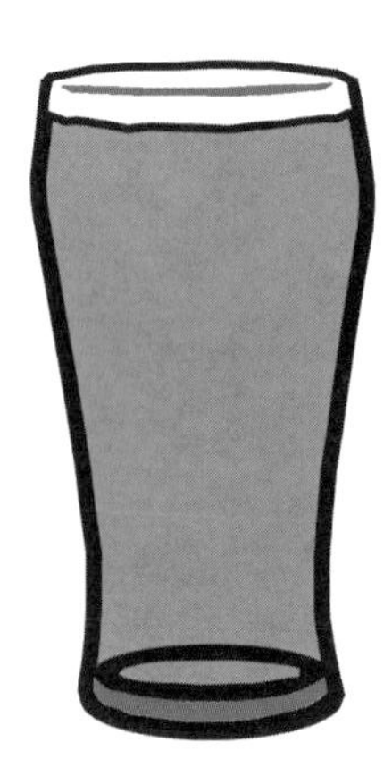

LUDLOW
Church Inn
Buttercross, SY8 1AW

▶ Behind the Buttercross in the town centre
T (01584) 872174
F (01584) 877146
W thechurchinn.com
Hobsons Mild, Town Crier; Hook Norton Hooky Bitter; Three Tuns Cleric's Cure; guest beers
Five double, one twin, two family rooms
£ ££ (single occupancy, weekdays £40)
Lunchtime and evening meals and snacks
Accepted

Local CAMRA's Pub of the Year 2005 the Church Inn, owned by a former mayor of Ludlow, is a great choice for ale lovers as it always has eight beers on handpump. Situated in the town centre, near the castle and market square, this free house stands on one of Ludlow's most ancient sites. Over the last seven centuries it has housed the blacksmith, saddler and barber-surgeon, but has been an inn since at least 1792. The inn's upstairs bar offers an excellent view of Ludlow church and the Shropshire Hills.

The pub's guest rooms all have en-suite facilities with a hospitality tray and television; four of the rooms feature spa baths. Children and pets are welcome to stay. A full English breakfast is served, or you can choose scrambled, fried or poached egg on toast.

Ludlow is a charming medieval market town with plenty to interest visitors, and has recently built up a reputation as something of a 'foodie' paradise, with many excellent restaurants – its annual food and drink festival in September is now a well established event. The Church Inn has its own busy restaurant, and bar meals are also available.

SHIFNAL
☆ Odfellows
Market Place, TF11 9AU

T (01952) 461517
F (01952) 463855
W odleyinns.co.uk
Beer range varies
Six double rooms, one family, all en-suite
£ £
Snacks and meals daily, lunchtime and evening
Accepted

A real ale wine bar offering fine beer, exciting food and accommodation at bargain prices, the Odfellows is one of a trio of Odley Inns. A pleasantly converted Victorian building, the hotel accommodation has separate access. Excellent value for money, all rooms provide TV, phone, fridge, tea, coffee, mineral water and fruit juice, comfy chair and workspace, plus CCTV monitored car park. The tariff includes a continental breakfast delivered to your room to keep in the fridge overnight or, after 10.30am when the restaurant opens, you can order full English including dry-cure bacon, free-range eggs and Shropshire pork sausages.

The former coaching house in the market place has a large, airy open plan room with fires in winter and offers a changing range of ales including local beers such as Salopian, Woods and Wye Valley, Belgian beers and draught cider. Also featuring in CAMRA's Good Pub Food guide, the inn serves a wide range of home-made food, inexpensive and tasty – sandwiches of Shropshire beef or local pork and leek sausage with Stilton, main dishes including well hung Shropshire sirloin steaks, Much Wenlock lamb chops, home-baked Shropshire ham with free-range eggs and hand-cut chips.

Local places of interest include Ironbridge Gorge and the Severn Valley railway. P

SHREWSBURY

Shrewsbury Hotel

Bridge Place, SY1 1PU

T (01743) 236203
W jdwetherspoonlodges.co.uk
Greene King Abbot Ale; Marston's Pedigree; Wood's Shropshire Lad; guest beers
Twelve double, eight twin, two family rooms, all en-suite
£ ££ (room only)
Snacks and meals all day
Accepted

Shrewsbury Hotel is the oldest of Wetherspoon's small (but growing) chain of Wetherlodges attached to its pubs or Lloyds bars. The 18th-century coaching inn in the centre of this medieval market town opposite the River Severn was privately run for over 70 years prior to becoming a Wetherlodge seven years ago.

The well-decorated and well-maintained rooms combine their 18th-century charm with the modern facilities of en-suite bathroom, tea and coffee making and TV. They occupy a warren of different stairs and levels in this listed building – Wetherspoon was not permitted to install a lift so the rooms are not wheelchair accessible. Like most Wetherlodges, prices are reasonable, and bargains are often available such as two nights for the price of one, so ask before booking (or visit the website). Breakfast is not included but starts at just £1.99 for a full English.

In the pub, a large, open-plan bar is decorated with pictures of local poets including Wilfred Owen. Tourists come from as far away as Japan to enjoy the area's history (Clive of India was one of Shrewsbury's favourite sons – his statue is in the main square) and black and white, half-timbered buildings. P

TELFORD

Coalbrookdale Inn

12 Wellington Road, Coalbrookdale, TF8 7DX

T (01952) 433953
W coalbrookdaleinn.co.uk
Hobsons Town Crier; Three Tuns XXX; Wye Valley Hereford Pale Ale; guest beers
Three double rooms, all en-suite
£ £70
Snacks and meals daily, lunchtime and evening
Accepted (not Amex)

This grade II listed pub was serving real ale to the ironworkers of Coalbrookdale in the 1830s and continues to offer a warm welcome to locals and visitors to the area. A former CAMRA National Pub of the Year, the staff here really know their beers – seven superb cask ales are always on handpump. The traditional bar has a real fire, quarry tiled floor and Victorian picture gallery.

A separate lounge/dining room serves notable food including smoked duck and bacon salad with hoi sin sauce, gnocchi with king prawns in pesto, pork ravini or chef's special beef fillet. Alternatively, the bar menu offers Coalbrookdale Cobbler, faggots and mash, fish and home-made chips or chicken, ham and asparagus pie, all around £7.

Accommodation is in three double rooms with solid oak floors and wooden furniture; the Victorian-style en-suites have cast iron baths and 'drench' showers. Included in the price is a choice of full English or continental breakfast.

Situated in the heart of the Ironbridge Gorge World Heritage Site, the pub is opposite the Museum of Iron and historic Darby Furnace, with Dale House and Darby House five minutes' walk away.
P

TELFORD

Golden Ball

Newbridge Road, Ironbridge, TF8 7BA

▶ Between Madeley Rd (B4374) and Waterloo St (B4373)
T (01952) 432179
F (01952) 433123
W goldenballinn.com
Everards Tiger; guest beers
Two double, two twin rooms, also available as singles, all en-suite
£ ££-£££
Lunchtime and evening meals
Accepted

'If you have time to visit one pub in the area, this is the one not to be missed,' say CAMRA members in the Good Beer Guide 2007. This charming 18th-century inn, which pre-dates the famous bridge itself, was once a brew house, but now offers a good choice of guest beers instead. The traditional bar retains original features such as the open fireplace where the mash was prepared, the waterpump and a host of small rooms with exposed beams and tiled floors. Good quality home-cooked food is served in the bar and pleasant restaurant with ingredients sourced locally where possible.

The World Heritage site of Ironbridge with its wealth of museums attracts many tourists, and the independently owned Golden Ball is always busy with visitors as well as locals. The four guest suites are all individually decorated, with TV and tea and coffee making facilities. The most expensive is the Paradise Suite, with its draped four-poster and en-suite bath and shower providing a romantic setting for a weekend à deux. The inn offers a full English breakfast in the morning. There is also a pleasant self-catering cottage available with two double and one single bedroom. Q ♣ P

Somerset

BAYFORD
Unicorn Inn
BA9 9NL

- ▶ On old A303, 1 mile east of Wincanton
- T (01963) 32324
- W theunicorninnbayford.com
- Draught Bass; Butcombe Bitter; guest beers
- Two double, one twin/family, one single room, all en-suite
- £ £-££
- Snacks and meals daily, lunchtime and evening
- Accepted

Entry to this 270-year-old former coaching inn on the old Exeter-London highway is gained through an impressive coach arch into the courtyard. Inside, the single-bar pub retains many of its original features – flagstone floors, beams, an open fireplace and a hidden well.

The Unicorn welcomes 'people with big appetites who don't want large screen TV, fruit machines, snooker or darts,' says the landlord. The inn, which also features in CAMRA's Good Pub Food guide, is renowned for its home-cooked, generous portions. Healthy appetites can wake up to the big breakfast which includes local duck eggs when available as part of a hearty full English. Later in the day meals include fresh fish such as skate, ling, Torbay sole and monkfish as well as the unusual fish cassoulet. All the home-made soups are vegetarian and gluten free.

Among the four en-suite rooms is a four poster, with all amenities for the modern traveller including secure car parking. An ideal place to stay if you are going to Wincanton racecourse – the Unicorn does get very busy on race days – it is also close to many other attractions including Stourhead House, Longleat, Glastonbury Tor and Stonehenge. Q P

CHEWTON MENDIP

Waldegrave Arms

High Street, BA3 4LL

▶ At village centre on A39 between Bath and Wells
T (01761) 241384
W waldegravearms.co.uk
Butcombe Bitter; guest beers
One double, one twin, one family room, all en-suite
£ £
Snacks and meals daily, lunchtime and evening
Accepted

A traditional, stone-built inn dating from 1852 at the heart of a pretty village, the Waldegrave has a big family garden and wins awards for its floral displays – in summer the frontage is a riot of colour with tubs and hanging baskets. The four cask ales are changed monthly, but always include local Butcombe Bitter.

Accommodation in this quiet and peaceful location is in three en-suite rooms, all equipped with TV and tea and coffee making facilities. The price includes full English breakfast with sausages from the local butcher, or you can opt for continental.

Featuring in CAMRA's Good Pub Food guide, meals are of a high standard, with Friday a highlight when there is a choice of up to 10 different fish cooked to your specifications – grilled, battered, fried. Steaks are also to the fore, right up to a 24oz T-bone or giant mixed grill with real chips, as well as three-egg omelettes, sandwiches and ploughman's. Sunday lunch is served all day.

On the edge of the Mendips, this is a good base for exploring Bath, Wells, Glastonbury, the Cheddar Gorge and Mendip hills.

Q P

CLEVEDON

Old Inn

9 Walton Road, BS21 6EY

▶ West of M5 jct 20
T (01275) 340440
Courage Best Bitter; Greene King Old Speckled Hen; guest beers
One double, three twin, one family, one single room, all en-suite
£ £
Meals served all day
Accepted

This 200-year-old whitewashed, single-room, beamed inn originally served the carriage trade from Weston-super-Mare to Portishead. The current landlady's great grandmother was once in charge here. It is now a favourite with local CAMRA members who enjoy the good community atmosphere, occasionally abetted by someone playing the piano or 'other jollity'. The guest beer choice is often unusual for the area and the food here, served all day, is good value.

The comfortable en-suite guest rooms, which were refurbished in 2004, are well-equipped with hospitality tray, hair dryer, television and DVD. At the Old Inn you can enjoy a lie-inn – a full cooked breakfast is available between 7 and 10.30am. Children and pets are welcome and the pub has a big, safe garden for families.

A convenient stop off for travellers on the M5, the pub is also ideal for people with business in Bristol or using the airport, which is just 15 minutes away. It makes a good base, too, for tourists as Wookey Hole, Cheddar Gorge and the National Trust's recent acquisition, Tyntesfield – a magnificent Victorian house and estate – are all nearby.

Q P

CORTON DENHAM

☆ Queen's Arms

DT9 4LR

- ▶ Off B3145 between Sherborne and Wincanton
- T (01963) 220317
- W thequeensarms.com
- Butcombe Bitter; Otter Bitter; Taylor Landlord; guest beers
- Four double, one twin room, all en-suite
- £ £££-££££
- Lunchtime and evening meals
- Accepted

Much care and attention has been lavished on the accommodation at the Queen's Arms to provide luxurious rooms for discerning guests. You could stay five times and enjoy a different experience on each occasion as each room has a style of its own (prices vary accordingly). One room has an antique walnut bed, a chaise longue and a deep cast iron bath for two, while another is furnished in contemporary colours, with a leather bed and suede bean bags for lounging on. All the rooms feature fine Egyptian bedding and stunning views over the rolling countryside around Corton Denham. And if you are not planning a romantic weekend à deux, z-beds are available for children.

A late 18th-century hostelry at the heart of the village, the bar's wood and flagstone floors, old pews, distressed leather sofas and muted colours provide a comfortable backdrop in which to enjoy real ale or a glass of Thatchers Cheddar Valley cider. The dining room offers an excellent menu that changes weekly based on seasonal produce. The inn keeps its own pigs and Maran hens that provide eggs for the classic English breakfast; porridge, eggs on toast or smoked haddock with poached egg can also be ordered. Q ♣ P

CREWKERNE

Old Stagecoach Inn

Station Road, TA18 8AL

▶ Off A30, between Chard and Yeovil
T (01460) 72972
F (01460) 77023
W stagecoach-inn.co.uk
Glastonbury Mystery Tor; guest beers
Six double, five twin, two family rooms, all en-suite; two rooms wheelchair accessible
£ ££ (£35 single occupancy)
Lunchtime and evening meals
Accepted

Next to the railway station, this former post house dates back to 1880 and is said to be the first in the area to be built of brick. The licensees left a bar in Ostend to come and run this inn so it's no surprise that they offer the best selection of Belgian ales in Somerset. The menu, too, features many dishes from their home country, with several that include beer in the ingredients. The annual Belgian beer evening is a popular event.

The guest accommodation is to the rear of the pub, away from the main road, so you can be assured of a restful night. Simply furnished, the rooms have television and hospitality tray. Children are welcome and a cot can be provided. Pets can also be accommodated. Breakfast is a traditional English affair with the usual sausage, bacon, egg and grilled tomato or you can have eggs or beans on toast. Most of the produce is sourced locally and special diets can be catered for with advance warning.

The pub has a large garden and there are plenty of places of interest to visit nearby including the Cricket St Thomas Wildlife Park and the Fleet Air Arm Museum.

Q ♣ P

CROSCOMBE

George Inn

Long Street, BA5 3QH

T (01749) 342306
W thegeorgeinn.co.uk
Butcombe Bitter; guest beers
Two en-suite double rooms, plus self-contained flat (one double, one single room) suitable for families, with wheelchair accessible bathroom
£ £-££
Lunchtime and evening meals and snacks
Accepted

The George has been dispensing hospitality since the early 1600s, and is the longest continuously running pub in the village. Back in 1666 an early landlord, James George, issued his own coinage depicting George and the Dragon. The house beer, King George the Thirst, is brewed by local brewery Blindmans.

The present landlords have been here since 2000 and in that time have put a lot of effort into renovating and updating the facilities, including the guest accommodation. The two double bedrooms have been upgraded by the provision of en-suite facilities and the old coach house has just been converted into a self-contained flat with one double and one single bedroom, and a bathroom adapted for use by disabled guests.

A generous breakfast is cooked and served by the landlord and landlady – with cereals, yogurt, eggs, bacon, local sausages or the full works if requested. Local, organic produce is used as available in the kitchen. Reasonably priced home-made meals are served in two dining rooms; the old tack room has been renovated to cater for small parties and, with a covered and heated terrace, meals can also be taken in the garden. Bar snacks are also available.

Q ♣ P

CROWCOMBE
Carew Arms
TA4 4AD

- ▶ Midway between Taunton and Minehead on A358
- T (01984) 618631
- W thecarewarms.co.uk
- Exmoor Ale, Stag; guest beers
- Three double, three twin rooms, all en-suite
- £ £££
- Snacks and meals daily, lunchtime and evening
- Accepted (not Amex or Diners)

Set in the Quantock hills in England's first area of outstanding natural beauty, the Carew Arms has been at the heart of the village for more than 400 years. The front bar has an inglenook fireplace and flagstones; a small lounge leads to a garden room bar and dining room, with doors onto the terrace and garden featuring a marvellous display of roses in summer. There is also a skittle alley and function room.

The bedrooms have been refurbished within the past couple of years, and are soothingly decorated, providing TV and tea and coffee making facilities plus excellent bath or shower rooms. Breakfast is included, comprising cereals including locally made muesli, eggs any way you like (omelettes, too), bacon, local sausages, lamb's kidney, flat mushrooms, grilled vine tomatoes and fried bread – as well as smoked haddock on occasion. There is a 10 per cent discount on the room rate for a three-night stay, a £15 surcharge for an extra bed in a room.

Close to fabulous walking country and several golf courses, local attractions include Exmoor national park, West Somerset Steam Railway, Dunster Castle and Coleridge Cottage. Q P

LANGFORD BUDVILLE
Martlet Inn
TA21 0QZ

- ▶ Just off B3187 between Wellington and Milverton, near M5 jct 26
- T (01823) 400262
- F (01823) 401555
- W martletinn.co.uk
- Cotleigh Tawny; Exmoor Ale; Masters Carnivale, Thunderbridge Ale
- Three double rooms, all en-suite; one room wheelchair accessible
- £ ££
- Lunchtime and evening meals
- Accepted

Built as a farmhouse around 400 years ago, this traditional village free house has seen some improvements over the years but its four rooms still bear original features. The main bar has flagstone floors, exposed beams and an attractive central fireplace housing a wood-burning stove.

The guest accommodation was created in 2006 in an adjacent barn. Three spacious bedrooms have been attractively decorated, with good en-suite facilities. A hospitality tray is provided along with TV and DVD player. One room has a pair of rocking chairs, another a comfy sofa. Children are welcome.

In the morning you can fill up on a full English breakfast with local produce such as sausages, or you can pick and choose what you would like. If you are in a hurry or setting off on a hike, breakfast butties can be provided to take with you. The pub stands on the West Deane Walk and National Cycle Route three. Fishing and golf can also be enjoyed nearby.

Renowned locally for good food, the finest local ingredients are used where possible in all meals from bar snacks to daily specials. The pub has award-winning gardens – at the front is a child-free adult sanctuary but the back garden has play facilities – as well as a skittle alley and function room.

LONG SUTTON
Devonshire Arms
TA10 9LP

- ▶ On B3165 off A372, four miles from Langport
- T (01458) 241271
- F (01458) 241271
- W thedevonshirearms.com
- Bath Ales Spa; Hop Back Crop Circle; Teignworthy Reel Ale
- Eight double, one twin room, all en-suite
- £ ££-£££
- Snacks and meals daily, lunchtime and evening
- Accepted

The Devonshire is a centuries old grade II listed former hunting lodge with a splendid frontage, its coat of arms displayed above the pillared entrance, set on a quintessentially English village green. The interior, by contrast, is unexpectedly contemporary with an open plan restaurant, main bar with open fire and locals' back bar.

The nine bedrooms, too, are modern, all individually designed with wide-screen TV and luxury touches, overlooking either the village green and church or courtyard and walled garden. The tariff includes a breakfast starting with fresh fruit or cereals, and full English featuring local produce down to toast sliced from locally-baked loaves.

Local produce also features on the main menu at a pub noted for its cuisine, from the splendid ploughman's of Keen's Cheddar, Somerset Brie, slow-roasted bacon and Dowerhouse chutney, to evening meals such as Quantock duck breast with rice noodles, grey mullet with chorizo, char-grilled lamb's kidney with confit beetroot or West Country beef fillet with cep sauce.

Close to the Fleet Air Arm Museum, Cheddar Gorge, Wookey Hole and Castle Cary, as well as Bath and Salisbury, the pub attracts a wide-ranging clientele.

P

MARTOCK
White Hart
East Street, TA12 6JQ

- ▶ Off A303, 4 miles from Yeovil
- T (01935) 822005
- F (01935) 822056
- W whitehartotelmartock.co.uk
- Otter Bitter; Sharp's Doom Bar; guest beers
- Four double, two twin, two family, two single rooms; all en-suite
- £ ££
- Lunchtime and evening meals
- Accepted

This imposing 18th-century building, a former coaching inn, is now a friendly, family-run hotel offering excellent four diamond rated accommodation. As a free house, the bar stocks a selection of guest ales, often from West Country brewers such as Dorset, Sherborne or Yeovil.

Warm and welcoming, the comfortable bar has chesterfield sofas by the fire and a piano that is sometimes played in the early evening. You can enjoy bar meals or dine in the restaurant; the inventive menu is based on fresh local produce. Conference facilities and a well-used skittle alley are in a separate building with its own bar.

The White Hart is popular with locals and visitors. Its ten guest rooms are all en-suite and well equipped. Children and pets are welcome here. The hotel garage provides secure parking for cycles and motorbikes. A continental breakfast is included in the B&B price, or for an additional £4 per person you can order a cooked meal, usually the full English, but if you want something else, just ask.

The hotel is well located for several stately homes, such as Montacute House and other NT properties; Yeovil Air Museum and Haynes Motor Museum will cater for transport enthusiasts.

Q P

MUDFORD
Half Moon Inn
Main Street, BA21 5TF

▶ On A359
T (01935) 850289
F (01935) 850842
W thehalfmooninn.co.uk
RCH Pitchfork, East Street Cream; guest beers
Nine double, three twin, two family rooms, all en-suite; eight wheelchair accessible
£ ££-£££
Food served all day
Accepted (not Amex)

The interior of this 17th-century inn has been carefully restored while maintaining its original rustic character. It features log fires, intimate corners and, outside, a lovely spacious cobbled courtyard for enjoying a pint of ale on a warm summer's evening. The Half Moon is a rare outlet in south Somerset for the RCH Brewery.

The former skittle alley and log store attached to the main pub has been converted to provide nine en-suite guest rooms, nearly all of them accessible for wheelchair-users. The bedrooms in the main pub building have also been updated and the inn has a four diamond rating from the ETB for its well-appointed accommodation. All rooms have wireless Broadband connection. The tariff is for the room only, but a self-service continental buffet is provided for just under £5 per person. Meals served throughout the day are home-cooked and of a very high standard, earning the inn a place in CAMRA's Good Pub Food guide.

Surrounded by stunning countryside and close to the 95-mile Jurassic coastline, the pub is an ideal base for walkers, riders and cyclists. Transport buffs might enjoy Haynes Motor Museum or the Fleet Air Arm Museum nearby. The medieval town of Sherbourne is a short drive away. Q ❀ ♿ P

ODCOMBE
Masons Arms
41 Lower Odcombe, BA22 8TX

▶ Off A3088, ½ mile from Montacute
T (01935) 862591
W masonsarmsodcombe.co.uk
Odcombe No. 1, Spring; guest beer
Two double, one twin room, all en-suite and wheelchair accessible
£ ££
Lunchtime and evening meals
Accepted

Early in 2005 the villagers of Odcombe were rescued from an awful threat – the loss of their local. When new owners finished essential work and reopened the Masons on April Fool's Day the villagers were so relieved they drank the pub dry of beer.

Regulars have continued to keep the pub busy, enjoying both the ale (they sometimes choose the guests) and the fine home-cooked food. With a little help from Shepherd Neame, the experienced licensees soon had the on-site brewery running again in the little brewhouse behind the pub.

The next project is to increase the number of guest rooms available – building work should start in 2007. At present there are just three rooms with country-style pine furnishings and en-suite showers. Situated away from the road, next to the pretty garden, you are assured of a peaceful night. Children and pets are welcome to stay. For breakfast there are various cereals and pastries, plus a cooked meal including free-range eggs and sausages from the local butcher. Organic produce is used as far as possible in all meals.

The pub also has a small campsite. Local places of interest include Ham Hill Country Park and Montacute House.
Q ❀ ♿ ♣ P

PORLOCK WEIR

Anchor Hotel & Ship Inn

TA24 8PB

▶ Take B3225 from Porlock, hotel is by the harbour
T (01643) 862753
F (01643) 862843
W theanchorhotelandshipinn.co.uk
Cotleigh Barn Owl; Exmoor Ale, Gold; guest beer
Eleven double, three twin, three family rooms, all en-suite
£ £££ (single occupancy from £49)
Lunchtime and evening meals
Accepted

According to local CAMRA members the Anchor & Ship has possibly the best view of any pub in Somerset. Situated above a little harbour, the panorama extends over the Bristol Channel to the coast of South Wales.

The premier guest bedrooms are at the front of the hotel, so benefit from this view, but are more expensive than the standard rooms. Traditionally furnished, all rooms have Sky TV, Internet connection and hospitality tray. Children under five can stay free of charge, older children are charged £20 per night sharing a parent's room, or 50% of the adult rate in a separate room. Pets are welcome.

Breakfast is varied: apart from the standard cooked English affair, there are also kippers, gammon, fruit and yogurt. Particular dietary requirements can be catered for.

The hotel dates from the early 1800s, while the thatched Ship Inn adjacent is over 400 years old. The Ship, with its friendly Mariners Bar, serves good bar meals, while the hotel has a more formal restaurant offering a daily changing menu, and an elegant drawing room, both with harbour views. Popular with walkers, the pub lies within Exmoor National Park, near Porlock Hill. Q P

WELLS

Crown at Wells

Market Place, BA5 2RP

T (01749) 673457
W crownatwells.co.uk
Butcombe Bitter, Blond, Gold; guest beers
Fifteen rooms, all en-suite
£ £££-££££
Snacks and meals daily, lunchtime and evening
Accepted

Thought to date back to 1450, the Crown was originally built as houses commissioned by Bishop Beckynton. Boarded up and in receivership in 1993, it was rescued by licensee Adrian Lawrence, to become a sister inn to the award-winning food pub the Fountain, also in Wells.

Adrian and his wife Sarah have turned the handsome building overlooked by the cathedral into a comfortable and welcoming hotel and pub with 'meeting place' bar and bistro. Accommodation includes double, single and family rooms, some with four poster beds and Jacuzzi baths, weekend rates available. The price includes an excellent breakfast – continental from a buffet table, traditional Somerset with eggs, bacon and sausages from local producers or vegetarian. Packed lunches are available.

The Crown is in CAMRA's Good Pub Food guide, featuring different home-cooked menus in bar and bistro, with a particularly good vegetarian selection. Choices include baked frittata with red onion and bell peppers, filo filled with roast vegetables, pine kernels and smoked cheddar, roast sea bass and duck breast with cherry and kirsch.

Close to Glastonbury Tor and the Vale of Avalon, there is also much to see in England's smallest city.

WIVELISCOMBE

Bear Inn

10 North Street, TA4 2JY

- T (01984) 623537
- Cotleigh Tawny, Golden Eagle; Sharp's Doom Bar; guest beer
- Three double, two twin rooms with shared facilities
- £ £ (£30 single occupancy)
- Lunchtime and evening meals and snacks
- Accepted

Just out of the town centre, the Bear is a lively pub that serves its local community well but is equally welcoming to visitors. The car park of this former coaching inn was once the site of the town's cattle market and retains various outbuildings. Wiveliscombe has a history as a brewing town and the pub serves ales from Cotleigh, one of the most successful brewers in the West Country. The comfortable bar has an area for pool and there is a skittle alley.

Accommodation here is excellent value for money. The country style bedrooms in this old building are full of original character, with sloping floors and low ceiling beams. Bedrooms do not have en-suite facilities but share two bathrooms between the five rooms. They are all equipped with hospitality tray and television. Children are welcome and the pub's large garden has a play area. Pets can be accommodated.

The generous, full English breakfast is included, with two sausages and two bacon rashers as well as black pudding and the usual accompaniments, but you can choose as much or as little as you like. The Bear offers a varied menu at other meal times, with home-made pizzas a speciality.

P

YEOVIL

Pall Tavern

Silver Street, BA20 1HW

- T (01935) 476521
- E pandaltd@aol.com
- Greene King Old Speckled Hen; guest beers
- One double, two family rooms, all en-suite; all available as singles
- £ £££
- Lunchtime and evening meals
- Accepted

CAMRA's 2007 Good Beer Guide says of the Pall, 'Pronounce the name of this excellent local "pal" and you get a good idea of its character'. Described by the licensees as a country pub in town, with a traditional pub atmosphere, it is a genuinely friendly place. Dating from the 1600s, the single comfortable bar is packed with artefacts and subdued music plays in the background. Two guest beers change as soon as the barrel is finished. Well-behaved dogs are welcome in the bar and overnight.

Children are also welcome and the pub can provide a cot or moses basket if required. All the bedrooms can accommodate up to four people and have tea and coffee making facilities, TV and video. At the time of writing, there are plans to convert the pub's snooker room into further guest accommodation.

For breakfast you can choose from a full English with scrambled, fried or poached eggs, or a lighter choice of eggs or beans on toast. Good value main meals are served in the bar or dining room, except Monday. The pub is close to both Yeovil Junction station and Pen Mill on the Bristol-Weymouth line.

Q

Staffordshire

COLTON
Ye Olde Dun Cow
73 High Street, WS15 3LG

- ▶ Near Rugeley
- T (01889) 584026
- W dun-cow.com
- Draught Bass; guest beers
- Three double, one twin room; two en-suite, two with shared bathroom
- £ ££
- Snacks and meals daily, lunchtime and evening
- Accepted

This former coaching inn, dating in parts back to the 18th century, has a traditional interior with beams and inglenook fireplace, outside is a welcoming beer garden. The spacious, newly-refurbished bedrooms have all mod cons: two are en-suite, all offer tea and coffee making facilities and TV. A full English breakfast is served in the breakfast room downstairs.

Popular, traditional pub meals, freshly cooked by the landlady, are available at lunchtime and in the evening. Main courses start at around £6 for steak and kidney pie, there is a good range of grills and steaks, plus several fish choices on a daily-changing specials board. On Sundays locals join visitors for a traditional Sunday lunch.

Surrounded by fabulous countryside, you can hire bicycles from the pub or take a walk through the rolling woodlands of Cannock Chase or along the Staffordshire Way. Shugborough Hall is close by and fishing can be arranged locally. Golf enthusiasts can play at the Belfry, home of the Ryder Cup – the pub will arrange tee times for you. And when you've had your fill of the countryside, Alton Towers is 20 minutes' drive away.

P

ECCLESHALL

George Inn

Castle Street, ST21 6DF

▶ On A519 between M6 jcts 14/15
T (01785) 850300
F (01785) 851452
W thegeorgeinn.freeserve.co.uk
Slater's Bitter, Original, Top Totty, Premium, Supreme, seasonal beer
Five double, two twin, one family, two single rooms, all en-suite
£ ££
Snacks and meals daily, lunchtime and evening
Accepted (not Diners)

Award-winning ales are dispensed at the George, brewed by the Slater family who own both the hotel and Slater's Brewery which was originally behind the pub but last year outgrew its premises and moved to a larger site in Stafford itself. Beer is supplied to 600 outlets direct, but the George is the brewery tap and its only tied house.

A coaching inn dating from the 17th century, Slater's ales on six handpulls are extremely popular, but not the only attraction. The building is full of character, from the mellow exterior to the old bar with beams and big inglenook fireplace. Innovative food is served either in the bar or more contemporary bistro.

Ten luxurious bedrooms all have tea and coffee making facilities; prices vary depending whether you stay midweek or at the weekend. Included is a full English breakfast with local black pudding, or continental if you prefer.

Eccleshall is a quaint market town close to Shugborough Hall, Weston Park, Stapeley Water Gardens, the Wedgewood Visitor Centre and factory shops and museums of the Potteries.

P

HANDSACRE

Old Peculiar

The Green, WS15 4DP

▶ Off A513, 4 miles from Rugeley
T (01543) 491891
E corinne.odonnell@ntlworld.com
Marston's Pedigree; Theakston Best Bitter, Old Peculier; guest beers
Two twin, two single, one family room, all en-suite
£ £
Lunchtime and evening meals
Accepted

A warm welcome is assured at this village inn. This cosy free house is basically one room split into three areas, with a great atmosphere in which to enjoy a pint or a bite to eat. The bar offers a weekly-changing guest beer, often from a local micro-brewery, as well as its namesake from Theakston, though note that the spelling is different. The good value food is popular with both locals and visitors.

The pub was originally a coaching inn and the former stables have been converted into guest rooms. The well-equipped bedrooms are on the ground floor so may suit guests with mobility problems. Children are welcome. A full English breakfast includes local free-range eggs and bacon and sausages from the butcher nearby; a vegetarian alternative and other choices are also possible.

The pub is in the village centre, just two minutes' walk from the Trent and Mersey Canal, and attracts boaters, walkers and cyclists. It is also convenient for visiting Lichfield five miles away, Alton Towers, Shugborough Hall and the National Memorial Arboretum near Alrewas.

Q ♣ P

NEEDWOOD

New Inn

5 Lanes End, Burton Road, DE13 9PB

- ▶ Four miles west of Burton-on-Trent
- T (01283) 575392
- W newinn.co.uk
- Marston's Pedigree
- Two twin, one family, one single room, shared bathroom
- £ £
- Snacks and meals Tues-Sun lunchtime, every evening
- Accepted

The New Inn is in fact not at all new and has quite a history. An 18th-century coaching inn and farmhouse, it provided accommodation and sustenance for travellers passing through what was once Needwood Forest. Records show an inn on the site around 1760, and the true age of the building can be seen by the bake oven still intact in a corner of the restaurant, and larder room with hooks for hanging game.

Bedrooms are clean and comfortable with TV and tea and coffee making facilities, and a full English or continental breakfast is included. Food here is very inexpensive with traditional pub grub such as pork chops and fish 'n' chips priced around £5-£6, and hot 'comfort' puds at £2.75, with Xmas plum pudding served all year round.

A jolly pub with biker nights and games such as bar billiards, darts, dominoes and crib played in the Poacher's Bar, the inn attracts walkers and motorcyclists for overnight stays. Handy for the brewing centre of Burton-on-Trent housing Coors Museum of Brewing, the pub is also close to Sudbury Hall with the Museum of Childhood, Tutbury Castle and crystal glass works, and Lichfield Cathedral.

Q P

TAMWORTH

Albert Hotel

32 Albert Road, B79 7JS

- ▶ Near rail station
- T (01827) 64694
- W tamworthhotel.co.uk
- Banks's Original, Bitter; Marston's Pedigree; guest beer
- One double/family, two twin, two single rooms, most en-suite
- £ £
- Lunchtime and evening meals
- Accepted

A straightforward, solid, Victorian brick pub, the Albert has retained its traditional layout with a separate bar and lounge, and pool/family room at the rear. In summer the secluded patio behind the pub and drinking area in front both get busy. Thursday is quiz night here. A former local CAMRA Pub of the Year, this friendly town-centre hostelry has a good regular clientele and offers reasonably priced accommodation to visitors, within easy walking distance of Tamworth station and on several local bus routes.

The Albert has five guest rooms – the double is big enough to accommodate a family and children are welcome. Not all rooms have en-suite facilities but they do have TV and hospitality tray. A full English breakfast is provided here, with toast and cereals, though a continental breakfast is also available on request. Local produce is used as much as possible in the kitchen – wholesome pub favourites are cooked to order at lunchtime and in the evening. The guest beers are usually from Wolverhampton and Dudley's range.

Places of interest nearby include Tamworth Castle, the Snowdome – great for practice runs before a winter sports holiday – and Drayton Manor Park.

Q P

Suffolk

ALDEBURGH

Mill Inn

Market Cross Place, IP15 5BJ

- ▶ Opposite Moot Hall
- T (01728) 452563
- W themillinnaldeburgh.com
- Adnams Bitter, Broadside, seasonal; guest beer
- Two double, one twin, one single room with two shared bathrooms
- £ £-££
- Snacks and meals lunchtime and Tue-Sat evenings
- Accepted (not Amex)

The Mill is a lively local with a delightful seafront location opposite the ancient Moot Hall. It is the favourite pub of the lifeboat crew (Dennis the landlord is a member) and local fishermen, so you can be sure of salty conversation and ripping yarns.

The B&B accommodation is extremely popular: two charming double rooms and a twin room all with sea views, plus a single room. All have TV and tea and coffee making facilities. The four rooms share two new bathrooms, each with a power shower as well as a bath. The full English breakfast includes local sausages, bacon and eggs.

Featuring in CAMRA's Good Pub Food guide, the Mill is renowned for excellent seafood at bargain prices. Fish supplied from the fishermen's huts on the beach can include cod, skate, Dover sole, local crab and lobsters, but there are also traditional favourites from cottage pie to filled Yorkshire puds. A bracing walk along the beach is just what you need before your evening meal and a couple of pints of Adnams. Local Aspalls cider is stocked, too.

Local attractions include Aldeburgh music hall and Snape Maltings.

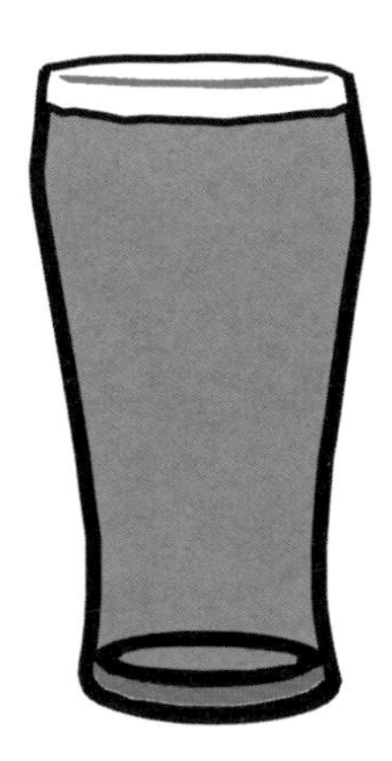

BRADFIELD ST GEORGE

Fox & Hounds

Felsham Road, IP30 0AB

- ▶ Off A134 near Bury St Edmunds
- T (01284) 386379
- Adnams Bitter; guest beers
- Two twin rooms, both en-suite
- £ ££
- Snacks and meals daily, lunchtime and evening
- Accepted

A Victorian country pub, the Fox & Hounds is on the outskirts of the village in a rural location close to the ancient coppiced woodland of the Suffolk Wildlife Trust. The attractive interior has been restored in keeping with the inn's Victorian origins; the public bar has a wood block floor, wood-burning stove and pine seating. There is a separate lounge bar with glazed area for dining to the front. Outside are a large car park, garden and petanque pitch.

Accommodation is in a converted barn behind the pub, just two twin rooms, both en-suite, promising peace and quiet, with uninterrupted views across open farm and woodland.

A free house, the inn serves Adnams Bitter plus a changing range of guest beers from other notable local independents such as Mauldons, Bartrams, Earl Soham and Nethergate. Real cider is occasionally available.

Attracting locals, walkers and diners, the Fox and Hounds is close to historic Bury St Edmunds with several superb pubs and plenty of history including the cathedral and monastery ruins, not forgetting Greene King Brewery with its fascinating museum showing local brewing traditions.

Q ♣ P

BRENT ELEIGH

Cock

Lavenham Road, CO10 9PB

- ▶ On A1141
- T (01787) 247371
- Adnams Bitter; Greene King IPA, Abbot
- One double, one twin room, both en-suite
- £ £
- No food available
- Not accepted

An architectural gem that will transport you right back in time, the Cock is a 15th-century thatched pub listed in CAMRA's national inventory for its unspoilt interior. An old-fashioned drinking house, it serves well-kept Adnams and Greene King ales, but no food. Both the snug and the tiny bar are cosy in winter with real fires, in summer the doors are opened and the bar is at one with its surroundings. Real draught cider is served and traditional pub games played.

Both the en-suite letting rooms are in self-contained accommodation with their own entrance, kitchenette with fridge and microwave oven, TV, and tea and coffee making facilities. The value-for-money tariff includes a self-service breakfast in the kitchenette of cereals, breads and eggs or, for an extra £3, you can order a full English cooked breakfast – the only meal prepared in the pub.

This is rural walking country with plenty of good footpaths, but the historic and pretty village of Lavenham is only a mile and a half away, while Bury St Edmunds is nearby.

Q ♣ P

BURY ST EDMUNDS

Old Cannon Brewery

86 Cannon Street, IP33 1JR

T (01284) 768769
W oldcannonbrewery.co.uk
Adnams Bitter; Old Cannon Best Bitter, Gunner's Daughter, seasonal; guest beers
Four double, one twin room, all en-suite
£ ££
Snacks and meals daily, lunchtime and evening
Accepted

This historic beer house, originally the St Edmunds Head, dates back to 1845, with the Cannon Brewery itself founded in 1887. Sadly, the brewery ceased production in 1917 and the pub was closed by Greene King in 1994. However, five years later it reopened as an independent free house complete with its own micro-brewery in the bar. The pub is renowned for its great atmosphere and friendly staff.

The five bedrooms are housed in what was once the brewhouse across the alley. All are comfortable, en-suite and attractively decorated, with TV and tea and coffee making, and include a hearty full English breakfast served in a cosy breakfast room downstairs.

The Old Cannon is justly feted for its excellent food, offering traditional pub meals at lunchtime such as toad-in-the-hole made with sausages containing their own 5.5 per cent Gunner's Daughter Ale. In the evening diners eat in a warren of connected rooms, enjoying dishes including roast Gressingham duck breast with apricot and ginger, and sautéed lamb's liver and Suffolk black pudding with redcurrant and thyme gravy.

Q

HORRINGER

Six Bells

The Street, IP29 5SJ

On A143 between Haverhill and Bury St Edmunds
T (01284) 735551
W thesixbellshorringer.co.uk
Greene King IPA, Abbot
One en-suite double room, two twins with shared bathroom
£ ££
Snacks and meals daily, lunchtime and evening
Accepted

The flower-bedecked Six Bells, an 18th-century pub that retains all its original character, is set in a beautiful, picture postcard English village. Oliver Cromwell is reputed to have stayed here.
Bedrooms are light and airy with TV and coffee making facilities. The double room, which can also be used as a family room, is en-suite, and the two twin rooms share a bathroom. A full English breakfast is included in the room rate.

Greene King ales are served, and sometimes a guest beer is added. Food is recommended – a changing mix of modern and traditional fare, including tasty pies, freshly battered cod, a choice of around four vegetarian dishes, a particularly good home-made lasagne, and popular Sunday lunch. Meals are served in a separate dining area, and there is a conservatory as well. Theme nights are held on occasion, featuring different cuisines.

Frequented by locals and visitors alike, there is ample car parking. The pretty garden with petanque is popular in summer. The fascinating Ickworth House and Gardens are right next door to the pub and well worth a visit. Bury St Edmunds, with its many historic buildings and Cathedral, is within easy driving distance.

P

LAVENHAM

☆ Angel

Market Place, CO10 9QZ

▶ On A1144
T (01787) 247388
F (01787) 248344
W theangelhotel.com
Adnams Bitter, Broadside; Greene King IPA; Nethergate Suffolk County
Six double, one twin, one family room, all en-suite
£ £££
Snacks and meals daily, lunchtime and evening
Accepted (not Diners)

Opposite the Guildhall and overlooking the market cross in what is considered to be England's finest medieval village, dotted with charming, crooked houses, the family-run Angel was first licensed in 1420. It retains many original features such as the Elizabethan shuttered shop window and pargetted ceiling in the guests' sitting room.

Bedrooms are delightful, with beams, fresh flowers and open brickwork. Breakfast offers a choice between the full English including local sausages, bacon and free-range eggs, smoked haddock or whole grilled kipper, or boiled eggs, while muesli mix and marmalade are both home-made.

The Angel is renowned for its award-winning food freshly prepared on the premises – all meat comes from nearby butchers in Lavenham and Long Melford, the game and vegetables are local and fresh fish is delivered daily.

At lunchtime in the bar expect traditional meals such as proper shepherd's pie or home-made pork pie with home-made chutney. At night savour sea trout with samphire or duck with apple, blackberry and mint compote. In summer you can eat out on a terrace overlooking the market place.

Q P

MILDENHALL
Queen's Arms
42 Queensway, IP28 7JY

▶ On A11 between Newmarket and Thetford
T (01638) 713657
W queensarms-mildenhall.co.uk
Greene King IPA, Abbot; guest beers
One en-suite double, two twin and one single room with shared bathroom
£ £
No food available
Not accepted

Very much a community local, the Queen's Arms offers good value B&B accommodation; guests are warmly welcomed and invited to join in any of the regular activities that are held here, from darts matches and quizzes to karaoke.

The homely, single bar pub with a traditional atmosphere has changed little since it was acquired by Greene King in 1887. Guest ales come from the Greene King list and an annual beer festival is staged in the large garden on August bank holiday to coincide with a cycle rally arriving in town. The bar also stocks a selection of Belgian beers.

The simply furnished but comfortable guest rooms are situated over the bar. Only the double room has private facilities. A full English breakfast is provided, but specific requests can be catered for if you prefer something else. No other meals are available.

The pub's location is handy for the races in nearby Newmarket. It is also close to Thetford Forest, Bury St Edmunds and Cambridge.

❀ ♣ P

THURSTON
Fox & Hounds
Barton Road, IP31 3QT

T (01359) 232228
F (01359) 232196
W thurstonfoxandhounds.co.uk
Adnams Bitter; Greene King IPA, Abbot Ale; guest beers
Two twin rooms, both en-suite
£ £
Snacks and meals daily, lunchtime and evening
Accepted

Local CAMRA activists helped save the Fox & Hounds from closure a few years ago, and this now thriving inn goes from strength to strength. It has featured in the Good Beer Guide for the past three years. As well as its three regular beers, guest ales are offered from breweries nationwide.

The building with a public bar with pool table and quieter lounge has recently been refurbished. The latest development by the enterprising owners is to add B&B accommodation: two en-suite twin bedded rooms with sofa beds for children if needed. Good value for money, a full English breakfast is included.

All meals are made with local produce as far as possible and include traditional pub dishes and snacks, as well as grills. The wood-fired pizzas are a popular choice. Specials change weekly.

Set in the Suffolk countryside, the pub is very close to Thurston station. It is a short distance from historic Bury St Edmunds where there is plenty to interest visitors, and some more great pubs to visit.

❀ ♣ P

WALBERSWICK

☆ Anchor

IP18 6UA

- T (01502) 722112
- W anchoratwalberswick.com
- Adnams Bitter, Broadside, seasonal
- Six double rooms, all en-suite
- £ £££
- Snacks and meals daily, lunchtime and evening
- Accepted

A beer and food lovers' paradise where gorgeous food is accompanied not only by Adnams' fine cask ales, but Belgian, Czech, Bavarian, Dutch and American bottled beers. You will find a beer recommendation alongside many dishes on the menu. The pub has been taken over by landlady and chef Sophie Dorber and her husband Mark Dorber, who famously ran the White Horse in Parsons Green, London, which celebrated 25 consecutive years in the Good Beer Guide in 2006.

The Anchor offers comfortable, simple accommodation for two night stays. The garden rooms (three are wheelchair accessible) have plain, bright bathrooms, small seating areas and cosy beds with crisp, white linen. Guests can wake up to a splendid breakfast with local sausages, bacon and eggs, home-baked bread and home-made marmalade.

This 1920s Arts and Crafts inn has roaring fires in winter, two cosy bars and a family room, large garden and small copse, terrace and restaurant looking towards the sea. Using plenty of locally caught fish and game in season, and vegetables grown on the inn's allotment, dishes range from seared scallops with streaky bacon and balsamic puy lentils to beer battered cod with hand cut chips and pease pudding.

Q ♿ ♣ P

Surrey

COPTHORNE

Hedgehog Inn

Effingham Road, RH10 3HY

- ▶ Off A264 near M23 jct 10
- T (01342) 716202
- E hedgehog@ep-ltd.com
- Fuller's London Pride; Harveys Hadlow Bitter; Theakston Old Peculier; Wells Bombardier; guest beers
- Seven double rooms, one wheelchair accessible twin room, all en-suite
- £ £
- Lunchtime and evening meals and snacks
- Accepted

Situated on the border with West Sussex, in an area that is good for walking, horse riding, fishing and golf, the Hedgehog is ideally placed for exploring this part of the country. A great place to stop over if you are flying from Gatwick Airport seven miles away, it is also convenient for Thorpe Park, the leisure complexes in Crawley and East Grinstead and the Hawth Theatre.

The eight modern, well-appointed guest rooms have TV, facilities for making hot drinks and a trouser press. At breakfast, as well as the full English, you can choose smoked haddock and poached eggs, Welsh rarebit or organic eggs cooked as you like them, or there is a buffet stocked with croissants, fresh fruit, cereals and yogurt. Children are welcome as overnight guests.

The pub, with an attractive landscaped garden and heated patio, serves food all day, including snacks, a children's menu and daily specials. The appetising main menu offers meals in different portion sizes depending on how hungry you are. A three-course meal will cost around £20 or so.

P

DORKING

Lincoln Arms Hotel

Station Approach, RH4 1TF

- ▶ 100 yards from Dorking station
- T (01306) 882820
- E lincolnarmshotel@virgin.net
- Fuller's London Pride; Shepherd Neame Spitfire; guest beer
- Four double, eight twin, four single, two family rooms, all en-suite
- £ £
- Snacks and meals daily lunchtime and evening (not Sun eve)
- Accepted (not Amex)

A genuine railway hotel, the Lincoln Arms is situated alongside the train station and railway line. The Lincoln Arms is one of Dorking's landmarks, built in 1867 when the railway came to town, and still welcoming rail travellers today. Originally called the Star & Garter, it once boasted an impressive veranda that stretched around the hotel.

The bedrooms are spread over two floors, recently refurbished, all with en-suite showers, very reasonably priced with a continental breakfast. If you prefer a full English, £5.49 buys you either the small cooked or the full Monty of double sausages, eggs and bacon plus hash brown, mushrooms, beans and toast. Special weekend rates are available.

Both lunch and dinner menus are served featuring English and continental dishes, plus a Sunday roast carvery. Locally-sourced ingredients are used where possible. On the ground floor is a traditional front bar with a games area and two pool tables, and modern back bar with Sky TV. Next to Dorking station, the hotel is also close to Deepdene station, three stops from Gatwick airport, near the M25 and a short drive from Box Hill. P

GOMSHALL

Compasses Inn

50 Station Road, GU5 9LA

- ▶ On A25 between Guildford and Dorking
- T (01483) 202506
- Surrey Hills Ranmore Ale, Shere Drop; guest beers in summer
- One double, two twin rooms, all en-suite
- £ £
- Snacks and meals daily
- Accepted

Originally known as God Encompasses, the Compasses Inn was built in 1830 and is a former Surrey Trust Company pub. It is separated from its beer garden by the meandering Tillingbourne River, with a bridge to take you to the other side. This traditional inn promises no big screen TV, pool table or juke box, though there is live music from 9pm on Fridays.

The ghost of a girl who drowned in the Tillingbourne is said to haunt the pub, but don't let that disturb your slumbers – a sighting is more likely to be the result of one too many pints of Shere Drop. The three clean, bright bedrooms are all en-suite with bath or shower, TV and tea and coffee facilities, the bargain price including breakfast ranging from toast up to full English.

Good, home-cooked food is served from noon all day, with meat and fish bought locally, a full bar menu supplemented by a daily specials board, and an à la carte menu in the restaurant from Wednesday to Saturday evenings.

Close to the village station, the pub is on the Dorking-Guildford bus route. Surrey Hills Brewery in nearby Shere offers brewery tours. The acclaimed RHS Wisley Gardens is also well worth a visit.

P

HERSHAM

Bricklayers Arms

6 Queens Road, KT12 5LS

▶ On A3, 10 miles from M25 jct 10
T (01932) 220936
F (01932) 230400
E ff@bricklayers-arms.fsworld.co.uk
Badger Tanglefoot; Boddingtons Bitter; Flowers IPA; Hogs Back TEA; Young's Bitter
Two double rooms, both en-suite
£ ££ (room only)
Snacks and meals daily lunchtime, Mon-Fri evenings
Accepted (not Amex or Diners)

Built almost a century ago in 1909, the Bricklayers Arms is a traditional village pub close to the village green, furnished to create a warm, welcoming atmosphere and popular with locals, businesses and visitors. In summer, its flower displays are a riot of colour, and its unusual garden features palm trees and tropical plants.

The accommodation has an English Tourist Board four diamond rating. Two double bedrooms are both well furnished with TV, tea and coffee facilities, direct dial phone, shoe cleaning materials and an iron and ironing board. Breakfast is an optional extra at £6 per head, but comprises the full English or whatever you fancy – let them know in advance and they will do their best to provide it for you. The pub is well-known locally for its excellent home-cooked food.

Room rates are good value for a location that provides a convenient base to visit London, as well as offering nearby attractions such as Hampton Court Palace, the Thames, Wisley Gardens and Painshill Park.

HORLEY

Coppingham Arms

263 Balcombe Road, RH6 9EF

▶ On B2036
T (01293) 782282
W coppinghamarms.co.uk
Greene King Old Speckled Hen; Harveys Sussex Best Bitter; Shepherd Neame Spitfire
One double, three twin, one single room, all en-suite plus shared bathroom
£ £
Snacks and meals daily lunchtime and evening (not Sun eve in winter)
Accepted

A traditional, 300-year-old inn built from two cottages on the edge of Horley. The main bar is divided into three areas: the older part split into public and saloon bars, the more modern extension created as part of a refurbishment three years ago used for dining. There is a pool table in the public bar, and live music is performed on the last Friday of the month.

B&B is at bargain prices in five simple but comfortable rooms, with the price of a night's stay including a continental breakfast of cereals, fruit juice, croissants, jam and marmalade and tea or coffee.

At other times the menu is more ambitious, including starters such as creamed garlic mushrooms, a duo of duck and Brussels pâtés and baby Camembert with Cumberland sauce, followed by home-made specials such as calves' liver with bacon, the pie of the day, steak and kidney pudding, moules marinière, roast of the day with all the trimmings, pork and leek sausages with mash and onion gravy, and various veggie choices.

This family-run, friendly pub is an ideal stop off for travellers using Gatwick airport close by. Q P

NEWCHAPEL

Blacksmith's Head

Newchapel Road, RH7 6LE

- ▶ On B2028, off A22
- T (01342) 833697
- W theblacksmithshead.co.uk
- Fuller's London Pride; Harveys Sussex Best Bitter; guest beers
- Three double, two twin rooms, all en-suite
- £ ££
- Snacks and meals daily, lunchtime and evening
- Accepted

Bordering three counties, Surrey, Sussex and Kent, the Blacksmith's Head is handy for Gatwick airport and, with en-suite rooms among the most luxurious pub accommodation in the area, an ideal stop over before or after a holiday or business trip. The rooms, two of them king size, are well fitted and equipped with en-suite facilities and the tariff includes a cooked English breakfast.

Built in 1924 on the site of an old forge, the family-run inn is a one-bar country free house with dining room, darts area and a beer garden plus car park. Occasional quizzes are held and two regularly changing guest ales come from small independents or micros. Real draught cider is served as well.

There is a Portuguese influence to the freshly-prepared dishes reflecting the nationality of the owners – with tapas, bar and restaurant menus to choose from.

The Blacksmith's Arms is ideally placed for visiting nearby stately homes and gardens including Hever Castle, Wakehurst Place, Chartwell, Nymans, Sheffield Park and Standen.

PEASLAKE

Hurtwood Inn Hotel

Walking Bottom, GU5 9RR

- T (01306) 730851
- W hurtwoodinnhotel.com
- Hogs Back TEA; King Horsham Best Bitter; Surrey Hills Shere Drop; guest beer
- Two twin, seventeen double, six family, three single rooms, all en-suite
- £ £££ (room only)
- Snacks and meals daily, lunchtime and evening
- Accepted

It's rare to find such a fine and thoughtful selection of real ales in a 'posh' hotel. The Hurtwood Inn Hotel, privately run for the past 12 years, and extensively refurbished, has a real country bar serving beer from small local breweries and micros.

Rated BTB three-star for quality, the hotel offers beautifully furnished en-suite rooms including two chalet rooms with wheelchair access. All have TV, tea and coffee making, wireless Internet access and hairdryers. Breakfast is £8.95 for a hearty full English or smoked haddock with poached egg, or £6.95 for continental including boiled eggs.

The hotel has an outstanding reputation for its high quality food. Bar meals might be beer-battered cod, home-made beef burgers, pork, leek and apple bangers, all around £8. In the à la carte restaurant dishes such as sirloin steak with wild mushroom pudding or monkfish with saffron pasta are around £17.

Built in 1920 by Surrey Trust Inns, the inn was owned for many years by Trusthouse Forte before being taken over by the current owners and restored to its former glory. Attracting walkers, cyclists, tourists and business folk, it is close to NT areas and 'substantial walks'.

East Sussex

FLETCHING

☆ Griffin Inn

TN22 3SS

▶ Off A275, three miles north-west of Uckfield
T (01825) 722890
F (01825) 722810
W thegriffininn.co.uk
Badger Tanglefoot; Harveys Sussex Best Bitter; King Horsham Best Bitter
Twelve double/family rooms, one twin, all en-suite; four rooms wheelchair accessible
£ £££-££££
Lunchtime and evening meals
Accepted

The Griffin Inn has served the village of Fletching for more than 400 years and these days customers come from far and wide to sample the excellent food and accommodation. It now offers a wide choice of bedrooms since purchasing the Victorian house next door and converting it into B&B accommodation to add to the four rooms in the pub itself and four in an adjacent coach house. All of them have been individually designed with considerable flair and respect for the original features. The four-poster beds and exposed beams look completely in keeping here, but the amenities are right up to date.

The inn is very atmospheric; the cosy bars with low ceilings have a mix of practical wooden and comfortable seating. A team of chefs conjures up enticing menus for the bar and restaurant, using produce from its own market garden and fish from Rye. You can start the day with buck's fizz (or even champagne) for a supplement, then choose between a cooked meal with free-range eggs and Fletching sausage, grilled Loch Fyne kippers or simply croissants, toast and home-made preserves.

The pub's delightful landscaped garden offers views over Sheffield Park and if you are lucky, fabulous sunsets. Q P

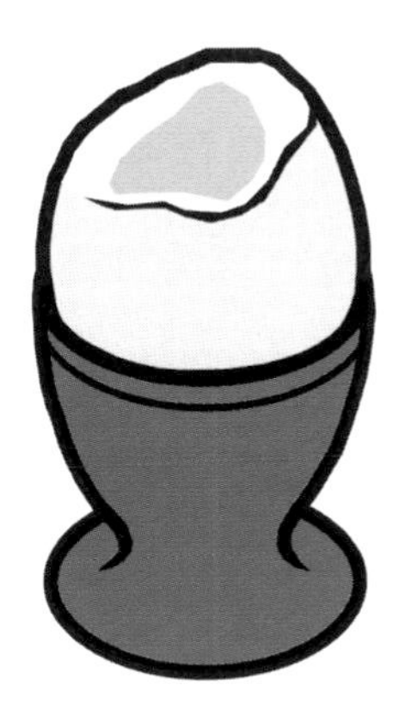

FOREST ROW
Brambletye Hotel
Lewes Road, RH18 5EZ

- ▶ On A22 between East Grinstead and Brighton
- T (01342) 824144
- F (01342) 824833
- W accommodating-inns.co.uk/brambletye
- Fuller's London Pride, Gale's HSB
- Nine double, eight twin, one family, three single rooms, all en-suite
- £ £££
- Lunchtime and evening meals
- Accepted

Situated at the edge of the Ashdown Forest, conveniently located in the centre of the village, the three-diamond rated Brambletye has served as a hotel since 1866. It was a favourite of Sir Arthur Conan Doyle who featured it in a Sherlock Holmes story, The Return of Sherlock Holmes.

Refurbished a couple of years ago, the pub has retained its rustic charm in the public areas and the guest rooms (one has a four-poster bed). All the bedrooms have their own shower, some a bathtub, too, plus hair dryer and facilities for making hot drinks. A full English breakfast is cooked to order in the morning. The restaurant serves an excellent, varied menu with all meals freshly cooked, and interesting lunchtime snacks.

An ideal base for visiting many of the historic and interesting sites in the area, children can take a ride on the Bluebell Railway, or call in at Pooh Corner in nearby Hartfield (which sells the world's largest collection of items related to the famous bear) and pick up a free map to find out exactly where in the Ashdown Forest they should head to play Pooh Sticks. There's plenty for grown-ups, too, including Hever Castle, Ashdown House and Nutley Windmill. P

HASTINGS
White Rock Hotel
1-10 White Rock, TN34 1JV

- ▶ On seafront, opposite the pier
- T (01424) 422240
- F (01424) 432350
- W thewhiterockhotel.co.uk
- Beer range varies
- Thirty double, five twin, five family rooms, all en-suite
- £ ££-££££ (room only)
- Lunchtime and evening meals
- Accepted

Hastings is enjoying something of a renaissance and work is on-going at the White Rock to cater for the needs of today's visitors who aren't looking for a traditional seaside B&B. A landmark in the town since the mid 1800s, the hotel is licensed for weddings in its elegant Promenade Lounge, while the spacious revamped café-bar boasts a large seafront terrace where you can soak up the sun and enjoy one of the local Sussex beers from breweries such as Harveys, 1648, Dark Star and Rother Valley. The bar is a Wifi hotspot.

The guest rooms are in the process of being updated. The refurbished premium rooms are stylishly decorated with pale colours and crisp white linen, equipped with TV, fridge and hospitality tray. First floor rooms have balconies and sea views, the rooms at the back are quieter. Standard rooms, with television and tea and coffee making facilities, are approximately half the price.

Breakfast is charged according to your selection from a varied menu – breakfast sandwiches, eggs, beans or cheese on toast or a fruit platter are all £2.50, while a full English or vegetarian equivalent is £5.75. Children are welcome throughout.

LEWES

Black Horse

55 Western Road, BN7 1RS

- On Western Road, A277
- T (01273) 473653
- Greene King IPA, Morland Original, Abbot; guest beer
- Four double, one twin, two single, one family room with shared bathroom
- £ ££
- Lunchtime and evening meals
- Accepted

Regulars of all ages treat this traditional town pub as their local and come here to play petanque, bar billiards or darts. The pub hosts live acoustic music and regular quizzes. The guest rooms are spacious and comfortable – some are above the public bar and some in a house across the road. Children are welcome to stay.

Breakfast is served in the pub's breakfast room, with a full English meal cooked to order. The organic eggs are absolutely fresh as they come from chickens kept by a member of staff and fed from the pub kitchen. They are happy to cater for special dietary needs.

Lewes is a fine old town with a medieval castle. Harveys Brewery is unusually situated right in the centre. The town has several pubs serving its ales, although the Black Horse doesn't normally keep them. Visitors in November can enjoy the famous bonfire celebrations. The countryside around here is delightful: Glyndebourne and Firle are well worth visiting, both close by, while in Alfriston a little further on, you can visit the Clergy House, the very first property acquired by the National Trust in 1896; Brighton is just 17 miles away.

LEWES

Crown Inn

191 High Street, BN7 2NA

- In town centre, off A27 between Brighton and Eastbourne
- T (01273) 480670
- W crowninn-lewes.co.uk
- Harveys Sussex Best Bitter; guest beers
- Four double, three twin, one family room, most en-suite
- £ ££ (single occupancy from £38)
- Lunches daily, evening meals Mon-Thu
- Accepted

Situated in the attractive county town, the Crown is probably the oldest continuously trading inn in Lewes, established in 1675 as the Black Lyon. Enjoying a prominent position on the High Street, this fine old building was extended in Victorian times with an elegant conservatory which, decorated in period style, remains a delightful spot for relaxing with a pint of beer brewed in the town or a home-cooked lunch. The hotel also boasts a fine wood-panelled bar where meals are also served.

All but two of the guest rooms have en-suite bath or shower and all have tea and coffee making facilities, hair dryer and TV with some Sky channels. Two rooms feature four-poster beds, one is a double, the other a family room. Children (and pets) are welcome here. A full cooked breakfast, accompanied by cereals, toast and fresh fruit, is based on local produce.

The hotel is the HQ of the bonfire societies responsible for the spectacular firework celebration on November 5th for which the town is renowned. Lewes has a Norman castle and lots of antique shops and galleries to discover. Trains run direct to London and transfers are available from the station to the inn by arrangement.

West Sussex

AMBERLEY

Sportsman

Rackham Road, Crossgates, BN18 9NB

▶ Just east of the village, off B2139 between A29 and A283
T (01798) 831787
F (01798) 839465
W amberleysportsman.co.uk
Fuller's London Pride; Harveys Sussex Best Bitter; Hogs Back TEA; guest beers
Three double, one twin, one family room, all available as singles, all en-suite; two wheelchair accessible
£ ££ (£45 single occupancy)
Lunchtime and evening meals daily plus bar snacks
Accepted

You meet some real Miserable Old Buggers in the bar at the Sportsman, but that's not an insult – the MOB Club was established to raise money for children's charities. Local brewery Hepworth brews a beer in the club's honour (MOB) that you might find on the bar. Apart from the MOBs this lovely old country pub attracts locals and visitors from all walks of life, particularly ramblers and cyclists who can pick up advice on routes – the South Downs Way passes nearby – and birdwatchers who enjoy glorious views over the Amberley Wild Brooks water meadows.

The guest rooms overlook the meadows or downland hills; they are attractively decorated with country-style furnishings. Two ground-floor rooms can accommodate wheelchairs and one has a specially adapted bathroom. Breakfast is the full English, but a continental version is available if preferred. Meals and snacks can be enjoyed in the conservatory restaurant or terrace, both benefiting from views of the Wild Brooks.

Amberley, with its thatched cottages, Norman church and medieval castle, has been dubbed 'the Pearl of the South Downs'. The Elizabethan Parham House, set in its own gardens and deer park, is nearby. Arundel, five miles away, has a famous castle and myriad antique shops and markets.

♣ P ⇌

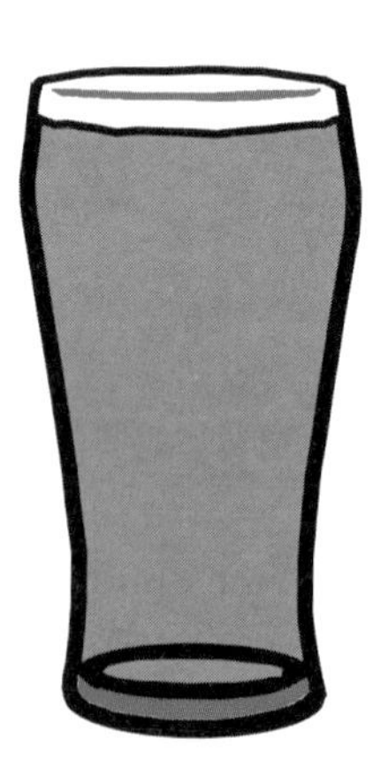

CHARLTON

Fox Goes Free

PO18 0HU

- ▶ Half mile east of A286 at Singleton
- T (01243) 811461
- W thefoxgoesfree.com
- Arundel Gauntlet; Ballard's Best Bitter; guest beers
- Three double, two twin rooms, all en-suite
- £ £££
- Snacks and meals daily, lunchtime and evening
- Accepted

This traditional Sussex flint inn started life as a farmhouse in the 16th century and became a pub in 1792. The red brick floors, inglenook fireplaces and original features reflect the 400-year-old history of a charming building with the added attraction of a large garden.

The five en-suite bedrooms with lovely country views over the South Downs were all refurbished at the end of 2005, the oak-beamed rooms repainted in pastel shades to create a light, airy feel. All mod cons are provided including TV and tea and coffee making facilities.

The Fox is renowned for friendly service, well kept real ales and fine food made with local produce where possible. It has two restaurants, offering bar food such as freshly battered cod, steak and kidney pie or honey roast ham ploughman's, and an à la carte menu including pan-fried guinea fowl with wild mushrooms, or roast wild boar with samphire, black pudding and chocolate jus.

A mile from Goodwood racecourse, the pub is also near Singleton Open Air Museum, West Dean Gardens, Cowdray Polo and Petworth Park in ideal walking country.

Q P

EAST ASHLING

Horse & Groom

PO18 9AX

- ▶ On B2178, 3 miles NW of Chichester
- T (01243) 575339
- W thehorseandgroomchichester.co.uk
- Dark Star Hophead; Harveys Hadlow Bitter; Hop Back Summer Lightning; Young's Bitter; guest beers
- Five double rooms, six twin/doubles, all en-suite
- £ ££
- Snacks and meals daily, lunchtime and evening
- Accepted (not Diners)

Local CAMRA Pub of the Year 2005, this 17th-century inn has a flagstoned floor, exposed red brick walls, inglenook fireplace, old settles and scrubbed wooden tables. It has been carefully extended using knapped Sussex flints.

There are 11 en-suite rooms: five doubles are in a converted barn with high, beamed ceilings, six double/twin rooms are in a new block built to match the barn. There is a choice of shower or bath en-suite, and all have TV and tea and coffee making. The room rate includes a full English breakfast complete with sausages from the local butcher.

The landlord regards the condition of his real ale as a 'constant pursuit of perfection', with a good selection of regular ales plus guests. Likewise, the food is excellent with two highly-qualified chefs producing a wide range of meals from steak and ale pie to grilled fillet steak, with an emphasis on freshly-caught fish.

Walkers, cyclists, horse riders and real ale fans swell the clientele at a pub just outside historic Chichester and close to the South Downs, Wittering beaches, Fishbourne Roman Palace and Goodwood.

Q P

EAST GRINSTEAD
Ship Inn
Ship Street, RH19 4EG

- ▶ Off High Street, near A264 and A22
- T (01342) 312089
- F (01342) 313501
- E shipinn@youngs.co.uk
- Wells Bombardier; Young's Bitter, Special
- Two twin en-suite rooms
- £ ££ (£ Fri & Sat)
- Lunchtime and evening meals
- Accepted

This traditional late Victorian town pub is situated on the edge of the town centre. Less than half a mile from the rail station, it is also convenient for Gatwick Airport eight miles away. Local attractions for visitors include the Blue Bell Railway, Ashdown Forest and the NT's Standen house and gardens close by.

The Ship is warm and welcoming, providing good real ale and meals from the Young's menu. Attracting a diverse range of customers, it hosts popular entertainment including live music staged at weekends and a fortnightly quiz on Thursday. The pub has two bars and the seating areas are limited, but the big armchairs are comfy. One bar is fairly quiet, the other has Sky TV and games. This is an excellent pub in summer with a fish pond and extensive decking on four levels providing plenty of outdoor drinking space.

The accommodation here is good value at all times with the rooms £10 cheaper at weekends. Breakfast is not included in the room rate; the full English is £8.95 per head. Children are welcome to stay.

P

MANNINGS HEATH
Dun Horse Inn
Brighton Road, RH13 6HZ

- ▶ On A281, 2 miles south of Horsham
- T (01403) 265783
- W dunhorseinn.co.uk
- Fuller's London Pride; Taylor Landlord
- One double, one single, one family room, all en-suite
- £ ££
- Lunchtime meals and snacks daily; evening meals Tue-Sat
- Accepted

A typical 1920s local (it was rebuilt after a fire destroyed the original pub) with stained glass windows and a large log fire, the Dun Horse bar offers darts and bar billiards, while the snug has a reference library for crossword addicts. Real ale is served straight from the barrel and the restaurant offers an extensive wine list. The menu concentrates mainly on pub staples but the food is good enough to have won the inn a place in CAMRA's Good Pub Food guide; there is plenty of choice for vegetarians and children can choose from their own menu.

The pub is very welcoming to families with children – it benefits from a secure garden and one guest room is equipped with a double and two bunk beds. All the bedrooms are bright and airy, simply but comfortably furnished, with TV and tea and coffee making facilities. At breakfast, a full English cooked meal is served, along with cereals, toast and a choice of fruit juice.

Families might enjoy a trip on the famous Bluebell Railway, just six miles away, and the lovely gardens of Leonardslee and Nymans, close by.

Q P

WEST CHILTINGTON

Five Bells

Smock Alley, RH20 2QX

- 3 miles from Pulborough railway station
- T (01758) 812143
- Arundel Sussex Mild; Palmer Copper Ale; guest beers
- Four double (one family), one twin room, all en-suite
- £ £££ (£50 single occupancy)
- Lunchtime and evening meals
- Accepted

An idyllic country free house, somewhat off the beaten track. The brick and stone, tile hung building, built in 1935, is typical of many of its period in Sussex. It comprises a main bar enlivened by leaded lights and a conservatory. The bar is fairly quiet – free from TV, juke box and piped music – and serves a good selection of up to five real ales, from both local breweries such as Harveys and Hogs Back and those further afield, for example Jennings. The conservatory offers good food from a blackboard menu that is chalked up daily; fresh fish and South Down lamb and beef are specialities as available.

The guest rooms are a recent addition, but have been carefully decorated and traditionally furnished in keeping with the style of the rest of the pub. The en-suite facilities include shower and bath; TV and a hospitality tray are provided. At breakfast you can opt for the full English, or any variation you would like.

The local train station is an hour and fifteen minutes from Victoria and just over half an hour from Gatwick. Q P

WHITEMANS GREEN
Ship Inn
RH17 5BY

- ▶ At B2036/B2114 jct, north of Cuckfield
- T (01444) 413219
- Beer range varies
- Two twin en-suite rooms
- £ ££ (single occupancy £45)
- Lunchtime and evening meals
- Accepted

The Ship is one of a diminishing number of pubs still around today serving real ale by gravity dispense, direct from the cask. It does have handpumps but these are just for display; the beers are kept in a cool room behind the bar. This is a free house where you are likely to find a beer from Brakspear, Fuller's or maybe Marston's Pedigree on the bar.

A friendly village pub, it is fairly compact and can get busy. The single bar with bare floorboards and wood panelling features an unusual double-sided fireplace with comfortable sofas on either side. There is also a games room and dining area where changing specials supplement a good regular menu.

This family-run establishment has just two rooms available. They can be let as singles, but are not suitable for children. The guest accommodation has its own entrance separate from the pub and both rooms have TV and tea and coffee making facilities. A full English breakfast is provided.

Whitemans Green is just 18 miles from Brighton, while Wakehurst and other gardens can be visited in the vicinity and there is a golf course nearby.

P

Tyne & Wear

NEWBURN

☆ Keelman

Grange Road, NE15 8NL

▶ Off A69/A695, 5 miles from Newcastle upon Tyne
T (0191) 267 1689
F (0191) 267 7387
W keelmanslodge.co.uk
Big Lamp Bitter, Summerhill Stout, Prince Bishop Ale
Six double rooms, all en-suite; one room wheelchair accessible
£ £ (£39 single occupancy)
Lunchtime and evening meals
Accepted

The Keelman is the tap for the Big Lamp Brewery, and both pub and brewery are situated in a converted Grade II listed water pumping station by the Tyne Riverside Country Park. The lovingly-restored, delightful old stone building lends itself wonderfully to its new purpose and creative interior design emphasises its original features such as exposed stone walls. A new conservatory and patio have been added to give more space for drinkers and diners. This is a family-friendly establishment and won Best Visitor Pub in the 2005 North East Tourism awards. Children can amuse themselves in the adventure playground while parents sample the award-winning Big Lamp ales.

The spacious guest rooms are in a purpose-built lodge. Each room has a double and single bed, and a cot can be provided; one room can accommodate a wheelchair. Rooms have country pine furnishings, TV and hospitality tray. Each room has a designated parking space. A full English breakfast is served in the pub.

The Keelman is just three miles from Gateshead's Metro Centre for great shopping, but healthier pursuits can be enjoyed at the leisure centre next door, where you can also hire mountain bikes.
❀P

Warwickshire

COUGHTON

Throckmorton Arms

B49 5HX

- ▶ On A435 between Studley and Alcester
- T (01789) 766366
- W thethrockmortonarms.co.uk
- Hook Norton Hooky Bitter; Purity Pure Gold; St Austell Tribute; Wye Valley Butty Bach; guest beers
- Five double, five twin rooms, all en-suite
- £ ££
- Lunchtime and evening meals and snacks
- Accepted (not Amex)

This traditional coaching inn, steeped in history and charm, is situated in rural Warwickshire, close to Birmingham and Stratford on Avon, attracting both business visitors and tourists exploring Shakespeare country. There is easy access from motorways; the nearest station is Redditch.

Guest rooms are all comfortable and well appointed; the three superior rooms are spacious with full-sized bathrooms and one is large enough for an extra bed for family use. A full English breakfast is provided, but guests can request a vegetarian or continental version if preferred. With a little notice all dietary requirements can be met.

The public rooms in the hotel have retained their original character, with exposed oak beams and open fires. The lounge and snug are served by a single bar that stocks a good range of real ales. The attractive restaurant is next to an extensive patio with views across open fields. Several public footpaths can be reached from the hotel grounds by crossing the river.

The village is known for the Throckmorton family home, Coughton Court, which is one of the finest Tudor houses in England. Now owned by the National Trust, it houses a fascinating exhibition about the Gunpowder Plot. P

EASENHALL

Golden Lion Hotel

CV23 0JA

- From Rugby, take B4112 and turn left at Harborough Magna
- T (01788) 833577
- W goldenlioninn.co.uk
- Beer range varies
- Seventeen double (three family), four single rooms, all en-suite, one wheelchair accessible
- £ £££
- Lunchtime and evening meals
- Accepted

An award-winning breakfast is something to savour after a comfortable night at the Golden Lion. The buffet provides fresh fruit juice from a juicing machine, local sausages, bacon, yogurt, cereal, pastries and fresh fruit; or if you do not see anything that takes your fancy, just ask. All meat and dairy produce is sourced locally and the restaurant menu changes on a daily basis, while on Sunday lunch there is a carvery for just under £14 for two courses or £17.25 for three courses.

Although situated in a village, this traditional inn and hotel dating from the 16th century is convenient for business travellers, a few minutes from the M6 and five minutes' drive from Rugby. The NEC, NAC and airports at Birmingham and Coventry are all easily accessible. For tourists, Althorpe, home of the Spencer family, and Warwick and Kenilworth Castles are nearby.

Accommodation is divided into traditional rooms, part of the original inn, and new executive rooms, but all are light and airy, individually designed for comfort and character, with free high-speed Internet connection. Q P

KENILWORTH

Old Bakery

12 High Street, CV8 1LZ

- Near A429/A452 jct
- T (01926) 864111
- F (01926) 864127
- W theoldbakeryhotel.co.uk
- Hook Norton Hooky Bitter; Taylor Landlord; guest beers
- Seven double, three twin, three family rooms, all en-suite
- £ £££
- No main meals available
- Accepted

This attractively-restored former bakery has nobly stopped serving food to concentrate on real ales instead, but a lot of effort goes into the one meal it does offer – a hearty breakfast for B&B guests. So enjoy fresh fruit and cereals followed by Mr Smith's sausages, locally-cured bacon, mushrooms, baked beans, fried tomatoes and free-range eggs fried, poached, scrambled or in an omelette.

The purpose-built accommodation in a quiet location behind the main building combines old-fashioned atmosphere with modern comforts – all 14 rooms have en-suite power shower, satellite TV, tea and coffee, trouser press and free Internet connection.

Situated in Kenilworth old town, the 400-year-old hostelry has two oak beamed drinking areas decorated in rustic style, and an attractive patio around an old well. Guest beers change regularly, focussing on ales from local micros. The inn is next to the Abbey fields and castle ruins, and close to Kenilworth Castle, with Warwick Castle and Stoneleigh Park in driving distance.

Q

Old Bakery, Kennilworth, Warwickshire

PAILTON
White Lion

Coventry Road, CV23 0QD

▶ Jct B4027/B4112, between jcts 1/2 of M6
T (01788) 832359
W whitelionpailton.co.uk
Greene King IPA, Abbot, Old Speckled Hen; guest beers
Seven twin, two family rooms, five en-suite, four with shared bathrooms
£ £
Snacks and meals daily, lunchtime and evening
Accepted

A 17th-century coaching inn, the White Lion is a handsome, white-painted village pub. It recently underwent a sympathetic modernisation, retaining the atmospheric bar with brick fire and original beams.

ETB three diamond rated, the olde-worlde style accommodation includes a private lounge for residents. Rooms have TV, telephone, baby listening service and tea and coffee making facilities. The unusually hearty English breakfast, included in the price, offers two sausages, two rashers of bacon, two eggs, two tomatoes and toast.

A busy food operation is catered by three chefs, with meals served in the dining room. Some local produce is used on a menu featuring home-made pies from steak and kidney, steak, Stilton and stout, to chicken, bacon and mushroom, or game. Other specialities are lamb shank braised with red wine and rosemary, poached halibut, Cajun spiced tuna, a wide range of grills and baguettes, and an amazing list of home-made puds – banana split, spotted dick, sticky toffee and treacle puddings, knickerbocker glory and lumpy bumpy cake. There is a Sunday lunch roast carvery.

The White Lion has an outside terrace to the front of the pub for alfresco drinking.

Q P

SAMBOURNE
Green Dragon

The Green, B96 6NU

▶ 1 mile from Studley, near jct 3 M42
T (01527) 892465
W greendragon.sambourne.com
Adnams Broadside; Hobsons Bitter; guest beer
Six double rooms, all en-suite
£ £
Snacks and meals daily, lunchtime and evening
Accepted

Dating from the 18th century, this traditional black and white timber-framed building facing the village green, with a war memorial and huge tree encircled by a wooden seat in front of it, is part of an idyllic, unchanging English scene. In more recent times, the late comedian Tony Hancock stayed here when his mother was the licensee.

Accommodation is in a separate modern block away from the main building, opposite the beer garden. Facilities include TV, tea and coffee making and Wifi broadband access, with a cooked breakfast from poached eggs to full English included in the price.

The pub comprises a main bar with three real ales, dining area and restaurant serving specials such as beef medallions, duck breast, sea bass and rib-eye steak with Stilton. The set menu has grilled steaks, liver and bacon and salad of scallops with smoked bacon, and Sunday roast at £6.95 for the main course, £9.50 for two courses.

For car enthusiasts, the MG Midget and Sprite Club meets every second Wednesday, and the pub is handy for Birmingham NEC, Ragley Hall, Studley Castle and Stratford-upon-Avon.

Q P

SHIPSTON-ON-STOUR
Black Horse Inn
Station Road, CV36 4BT

T (01608) 661617
E blackhorse3@aol.com
Greene King IPA, Abbot Ale; guest beers
One double, one twin, one family room, all en-suite
£ £-££
Snacks and meals daily, lunchtime and evening
Accepted

Built in 1194, this traditional stone-built inn is the only thatched building in Shipston, its licence dating back to 1540, though it was brewing illegally before that. A pub for the discerning drinker, offering two regularly-changing guest ales alongside the two Greene King beers, and real cider, it has a cosy, welcoming lounge with a large inglenook and roaring log fire.

Comfortable accommodation is popular with tourists and business people; two of the rooms are wheelchair accessible, and children and pets are welcome. The three rooms have TV, tea and coffee making, hairdryer and iron, and the price includes a full English breakfast with yoghurt, fresh fruit and cooked breakfast with eggs any way you like and sausages from the local butcher. Local meat and vegetables are also used in lunches and evening meals.

Aunt Sally is played here, as well as crib, darts and dominoes, while folk musicians gather once a month for an informal music session. The pub has a beer garden, is close to both North Cotswold and Wizard breweries and within driving distance of the county town of Warwick.

Q P

TEMPLE GRAFTON
Blue Boar
B49 6NR

T (01789) 750010
W theblueboar.co.uk
Greene King Old Speckled Hen; Purity Pure UBU
Seven double, one twin/single (wheelchair accessible), five family rooms, all en-suite
£ ££
Lunchtime and evening meals; food served all day Sat and Sun
Accepted

The Blue Boar is an ideal base for exploring Shakespeare country – indeed the story goes that the Bard was married in Temple Grafton Church (where his wife's name was apparently incorrectly recorded as Whateley instead of Hathaway). Stratford is just three miles away, while Warwick, with its glorious castle, is eight miles distant. For business guests who prefer rural surroundings, the pub is 18 miles from the NEC.

Temple Grafton was mentioned in the Domesday Book and the Blue Boar itself dates back in part to the 16th century when it was an ale house – landlords have been traced right back to 1776. The well that provided pure water for brewing for many years is preserved in the restaurant bar, covered by glass. Brewing no longer takes place here but the bar stocks real ale from one a local micro-brewey – Purity.

Warmed in winter by open fires, the restaurant serves good food with traditional favourites and exciting specials and a dessert menu that changes daily. For overnight guests, a full English breakfast is offered, based on local produce. The newly refurbished bedrooms offer TV and refreshments and there is a laundry service.

Q P

WARWICK

☆ Old Fourpenny Shop Hotel

27-29 Crompton Street, CV34 6HJ

- ▶ Near racecourse entrance, between A429 and A4189
- T (01926) 491360
- W fourpennyshophotel.co.uk
- RCH Pitchfork; guest beers
- Six double, two twin, one family, two single rooms, all en-suite
- £ £££
- Snacks and meals daily, lunchtime and evening
- Accepted (not Amex)

Celebrating 16 consecutive years in the Good Beer Guide, the Old Fourpenny has just one regular beer, RCH Pitchfork, alongside five guests; 1,500 different cask ales have been served over the years. A blackboard behind the bar lists the beers – locals order by number.

The recently refurbished guest accommodation is in individually furnished rooms on three floors, all with bathroom or shower en suite, plus TV, telephone and tea and coffee making. Breakfast is included in the tariff; a cold buffet table provides cereals, yoghurt, fresh and stewed fruit plus four teas including Earl Grey and herbal, and Arabica coffee or decaff. Hot options range from eggs any way you want with a choice of smoked or unsmoked bacon, pork sausages, mushrooms and tomato; grilled kipper, poached smoked haddock or smoked salmon with scrambled eggs. At other times the restaurant serves a wide choice of good food from table d'hote and à la carte menus.

Located near Warwick Castle and the racecourse, this was once a racing inn and stables, later loved by canal navvies for cheap coffee and rum – hence the name.

❀P ⇌ 🚌

WELLESBOURNE

Stag's Head

1 Chestnut Square, CV35 9QS

- ▶ Five miles from M40 jct 15 on A429
- T (01789) 840266
- Fuller's London Pride; Greene King IPA, Abbot; Shepherd Neame Spitfire; Taylor Landord; guest beers
- One double, two twin, one family, one single room, all en-suite
- £ ££
- Snacks and meals daily, lunchtime and evening
- Accepted

Dating back to 1640, the Stag's Head has been licensed as a pub for around 150 years. It is a traditional village pub with thatched roof, a two-room public area with beams and stone floor, and a real fire in winter. As well as a good range of real ales with changing guests, real cider is served, too. You can enjoy a cosy evening with traditional pub games, and in summer have a drink outside in the beer garden.

The stable block has been converted to five en-suite rooms providing comfortable bed and breakfast accommodation with a separate entrance from the pub. Two rooms are wheelchair accessible. Tastefully furnished, the rooms provide tea and coffee making and TV. The price includes a full English breakfast of juice, cereals, sausage, bacon, eggs, mushrooms, tomatoes, baked beans and toast, and meals are also served lunchtime and evening.

The inn attracts walkers, cyclists and tourists as well as locals. It is well placed for visiting Stratford-upon-Avon, Warwick, Leamington Spa and Compton Verney art gallery and museum.

Q ❀ ♿ ♣ 🚌

West Midlands

BIRMINGHAM

Bull

1 Price Street, B4 6JU

- ▶ Off St Chad's Queensway
- T (0121) 333 6757
- F (0121) 359 1168
- W thebull-pricestreet.com
- Adnams Broadside; Ansells Mild; Marston's Pedigree; guest beers
- Four double, two twin, three single, one family room, all en-suite
- £ £
- Meals served all day
- Accepted

Dating from 1729 and a listed building, this is one of the oldest pubs in Birmingham. Situated in the city's famous Gun Quarter, the Bull (formerly Bull's Head) has a fascinating history. This area was at one time the largest centre of arms production in the world. The workers were often paid their wages in the Bull, which led to heavy drinking and brawling so the landlord would summon the local priest (rather than the 'peelers') to sort out his unruly customers.

Now that the inn's clientele is rather better behaved, the pub is able to line the walls and decorate the bar with a vast collection of china – teapots, jugs and tea sets. Combine that with a pretty courtyard garden and guest rooms dressed in Laura Ashley fabrics and the transformation is complete. The good value accommodation has recently been refurbished and all the rooms have a TV. A full English breakfast is served here, but omelettes, scrambled eggs or kippers can be provided on request if preferred.

The public rooms include a single bar, lounge and snug, much used by local groups. The pub is now a Wifi hotspot. Good home-cooked meals and daily specials are available all day (note: the pub is closed on Sunday). Q

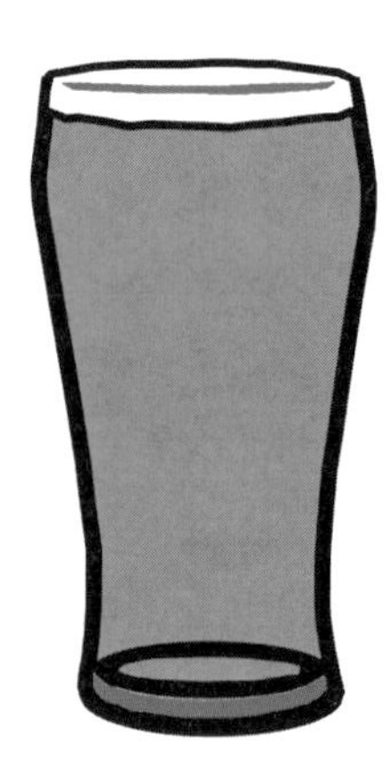

DUDLEY
Lamp Tavern
116 High Street, DY1 1QT

T (01384) 254129
Batham Mild, Best Bitter, XXX (winter)
One double, two twin, one single, one family room, four en-suite
£ £-££
Snacks and meals daily lunchtime, snacks only evening
Accepted (not Amex)

This is a smashing Batham's local with four rooms including a lively bar with sports TV, quiet lounge, dining room providing good value weekday lunches, and function room with weekly entertainment in the adjoining old Queen's Cross Brewery, an imposing red brick industrial building.

Accommodation is in pleasant, simply furnished bedrooms in the old cottage, reached by a covered passageway from the pub. All rooms are en-suite except the family room which has its own private bathroom. All have TV and tea and coffee facilities, iron and trouser press available on request. The car park is CCTV monitored. Room rates vary depending on whether you are staying mid-week or at the weekend, there are reduced rates for CAMRA members. The tariff includes a full cooked breakfast with sausage, bacon, eggs and beans. Vegetarians can be catered for.

The Lamp makes a good base for visiting the Black Country Museum, Dudley art gallery and Stourbridge Glass.
❀ ♿ ♣ P

WALSALL
Lyndon House Hotel
Upper Rushall Street, WS1 2HA

T (01922) 612511
W lyndonhousehotel.co.uk
Courage Directors; Greene King Abbot; Highgate Dark; Theakston Best Bitter; guest beers
Seventeen single, six twin rooms, all available as singles, all en-suite
£ ££ (£49.50 single occupancy)
Lunchtime and evening meals
Accepted (not Amex)

This hotel in the heart of the town has a bar to suit you, whatever your mood. The Lyndon Bar is warm and friendly, traditional in style and offers bar meals, while Sally Ann's Cocktail Bar is the place to relax with a cocktail, naturally, but also serves tea and coffee and has a terrace for good weather. The most unexpected is the Stein Bar, with an alpine theme, offering a good choice of beers and lagers, where you can dance until 2am at weekends. The hotel mostly attracts the over-40s partly due, perhaps, to its dress code (baseball caps, for example, are frowned upon).

The building dates back almost 300 years and the guest rooms are individually designed in traditional style, some with four-poster beds. Satellite TV and hospitality tray come as standard. A generous breakfast is served, including two fried eggs and two sausages but you can have kippers if you prefer. The kitchen sources much of its produce locally and the restaurant specialises in Italian and Mediterranean dishes.

Walsall is just nine miles from Birmingham city centre, but has attractions of its own such as the Leather Museum – Walsall has a long history of producing saddlery and leather goods. Q ❀ P ⇌

Wiltshire

CORSHAM

Quarryman's Arms

Box Hill, SN13 8HN

▶ Off A4, 4 miles from Bath
T (01225) 743569
F (01225) 742610
W quarrymans-arms.co.uk
Butcombe Bitter; Moles Best Bitter; Wadworth 6X; guest beer
Two double, one twin, one family room, all en-suite
£ ££
Lunchtime and evening meals and snacks
Accepted

As the name suggests, this pub served the men quarrying Bath stone, and memorabilia connected with the industry is are displayed around this 300-year-old country pub. Tours of the mines can be arranged (ask at the pub). Just outside Bath, but hard to find down country lanes, it sits almost on top of the Brunel railway tunnel and benefits from superb views over Box Valley (particularly from the top bedroom). It attracts walkers, cavers, cyclists, riders and tourists.

The inn has just four guest rooms, but the family room is spacious with two double beds and a put-u-up. Cots are also available. A room is presently being adapted for wheelchair users. A very full English breakfast is provided, or alternatively you can have smoked haddock, kippers or smoked salmon. Fish features prominently, too, on the main menu, which combines traditional pub food with more contemporary dishes, based as far as possible on local produce.

Children are welcome to stay and no doubt will want to take a trip to nearby Laycock Abbey (NT) which has found new fame as the location for scenes in the Harry Potter films.

Q P

CORTON

☆ Dove

BA12 0SZ

- ▶ On Wylye Valley road, south of Sutton Verry
- T (01985) 850109
- W thedove.co.uk
- Hop Back GFB; Shepherd Neame Spitfire; guest beers
- Four double, four single, one family room, all en-suite
- £ ££
- Snacks and meals daily, lunchtime and evening
- Accepted

This thriving, lovingly-refurbished village pub is situated in the delightful Wylye Valley. It is known for its interesting beers – one guest in winter, two in summer, from breweries including Butcombe, Sharp's, Timothy Taylor and Milk Street – and excellent food. A feature open log fire is set on a platform in the centre of the bar. The large, attractive garden holds regular barbecues in summer.

Courtyard accommodation is in cottage-style bedrooms each with a front door, all en-suite, and one wheelchair accessible, providing TV and tea and coffee making. The full English breakfast uses local produce, kippers or smoked haddock and, on special occasions, smoked salmon with scrambled eggs and Buck's Fizz.

The Dove is popular for its excellent food, including a seasonal menu which includes pigeon breast with redcurrant, wild mushroom risotto, hand-made sausages with mash, sea bass baked with fresh herbs or venison with red wine. Specials change daily.

Close to Longleat, Bath, Salisbury and Stonehenge, and on the Wiltshire Cycle Way – the pub will help you organise walking, horse riding and cycle routes.

Q P

CRICKLADE

Red Lion

74 High Street, SN6 6DD

- T (01793) 750776
- W theredlioncricklade.co.uk
- Moles Best Bitter; Ramsbury Gold; Sharp's Doom Bar; Wadworth 6X; guest beer
- One double, one twin room, both en-suite
- £ £-££
- Snacks and meals daily, lunchtime and evening
- Accepted

A past winner of CAMRA South West Regional Pub of the Year, the 16th-century Red Lion continues to live up to its reputation for providing the best of local and national brews, serving up to nine ales, the guest from small local micros.

The letting rooms, in the courtyard, are full of character with exposed stone walls, beams, attractive tiled floors and handsome wooden beds plus two-seater settees. Both en-suite rooms are equipped with TV/DVD, fridge, tea and coffee, trouser press and desk. A hearty, full English is included in the room rate and will fortify you for a day discovering the surrounding attractions.

The Thames path runs outside the pub door, making the inn particularly popular with walkers. The Cotswold Way and Ridgeway are also nearby. You can visit the waterpark and nature reserve, flower-rich North Meadow, Wilts & Berks Canal, or explore the Cotswolds.

Good food is served in the restaurant, which used to be the back bar. Enjoy a starter from the cold buffet followed by roast Scotch silverside and Yorkshire pudding, North Sea haddock, or mushroom, cranberry and Brie Wellington. Outside is a large beer garden for alfresco drinking.

EBBESBOURNE WAKE
Horseshoe Inn
SP55 5JF

T (01722) 780474
Otter Bitter; Ringwood Best; guest beers
Two double rooms, both en-suite
£ ££
Snacks and meals daily, lunchtime and evening
Accepted

This welcoming, unspoilt 18th-century inn serves two excellent regular beers and guests including ales from micros direct from casks stillaged behind the bar. Service is either via the bar or through the original serving hatch, just inside the front door.

A friendly village pub, where visitors are always made to feel welcome, it comprises two small bars, a restaurant and conservatory. The bars, warmed by a real fire, feature an impressive collection of old farm implements, tools and lamps. As well as real ales, the Horseshoe serves Thatcher's Cider. Popular with diners, it is known for good cooking using local produce, including vegetarian options.

Accommodation is in two en-suite rooms. Both enjoy facilities including TV and tea and coffee making, with a full English breakfast provided.

In a remote rural setting at the foot of an old ox drove, the pub is ideal for enjoying country walks and outdoor pursuits, and is not far from Stonehenge and Cranbourne Chase. There is a large, attractive beer garden with a children's play area for sitting out in summer.
Q P

HOLT
☆ Tollgate Inn
Ham Green, BA14 6PX

T (01225) 782326
W tollgateholt.co.uk
Beer range varies
Four double rooms, all en-suite
£ £££
Snacks and meals daily, lunchtime and evening
Accepted (not Amex or Diners)

Renowned for its dedication to real food and its ever changing range of real ales, many of them from small West Country brewers, the Tollgate is 'a gem of an old village pub', according to local CAMRA. The 16th-century inn has a cosy bar with wood burning stove, upstairs restaurant, and two acres of grounds where the goats and chickens live.

Four en-suite luxury rooms with beams and antique furniture have mini bars, fresh fruit, daily papers, and comfy seating overlooking the village green or, in the distance, Westbury White Horse. Choose your breakfast from locally-smoked kippers topped with a poached free-range egg from one of the pub's own hens, Valley Smoke House smoked salmon and scrambled eggs on toasted brioche or the full English of Sandridge Farm bacon, Church Farm sausages, home-laid eggs, sautéed Bromham new potatoes, Bury black pudding, mushrooms, tomatoes and home-made fried bread; jam and marmalade are home-made, too.

Dedication to fresh, local produce follows through to main meals: a tempting menu of game from nearby shoots, Church Farm beef, fish direct from Brixham and West Country cheeses.

The Courts NT gardens are in the village, Lacock NT village is nearby and Bath is seven miles away. P

Tollgate Inn, Holt, Wiltshire

MARKET LAVINGTON

Green Dragon

26-28 High Street, SN10 4AG

- ▶ B3098, near Devizes
- T (01380) 813235
- E greendragonlavington@tiscali.co.uk
- Wadworth IPA, 6X, JCB, seasonal; guest beers
- Two double (one en-suite), one single room sharing bathroom
- £ £
- Snacks and meals daily, lunchtime and evening
- Accepted

The Green Dragon led the village's cask ale revival, and now demonstrates similar dedication to local produce – sausages and bacon from the butcher next door, honey from the local beekeeper, bread from the nearby Italian baker and home-made marmalade all on the breakfast menu – even tea from the Wiltshire Tea Company.

This 17th-century coaching inn on the edge of Salisbury Plain is a quiet, peaceful retreat – unless the army is on manoeuvre. It features a Bath stone porch, beer garden with pets' corner and barbecue, bar with real fire and dining area offering meals from fresh haddock in Wadworth beer batter to pork and herb sausages with three home-made Yorkshire puddings.

Accommodation is provided in three guest rooms. The en-suite room is part of the old cottage next door, with beams and a fireplace. The double can also be used as a twin or family room with a futon added. All have tea and coffee making and use of the residents' TV lounge.

Close to the Ridgeway, the pub attracts walkers and cyclists, providing storage for bikes and drying facilities. A small museum behind the village school houses a Victorian kitchen.

Q ♣ P

NORTH WROUGHTON

☆ Check Inn

Woodland View, SN4 9AA

▶ From M4 jct 15 follow Swindon then Wroughton/Devizes signs
T (01793) 845584
F (01793) 814640
W checkinn.co.uk
Beer range varies
One double, one twin, one family room, all en-suite
£ £ (room only)
Lunchtime and evening meals
Accepted (not Amex)

CAMRA's national Pub of the Year runner up in 2005 always has ten beers on handpump, with ales changing on a daily basis and local breweries well represented. Converted from a pair of farm cottages, the inn has been updated and extended over the past few years and there are plans to add more guest rooms.

A modern, sympathetically designed extension houses the three guest rooms. Well appointed, they have desk space, power shower and full length mirror. The family room has a shower and bathtub. The rooms can be let for single occupancy. Rates are for room only, so guests can choose whatever they like for breakfast in the morning, from tea and toast up to a full English and anything in between; the price varies accordingly from £3.95 to £7.95 per person. A good home-cooked menu of main meals includes local crayfish as a speciality.

Outside, the attractive, landscaped patio has a floodlit petanque court. Attractions nearby include the GWR Railway Museum in Swindon, Cotswold Water Park and the prehistoric sites of Avebury and Silbury.

P

OGBOURNE ST GEORGE

Inn with the Well

Marlborough Road, SN8 1SQ

▶ Off A346
T (01672) 841445
W theinnwiththewell.co.uk
Wadworth 6X, guest beer
Three double, two twin, one family room, all en-suite
£ £
Snacks and meals daily, lunchtime and evening (not Mon)
Accepted

The well that gives this pub its name is 90-feet deep, in the dining room, with a bullet proof glass cover. A traditional coaching inn dating from 1647, the inn is well placed for walking the Ridgeway or Og Valley, spotting crop circles, and visiting nearby historic sites, stately homes and towns.

A village local with darts and crib teams, the inn also caters for guests far and wide. It is known for its good food and real ale; don't be fooled by the handpumps, the Wadworth and one guest beer are served by gravity straight from the cellar.

Accommodation is in six rooms, all en-suite with shower and bath, thoughtfully providing a duck for the bath as well as a TV, hairdryer and hospitality tray. Four rooms are on the ground floor, two of them wheelchair accessible.

The executive chef and co-owner trained at Leith's so good food is to be expected, with traditional favourites on the bar menu and more eclectic choices on the main menu. The bistro evening on Friday offers three courses for £10, Sunday lunch is £6.95, and special gourmet evenings are held in winter.

P

SALISBURY

King's Head Inn

Bridge Street, SP1 2ND

- ▶ On River Avon, just off High Street
- T (01722) 438400
- W jdwetherspoonlodges.co.uk
- Courage Best, Directors; Greene King Abbot Ale; Marston's Pedigree; Ringwood Fortyniner; guest beer
- Fifteen double, fourteen twin, three family rooms, all en-suite
- £ ££ (room only)
- Snacks and meals during opening hours
- Accepted

The King's Head is a spectacular building, built in 1874 for Richardson Bros wine merchants, importers and shippers. Originally known as City Chambers, it was occupied by various wine merchants until the late 20th century.

Today it is a Wetherspoon Lloyds downstairs, offering four real ales – the Courage Best and Directors rotate and there is often a guest from a regional brewer. The premises were refurbished in 2004 when the rooms above were converted to stylish en-suite accommodation with either baths or showers and modern facilities. The room rate is excellent value for the centre of this tourist city, with special deals at weekends. The tariff does not include breakfast but Lloyds serves the full English from £1.99. A lift accesses the bedroom floors, and two rooms are converted for disabled use.

The bar is a huge open room with a 'chill out' area but there are more secluded alcoves and a library space. Dining is in a separate open-plan area offering the usual Lloyds menu. The bar gets extremely busy at weekends and the music can be very loud – perhaps not a place for older folk seeking serenity. There is no parking but a public car park is close by.

WINTERBOURNE MONKTON

New Inn

SN4 9NW

- ▶ On A4361, 6 miles from M4 jct 15/16
- T (01672) 539240
- W thenewinn.net
- Wadworth IPA, 6X; guest beers
- Two double, two twin, one family room, all en-suite; one room is wheelchair accessible
- £ ££
- Lunchtime and evening meals (not every day)
- Accepted

Surrounded by wonderful walking country, the New Inn lies a mile from Avebury Stone Circle (the largest of its kind in Europe). A lovely walk will take you there past old Monkton church or for more serious ramblers there is an alternative route via the Ridgeway Path. Silbury Hill and the Long Barrows are also nearby.

Dating back in parts 300 years, the New Inn is a traditional country pub where the locals are keen on darts. It has a big garden and in winter you can warm yourself by the log fire. The pleasant guest rooms are well equipped with TV, hospitality tray and hair dryer. The family room and one double are above the pub, the others are in a converted coach house next door. Local butcher's sausages are included in the full English breakfast or you can have a vegetarian cooked alternative or continental if you prefer.

The pub is close to Devizes, home of Wadworth Brewery. The brewery still delivers beer to its pubs within a two-mile radius by horse-drawn dray and its stables are open to the public in the early afternoon, Monday-Thursday.

Q P

Worcestershire

BERROW GREEN

☆ Admiral Rodney

WR6 6PL

- ▶ On B4917
- T (01886) 821375
- F (01886) 822048
- W admiral-rodney.co.uk
- Wye Valley Bitter; guest beers
- Two double, one twin room, all en-suite
- £ ££
- Snacks and meals daily, lunchtime (not Mon) and evening
- Accepted (not Amex or Diners)

Originally a 16th-century farmhouse, this free house is full of character, with two bars and a three-tier restaurant in a converted barn crammed with old beams. The beer here is Wye Valley Bitter, plus three guest ales often from local micros, real cider and perry.

ETB commended accommodation is in three rooms, recently refurbished and beautifully decorated, all with en-suite including bath and shower, TV, hair dryer and courtesy tray. The Admiral's Room has a four-poster bed. Breakfast is a hearty meal of award-winning Teme Vale sausages, local bacon, black pudding and eggs, honey from Berrow Green and home-made marmalade; there is a veggie alternative.

Food is important at the Admiral Rodney, on seasonal menus using local produce. The bar menu has traditional dishes such as boiled ham with parsley sauce, Herefordshire rump steak and imaginative veggie options, all under £10; the restaurant menu includes meals such as lamb shank faggot in Savoy cabbage leaf or roast pork loin stuffed with sage and onion in thyme sauce, main dishes around £15.

The floodlit garden has a heated patio and there is a field to walk your dog – or stroll along the Worcestershire Way nearby.

Q P

BROADWAY

Crown & Trumpet Inn

Church Street, WR12 7AE

▶ Just behind village green
T (01386) 853202
Greene King Old Speckled Hen; Hook Norton Hooky Bitter; Stanway seasonal beers; Taylor Landlord; guest beers
Three double, one twin, one family room, all en-suite
£ ££
Snacks and meals daily, lunchtime and evening
Accepted

A fine 17th-century Cotswold stone inn with oak beams, log fires and brewery memorabilia, situated just off the village green. The Crown and Trumpet serves an especially good selection of beers, the four regular ales include a seasonal from Stanway Brewery produced especially for the pub. An interesting range of pub games is played including ring the bull; the clientele includes ramblers enjoying the Cotswold Way, cyclists, locals and Morris Men.

The bedrooms are all en-suite, rates are cheaper mid-week than at the weekend and include a full English breakfast. Food here is excellent with meat pies a speciality, all beef coming from a Cotswold herd. Local beef is also used for the Sunday roast with Yorkshire pudding, and served in a baguette with Tewkesbury Mustard.

Jazz and blues nights are hosted monthly and Saturday night entertainment is often live music. Situated just off the Cotswold Way, the pub is in wonderful walking area, and central for touring Shakespeare's country and both the Cotswold and Malvern Hills. Nearby are the 18th-century Gothic folly Broadway Tower and country park, the market town Moreton-in-Marsh and the pretty village Bourton-on-the-Water. P

BROMSGROVE

Ladybird Inn

2 Finstall Road, Aston Fields, B60 2DZ

▶ On A448, next to Bromsgrove station
T (01527) 889900
Batham Best Bitter; Hobsons Best Bitter; guest beers
Forty-five bedroom hotel offering double, twin, single and family rooms, all en-suite
£ ££
Snacks and meals daily, lunchtime and evening
Accepted

Originating in 1905 as a small railway hotel, the pub was once known as the Dragon, but was renamed by the owner Chris Bird in memory of his wife, whose portrait hangs over the fireplace in the lounge. Now a free house, over the past few years it has been extended to include a newly-built 45-bedroom hotel, complete with front bar for drinkers where real ales and cider are served, light and airy lounge with polished wooden floors, Italian restaurant Rosado's as well as a function room and garden.

Bedrooms have oak furnishings and facilities include Sky TV with DVD player, radio alarm, modem for Internet access, hair dryer, sofa and king size bed, with full English breakfast included.

Its position right next to Bromsgrove station, with frequent trains to Birmingham, as well as its proximity to the motorway network, makes it a popular place to stay for both business people and tourists who can enjoy views over the north Worcestershire countryside. It is close to Avoncroft Museum of Historic Life where 25 historic buildings have been rescued and rebuilt on an open-air site. Not far away are historic Worcester and Stratford-upon-Avon.
Q P

FLYFORD FLAVELL

Boot Inn

Radford Road, WR7 4BS

▶ Off A422 between Worcester and Stratford-upon-Avon
T (01386) 462658
W thebootinn.com
Adnams Bitter; Fuller's London Pride; Greene King Old Speckled Hen; guest beers
Three double, two twin rooms, all en-suite; two wheelchair accessible
£ ££-£££ (single occupancy £50)
Lunchtime and evening meals (not Sun eve) and snacks
Accepted

The Boot is a good choice for a golfing break as the pub holds corporate membership at the nearby 27-hole Vale golf club and guests can enjoy a round free of charge. For business people who like to combine work and pleasure, the pub is convenient for Birmingham, the NEC and the NIA, while tourists can visit Stratford-upon-Avon or explore the Malverns and the Cotswolds.

Set in glorious countryside, this award-winning pub dates back in part to the 15th century. The five guest rooms are in a recently converted coach house where care has been taken to make the most of the original building; the spacious bedrooms feature bare brick walls and exposed ceiling timbers. Children are welcome to stay and two rooms can accommodate wheelchairs. The breakfast includes locally-made sausages, the best back bacon, free-range scrambled eggs, tomato and mushrooms.

The pub is popular for its food; meals can be taken in the heavily beamed restaurant or in the light, airy conservatory. In summer you can eat out on the patio. Snacks are available at lunchtime. Sunday lunch is served from noon until 5.30pm but the kitchen is closed Sunday evening. ♣ P

GREAT MALVERN

Great Malvern Hotel

Graham Road, WR14 2HN

▶ Next to Church Street crossroads
T (01684) 563411
F (01684) 560514
W great-malvern-hotel.co.uk
Draught Bass; Flowers IPA; Wood Shropshire Lad; guest beer
Seven double, six twin, one family, one single room, all en-suite
£ £££
Snacks and meals lunchtime and evening, Mon-Sat
Accepted

An imposing white fronted family-run hotel close to the station and just a short walk from the Malvern Theatre complex, it has a busy public bar, popular with those seeking pre or post theatre refreshment, and brasserie for informal dining and theatre suppers. Or you can relax in the comfortable lounge supplied with daily newspapers and board games. The guest beer often comes from a local brewery, including the nearby Malvern Hills Brewery.

All 15 rooms are en-suite, with direct dial phone, TV, hair dryer, radio alarm and tea and coffee making facilities. The room rate includes a breakfast buffet in the morning room with full home-cooked English breakfast, and also gives you free temporary membership of Splash Leisure Centre and gym nearby. Theatre packages offer B&B accommodation and theatre tickets.

In an ideal location for exploring the Welsh Border country, the historic spa town of Malvern is on the edge of the Malvern Hills. The hotel is five minutes' walk from the path to the top of the hills, with views over Worcestershire and the Severn Valley. It is within easy driving distance of Worcester, Hereford and Ross-on-Wye.

P

KNIGHTWICK

☆ Talbot

WR6 5PH

▶ On B4197, just off A44
T (01886) 821235
F (01886) 821060
W the-talbot.co.uk
Hobsons Best Bitter; Teme Valley T'Other, This, That, seasonal beer
Six double, three twins, two single rooms, all en-suite
£ £££
Snacks and meals daily, lunchtime and evening
Accepted

Recently awarded local CAMRA Pub of the Year, this 14th-century brew pub, in a peaceful riverside setting with fishing rights, serves award-winning food made with vegetables and herbs from its own kitchen garden. The emphasis is on organic and locally produced ingredients and traditional, seasonal and sometimes ancient recipes.

Creative chef sisters Annie and Wiz Clift get your tastebuds going from first thing with a full English breakfast including bread, black pudding, marmalades and preserves made in their own kitchen plus Gloucester Old Spot bangers and bacon. As the day goes on old-fashioned treats like pig's head brawn, ham hock and caper terrine, confit belly pork with pearl barley and cider might be on the menu. All suppliers are listed including walnuts from Knightwick Manor, 'surplus from the locals' gardens' and wild food gathered from the fields such as edible fungi.

The restful bedrooms, all en-suite, come with a jar of home-made biscuits as well as the usually facilities.

Teme Valley micro brewery behind the pub produces three regular ales as well as seasonal ales, served in a small bar near the entrance, leading to larger dining bar and separate cosy restaurant. The inn hosts a Green Hop festival in early October. Q P

OFFENHAM

Fish & Anchor

The Crossing, WR11 8QT

▶ 2 miles east of Evesham
T (01386) 41277
F (01386) 45542
W fishandanchor.co.uk
Adnams Broadside; Brains Rev James; guest beers
One double, one twin, one family, one single room
£ ££
Snacks and meals daily, lunchtime and evening
Accepted

A large black and white pub on Offenham Weir, in a tranquil position on the River Avon, it has its own fishing rights on the river available to guests at £5 per day if booked in advance. If you arrive by boat, advance booking secures you a mooring.

The Fish & Anchor is a family-run pub dating back to the late 1800s with a cottage bar, second bar to the rear, 50-seater restaurant and garden with its own outside bar in summer. Home-cooked meals and snacks are served from the traditional bar menu, as well as a comprehensive menu in the restaurant, with the popular Sunday roast lunch a speciality. Real cider is on handpump as well as real ale.

A range of modern letting rooms is available including an en-suite family room that sleeps four. The room rate includes a full English breakfast. There is a large area outside for caravans and motor homes, open in summer.

Close to the site of the Battle of Evesham, and only a 15-minute drive from Evesham itself, the Fish and Anchor is also close to Broadway Tower and park, Stratford-upon-Avon, Chipping Campden and the Cotswolds, attracting river users, cyclists and walkers.

Q P

UPPER COLWALL

Malvern Hills Hotel

Jubilee Drive, WR13 6DW

- ▶ On A449, midway between Malvern and Ledbury
- T (01684) 540690
- F (01684) 540327
- W malvernhillshotel.co.uk
- Malvern Hills Black Pear; Wye Valley Bitter, Hereford Pale Ale; guest beers
- Eight double, four twin, one single and one family room; all en-suite
- £ £££
- Lunchtime and evening meals
- Accepted

The hotel dates from the 19th century but there has been a hostelry on this site for hundreds of years. It stands high in the Malverns opposite the ancient hill fort British Camp (also known as the Herefordshire Beacon), commanding a panoramic view far over Worcestershire and Herefordshire in a designated area of outstanding natural beauty.

Walkers number among the visitors to the hotel where the guest rooms have recently been refurbished in individual style to a high standard. You can stay in the Georgian room with its lovely antique king-sized bed, or the romantic four-poster room; the family room, with one double and one single bed, has a DVD player with children's titles provided. The bathrooms have modern fittings.

In the morning you can help yourself to a buffet table with stewed fruits, cereals, yogurt and home-made muesli, then consult a lengthy choice on the cooked menu, including the full English with award-winning Malvern sausages, a selection of omelettes made with free-range eggs, natural oak-smoked haddock poached in milk, or Wiltshire ham with tomato and Herefordshire cheeses. For main meals a varied menu with good vegetarian choices is served in the lounge bar, restaurant or on the terrace. P

UPTON-UPON-SEVERN

White Lion Hotel

21 High Street, WR8 0HJ

- ▶ In town centre, off B4104, near jct 7/8 of M5
- T (01684) 592551
- F (01684) 593333
- W whitelionhotel.biz
- Greene King Abbot, guest beers
- Eight double, four twin, one single room, all en-suite; one ground-floor room is suitable for disabled guests
- £ £££
- Lunchtime and evening meals
- Accepted (not Diners Club)

The White Lion is a far cry from the quaint rural inns that largely fill this guide, but this splendid hotel retains all the charms of its early 16th-century origins, just on a rather grander scale than most B&B pubs. The atmosphere is nonetheless relaxed and unstuffy and non-residents are welcome to drop in for a pint – three guest ales usually include one from a local brewery.

The hotel can still claim to be 'a house of exceedingly good repute' as it was described by Henry Fielding in Tom Jones in 1749. The public areas and guest rooms are all beautifully furnished with an emphasis on comfort. Excellent food is served in the restaurant or you can relax over a less formal meal in the bar (not Saturday evening or Sunday lunchtime). Breakfast can be as hearty as you wish – you can choose any or all of the components of a full English, accompanied by cereals, toast and preserves.

Famous for its landmark 'Pepperpot' church, Upton has much to offer visitors, including specialist shops (instead of the ubiquitous chain stores) and diverse cultural events. The hotel hosts the Lion and Pepperpot beer festival in May.

Q P

UPTON SNODSBURY

☆ Bants

Worcester Road, WR7 4NN

- ▶ On A422 between jct 6/7 of M6, near Worcester
- T (01905) 381282
- F (01905) 381173
- W bants.co.uk
- Draught Bass; Fuller's London Pride; Whittington's Cats Whiskers; guest beers
- Five double, one twin, three single rooms; ground-floor rooms wheelchair accessible
- £ ££-£££
- Lunchtime and evening meals
- Accepted

The pub's unusual name dates back to 2004 when the owners took the bold decision to adopt their surname to celebrate 20 years in charge here. This 16th-century establishment combines olde-worlde charm with contemporary facilities; the lounge bars, replete with exposed beams and blazing log fires, contrast with the conservatory restaurant that serves modern English with a Mediterranean twist. Meals are home-cooked, based on local produce, including daily specials.

Four guest rooms are in the pub and five in converted 16th-century barns in the grounds. A twin and single share a bathroom, the rest are en-suite. For ultimate luxury, the Cider Mill suite has a super king-sized bed, flat screen TV/DVD and spacious bathroom with a jacuzzi – an overnight stay here costs £150, but special rates can be negotiated for short breaks and dinner, bed and breakfast packages. In the morning you have a fine choice of food from a full list of cooked ingredients or fresh fruit and yogurt. Luxury breakfasts are an option; for a £6 supplement you can indulge in a smoked salmon and prawn platter with a glass of Bucks fizz or medallions of fillet steak with fried eggs, sauté potatoes, mushrooms and a glass of port.

Q P

East Yorkshire

BEVERLEY

Dog & Duck Coaching Inn

33 Ladygate, HU17 8BH

- ▶ Off Saturday Market square, near bus and rail stations
- T (01482) 862419
- F (01482) 862419
- E muc65@hotmail.co.uk
- Caledonian Deuchars IPA; Greene King Abbot; John Smith's Bitter; guest beers
- Two double, two single, two twin rooms (one room can accommodate a family), all en-suite
- £ £
- Lunchtime meals and snacks
- Not accepted

Close to the historic centre of Beverley by the 200-year-old market, this traditional pub has been run by the same family for more than 30 years, with grandson Mark now in charge. The pub has kept its original 1930s styling although dividing walls have been removed. The former tap room has a period fireplace and bentwood seating, the lounge has a snug area at the rear. The bar usually stocks beers from Copper Dragon, over 40 whiskies and a good wine list with bottles starting at just £7.

The purpose-built, self-contained guest rooms behind the pub were opened in 1992. Three on the ground floor are wheelchair accessible and customers benefit from secure parking. Overnight guests tick their requirements on a breakfast list before retiring, and any special requests can usually be met.

Home-cooked, inexpensive lunches are popular here, but no evening meals are served, although you won't have far to go to find something in town. While you are exploring this charming old town, make a point of visiting The White Hart Inn (Nellie's) in Hengate. Listed in CAMRA's national inventory of heritage pubs, it has gas lighting and stone-flagged floors.

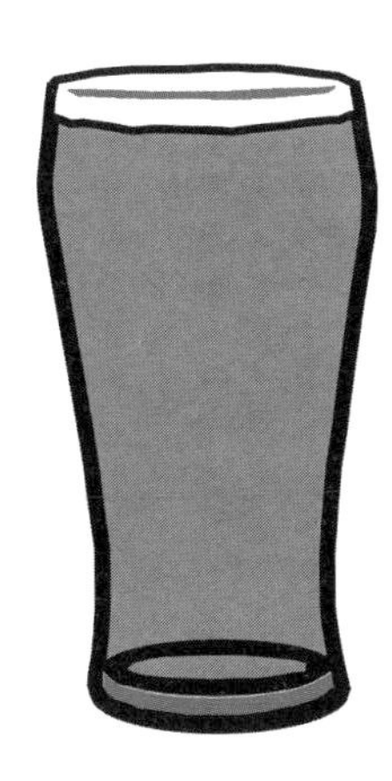

DRIFFIELD
Bell Hotel
Market Place, YO25 6AN

- ▶ Off A614 at town centre
- T (01377) 256661
- F (01377) 253228
- W bw-bellhotel.co.uk
- Beer range varies
- Twelve double, two twin, two single rooms, all en-suite; three rooms wheelchair accessible
- £ £££
- Lunchtime and evening meals and snacks
- Accepted

The Bell is owned by the largest hotel chain in the world but retains its own charm and individuality, and was awarded Town Pub of the Year by local CAMRA members in 2005. Two or three mostly local beers are always available (not to mention 300-plus malts) in the warm and welcoming wood-panelled bar. Outside is a pleasant covered courtyard for alfresco drinking and dining.

Residents have use of a full leisure complex including swimming pool, sauna, steam room, jacuzzi, super spa, flotation tank, gym and squash court. The individually styled guest rooms or suites are well equipped and furnished with antiques, and have all the amenities you would expect from a Best Western including Internet connection, TV, desk, iron and trouser press. The comprehensive breakfast menu offers a full English (or vegetarian version) alongside porridge, smoked haddock with poached eggs, scrambled eggs with or without smoked salmon, smoked fish kedgeree or grilled oak-smoked kippers.

Main meals are served in the beautiful oak-panelled dining room, offering fine dining in elegant surroundings. An excellent lunchtime carvery is available. Children under 16 are not permitted. Q P

DUNSWELL

Ship Inn

Beverley High Road, HU6 0AJ

- ▶ On A164 between Hull and Beverley
- T (01482) 859160
- F (01482) 859160
- W theshipsquarters.co.uk
- Black Sheep Best Bitter; Taylor Landlord; guest beers
- Four double, one twin room (adapted for disabled customers), all en-suite
- £ £
- Lunchtime and evening meals
- Accepted

This free house dates from the early 19th century and once served traffic on the nearby River Hull. Nautical memorabilia features in the friendly bar that is warmed by two log fires and has a dining area serving good food. The inn also has a large garden and paddock where barbecues are held regularly in summer.

The Ships Quarters is attractive newly-built motel-style accommodation behind the pub, offering good value B&B. Four rooms have a double bed plus a sofa bed, while the twin room is adapted for disabled use with a properly equipped bathroom with wheelchair access. Children are welcome to stay, but are not admitted in the pub. The rooms are light with modern furnishings including a TV, desk and fridge. A continental breakfast is provided in the room with fruit juice, cereals, fruit, yogurt and croissants.

The pub is ideally situated for visiting historic Beverley three miles away and Hull just a mile away, and is on the bus route between the two towns. Visitors to the area will enjoy the gothic cathedral of Beverley Minster, while in Hull the futuristic attraction The Deep gives fascinating insights into the marine world. ♣ P

FLAMBOROUGH

Ship Inn

Post Office Street, YO15 1JS

- ▶ Village centre, 5 miles from Bridlington
- T (01262) 850454
- Beer range varies
- Four double/twin rooms, two en-suite
- £ £
- Lunchtime and evening meals
- Accepted

This 17th-century coaching inn right at the heart of the village is grade II listed and is the longest continuously trading pub in Flamborough. Its original stained glass windows have survived, their lettering declaring the purpose of each room. Inside, there is an abundance of dark wood.

The bar stocks a range of real ales that changes on a monthly basis, featuring a wide range of northern breweries including John Smith's, Timothy Taylor and Jennings, plus some more southerly outfits such as Greene King and Wells. A varied bar menu is supplemented by daily specials.

The bedrooms on the first floor are both en-suite, those on the second floor, which are £10 per night cheaper, have wash basins and share a WC. TV and tea and coffee making facilities are provided in all the rooms. Children and pets are welcome to stay. A full English breakfast is served. Opposite the pub, self-catering accommodation is also available in a two-bedroom cottage.

Flamborough attracts walkers and birdwatchers to its spectacular cliffs and the RSPB sanctuary nearby. If you are staying several nights, make a point of visiting the Seabirds also in the village, which features in CAMRA's Good Pub Food guide.

P

SOUTH CAVE

Fox & Coney Inn

52 Market Place, HU15 2AT

- T (01430) 422275
- Caledonian Deuchars IPA; Taylor Landlord; Theakston XB; guest beers
- Four double, five twin, two family, one single room, all en-suite; one room with wheelchair access
- £ ££
- Lunchtime and evening meals and snacks
- Accepted

Built in 1739 as a coaching inn, the Fox and Coney is one of the oldest buildings in this picturesque Wolds village. Just off the Wolds Way Walk, the pub is a popular night stop for walkers. It has facilities for drying damp clothes and boots, and can organise packed lunches and transportation of luggage.

Hot meals are served seven days a week in both the bar and the restaurant. Made with local produce where possible, daily specials complement the regular menu, while a carvery is served on Sunday lunchtime. If you don't want a full meal, snacks are usually available.

A traditional rural inn, the homely atmosphere is enhanced by three open fires. A favourite with local customers in this large village, it hosts a regular quiz. Children are welcome to stay overnight in the well-equipped guest rooms that have satellite TV, hospitality tray, trouser press and hair dryer. A full English breakfast is offered here but individual requests can usually be catered for.

The pub is handy for Hull and Beverley, and just 30 miles from York. Local places of interest include Cave Castle, Rowley Manor and Walkington Manor. Q P

North Yorkshire

ALLERSTON
Cayley Arms
YO18 7PJ

- ▶ Off A170, just east of Pickering, towards Scarborough
- T (01723) 859338
- W thecayleyarms.co.uk
- Black Sheep Best Bitter; guest beer
- Three double, one twin, one family room, all en-suite
- £ £
- Lunchtime and evening meals and snacks
- Accepted

Built in the 1880s as a small farm, part of the Cayley estate, the pub has seen many changes. It has just been refurbished with a fresh coat of paint and new carpets throughout the traditional country-style interior.

The accommodation here is very good value; the bedrooms are spacious and light, well equipped and attractively furnished. The family room includes a bunk bed and children are welcome. At breakfast you can help yourself to cereals, toast and juice before tucking into a full cooked meal including local sausages and black pudding. The pub restaurant with its warm tones is equally inviting for main meals which range from pub favourites, roasts and vegetarian options through to innovative new dishes. Snacks are also served in the bar where you will be made to feel welcome by the friendly locals.

In fine weather the lovely garden with a stream running through it is the place to be. Tracks from the side of the pub lead directly into the Dalby Forest, which is very popular with walkers, cyclists and lovers of wildlife.

Q P

ASKRIGG
White Rose Hotel
Main Street, DL8 3HG

▶ Off A684 (signed from Bainbridge)
T (01969) 650515
F (01969) 650176
W thewhiterosehotelaskrigg.co.uk
Black Sheep Best Bitter; Theakston Best Bitter; guest beers
Ten double, one twin room, all en-suite
£ £££ (single occupancy £50-£55)
Lunchtime and evening meals
Accepted (not Amex or Diners)

At the centre of village life, the hotel has a handsome, early Victorian frontage opening onto a homely, comfortable lounge bar serving local beers. The building was renovated during 2005 after being closed for five years, but its essential character remains. The attractive restaurant with exposed stone walls leads to a further dining area in the conservatory. Good food is based on local produce and every effort is made to cater for special dietary requirements.

The bedrooms have all been refurbished, too; four have king-sized beds and they all have TV and tea and coffee making facilities. The residents' lounge has a TV and pool table. Children are welcome to stay and pets can be accommodated. A hearty cooked breakfast of eggs, bacon, sausage, tomato, mushroom and black pudding is accompanied by cereals and toast.

Askrigg lies in the Yorkshire Dales National Park and there is plenty to see and do around here, especially for families. Children will be delighted by the Forbidden Corner near Middleham – a labyrinth of tunnels, chambers, follies and surprises created in a four acre garden – and there is free entry to the Dales Countryside Museum in Hawes. You can see how 'cracking cheese' is made at the Wensleydale Experience in Hawes and there are several National Trust properties in the area. P

BLAKEY RIDGE
Lion Inn
YO62 7LQ

▶ Between Castleton and Hutton-Le-Hole
T (01751) 417320
F (01751) 417717
W lionblakey.co.uk
Theakston Black Bull, XB, Old Peculier; Greene King Old Speckled Hen; guest beers
Six double, one twin, three family rooms, all en-suite
£ ££
Snacks and meals daily, lunchtime and evening
Accepted

In winter open fires burn all day and evening in the ancient fireplaces of the Lion Inn, creating a warm welcome for travellers to this remote 16th-century hostelry. Standing on Blakey Ridge, at 1,325 feet the highest point of the North Yorks Moors national park, it has spectacular views over Rosedale and Farndale Valleys. The original, low-beamed ceilings add to the atmosphere of the family-owned free house, founded by the Crouched Friars to ease their poverty. Cockpit Howe, a Neolithic burial mound, stands behind the pub.

Ten letting rooms, including a honeymoon suite with four-poster bed, are equipped with TV and tea and coffee making. Full English breakfast with black pudding and fried bread is included, kippers if you'd rather.

A bar menu served all day offers dishes such as home-cooked ham, egg and chips, pork with apple and white wine sauce, and Old Peculier casserole, all around £8. At night an à la carte menu is served in the candlelit dining rooms.

Close to Rosedale Abbey in magnificent walking and cycling country, secure storage is provided for mountain bikes.
P

CASTLETON
Eskdale Inn
Station Road, YO21 2EU

- ▶ Off A171
- T (01287) 660234
- W eskdaleinn.co.uk
- Black Sheep Best Bitter; Tetley Bitter; guest beers (summer)
- One double, one twin room, both en-suite
- £ ££ (£32.50 single occupancy)
- Lunchtime and evening meals and snacks
- Accepted

The Eskdale Inn is served by the North Yorkshire Moors single track railway that runs for 35 miles between Middlesborough and Whitby. On Friday nights a special 'music train' runs the full length of the line and customers stop off at the inn for a meal and pick the train up again on its return journey.

The building was originally the station house – at first it was just a waiting room, then a small bar was installed in one corner and it evolved from there into a fully-grown inn. After many changes of ownership, it is now an award-winning hostelry. A halfway house for the Esk Valley walk, it stands at the start of many other walking routes and free route maps are available at the pub.

A weekly-changing guest beer is stocked in summer and the kitchen provides tasty meals based on local produce – rabbit pie and home-made crumbles are specialities, and an all-day breakfast features on the menu. For B&B guests a very full English breakfast is included in the reasonable room rate, children are welcome and dogs are accommodated (£5 per night). The guest rooms are simply but comfortably furnished, with hospitality tray.

CAWOOD
☆ Ferry Inn
2 King Street, YO8 3TL

- ▶ B1299 (off A19) next to Cawood Bridge
- T (01757) 268515
- W theferryinn.com
- Caledonian Deuchars IPA; Taylor Landlord; Theakston Best Bitter; guest beers
- Two double, one family room, all en-suite
- £ £
- Snacks and meals daily, lunchtime and evening
- Accepted

The sound of rushing water will lull you to sleep at the Ferry, a delightful inn just by the swing bridge over the River Ouse with a large beer garden fronting the river. The traditional bar, with low ceilings and inglenook, displays the village's connections with Cardinal Wolsey – ruins of his castle are in Cawood – and the great feast of 1464.

The light and airy bedrooms are decorated in green shades, all with new en-suite shower rooms. One double has a fireplace and window seat, another is a beamed attic room, the third has a river view. Breakfast is an additional £5, and what an imaginative choice. Eggs Florentine of fresh baby spinach and poached eggs with Hollandaise on a muffin, eggs Benedict of honey roast ham and poached eggs on a muffin, smoked salmon with scrambled eggs and mushrooms or the full English (children's portions available).

Freshly-prepared main meals are excellent here, changing frequently depending on the season, and always supplemented by a specials board. Weekend barbecues and a riverside marquee bar are available during the summer months (weather and river permitting).

York is just a 20-minute drive away, but a bus passes too. P

CRAY

White Lion Inn

BD23 5JB

- ▶ On B6160, north of Buckden
- T (01756) 76262
- W whitelioncray.com
- Copper Dragon Golden Pippin, Scotts 1816; Taylor Golden Best; guest beers
- Seven double, three twin, one family room, all en-suite except one room with shared facilities
- £ ££-£££
- Lunchtime and evening meals
- Accepted

The highest pub in Wharfedale, the White Lion is situated beneath Buckden Pike and originally served a drover's route. It is an ideal choice for those who truly want to get away from the pressures of modern life as there is no mobile phone or terrestrial television reception. Popular with walkers, help can be given with route planning and picnic baskets and cool boxes hired.

The pub has been sympathetically restored retaining old beams, open fires and stone-flagged floors. The bar is blissfully free of background noise, except the hum of conversation or click of dominoes being played.

If you hate to be cut off completely, you can book one of the four premium rooms with free satellite TV channels. The rooms are decorated in a simple country style with pine furnishings and tea and coffee making facilities. Children are welcome; a travel cot, playpen and baby listening service are available, but must be reserved when booking. Pets can be accommodated in three ground floor rooms.

A full English breakfast is served with eggs cooked to your liking, and special requests such as porridge can usually be fulfilled. The kitchen uses as much local produce as possible in all its meals. Q P

EN-SUITE ACCOMMODATION
BAR MEALS
REAL ALE
HOT DRINKS
FOOD

OULSTON 3
COXWOLD 5
THE DURHAM OX

CRAYKE
Durham Ox
Westway, YO30 2BN

- ▶ Off A19 near Easingwold
- T (01347) 821506
- F (01347) 823326
- W thedurhamox.com
- Theakston Best Bitter; guest beers
- Four suites all en-suite
- £ £££-££££
- Lunchtime and evening meals
- Accepted

The splendid 300-year-old Durham Ox is ideal for a weekend retreat, surrounded by breathtaking views over the vale of York, and down the hill from the medieval church. It is only 20 minutes' drive from York city centre and many other tourist attractions such as Castle Howard.

This family-owned inn has a real country feel to its beamed and flagged bars, with blazing log fires and lovely old furnishings, while the restaurant has won awards for its locally-sourced food.

The guest suites are mostly in refurbished farm buildings in the courtyard; the tariff varying depending on the number of guests. The most luxurious suites have two bedrooms – one double and one twin, with a jacuzzi bathroom, lounge and galley kitchen. The General's Quarters (in the pub itself) has two bedrooms and a bathroom and is suitable for families. Junior suites – a double room, en-suite bathroom and small seating area – can also be let for single occupancy. Beautifully decorated, the rooms all have TV, video, CD player, hospitality tray and hair dryer. An excellent breakfast choice is offered including omelettes, eggs cooked as you like them, smoked haddock or kippers and, of course, the full English. If you have an early start a continental hamper can be delivered to your room.

Q P

CROPTON
☆ New Inn
YO18 8HH

▶ Off A170 near Pickering
T (01751) 417330
F (01751) 417582
W croptonbrewery.com
Cropton Brewery's range plus seasonal beer; guest beers
Eleven double rooms plus cottage suite, all en-suite
£ ££
Snacks and meals daily, lunchtime and evening
Accepted

Here you can sleep in a fine old stone inn that is also the home of award-winning Cropton Brewery. Ale has been brewed on the site since 1613, illegally in the early days, with wrongdoers sent to York Gaol. In 1984 the craft was revived when the brewery opened in the pub's cellars, Two Pints the first ale brewed. A decade later a modern brewhouse was erected behind the pub – a guided tour is a highlight for any visitor.

Accommodation is in newly-decorated bedrooms, two wheelchair accessible, one with a four-poster. Four are available as twin or family rooms, and there is also a cottage with its own sitting room in the brewery grounds. A full English breakfast is included in the room rate.

Good food accompanies the excellent range of ales, served in the beamed village bar and separate restaurant. Dishes include cod in the inn's own beer batter, steak and stout pie, and a sausage ring flavoured with Two Pints.

On the edge of the North Yorkshire moors, the inn is set in wonderful walking country, and is close to the North Yorkshire steam railway, Whitby and Castle Howard.

P

DANBY
☆ Duke of Wellington
2 West Lane, YO21 2LY

T (01287) 660351
W danby-dukeofwellington.co.uk
Copper Dragon Scotts 1816; Daleside Bitter; Tetley Imperial; guest beers
Four double, one twin, one family, two single rooms, all en-suite
£ ££
Snacks and meals daily, lunchtime and evening
Accepted

Dating back to 1765, the inn was used as a recruiting post by local regiments during the Napoleonic Wars, and a cast iron plaque of the great man, unearthed during restoration work, has pride of place over the open fireplace.

With timber-beamed bars and open fire, the ivy-clad pub has expanded over the years to incorporate what was once a row of cottages overlooking the village green. Food is delicious and good value – even the ham for the sandwiches is home-cooked in cider.

Several bedrooms enjoy fine views of the Danby Dale and surrounding moorland. All the en-suite rooms are individually decorated with LCD flat screen TV and tea and coffee making. There is a sitting room for guests. A full English breakfast is included in the tariff.

At the heart of the North Yorkshire moors, this pub is perfect for walkers. Information about local walks, from light strolls to longer treks, is available including maps with a list of safety tips on the back. Packed lunches and drying facilities can be provided. Places of nearby interest included Danby Castle, and further afield Whitby, Castle Howard and the North York Moors Railway.

Q P

ABOVE: Duke of Wellington, Danby.

EAST WITTON

☆ Cover Bridge Inn

DL8 4SQ

- ▶ ½ mile north of village on A6108, near Leyburn
- T (01969) 623650
- W thecoverbridgeinn.co.uk
- Black Sheep Best Bitter; Copper Dragon Golden Pippin; Taylor Landlord; Theakston Best Bitter, Old Peculier; guest beers
- Two double, one twin room plus an additional bed for family use; all en-suite
- £ £ (single occupancy £32)
- Lunchtime and evening meals
- Accepted

A multiple CAMRA award winner, the inn is described by local members as a 'mini beer exhibition', with a good range of real ales supplemented by three guests. Once you have fathomed out the door latch you enter a wonderful old bar that has changed little over the last 300-odd years. A flagged floor, exposed beams, wood settles and roaring fire will encourage you to linger over a beer or two. There is also a tiny lounge, which leads out to an extensive riverside garden with a children's play area, and a small dining room that serves great food, including a full English breakfast for overnight guests.

Comfortable B&B accommodation here is good value. The two double rooms overlook the garden, while the twin-bedder is spacious enough to accommodate a third bed for a child. Families (and their pets) are welcome to stay.

The pub stands on the River Cover, just upstream from its confluence with the River Ure; day fishing permits can be obtained. There are good local walks to be had, too. A little further afield are the ruins of Jervaulx Abbey and Masham where the Black Sheep Brewery has an excellent visitor centre.

Q P

GRINTON
Bridge Inn
DL11 6HH

▶ On B6270 one mile east of Reeth
T (01748) 884224
W bridgeinngrinton.co.uk
Jennings Cumberland Ale, Cocker Hoop, seasonal beers; guest beer
Two double, one twin, two family rooms, all en-suite
£ ££
Lunchtime and evening meals
Accepted

The Bridge is set in an enviable location, beneath Fremington Edge on the bank of the River Swale at the heart of the Yorkshire Dales National Park. The pub is almost as old as the 12th-century church that stands opposite, known as the Cathedral of the Dale. The interior, which has a comfortable rustic feel, comprises a central lounge, public bar and games room as well as a hotel lounge and dining room. Open fires and exposed beams add to the warm atmosphere. Frequented by walkers and cyclists, it also attracts many other visitors from anglers, musicians and beer lovers to tourists.

The guest rooms, which all benefit from views of the church or the wonderful surrounding Swaledale scenery, are well appointed with beverage tray and TV. Breakfast caters for all appetites, with either a full English cooked meal, eggs – scrambled, boiled or poached – with toast, or smoked haddock. The inn has a good reputation for its food, based as far as possible on locally-sourced produce. The extensive menu is further boosted by a good selection of specials, which may include Grinton lamb and barley casserole or game in season.
Q P

HARDRAW
Green Dragon Inn
DL8 3LZ

▶ Off A684
T (01969) 667392
W greendragonhardraw.com
Taylor Landlord; Theakston Best Bitter, Old Peculier; guest beers
Fifteen double, two twin, four single, three family rooms, all en-suite and some wheelchair accessible, plus self-catering apartments
£ ££
Lunchtime and evening meals
Accepted

The Green Dragon, some 700 years old, is perhaps the oldest pub in the Yorkshire Dales, and retains its original stone flag floors, ancient furniture and old ranges in the fireplaces. But the inn also hides another record breaker: in the extensive grounds behind the pub is reputedly England's highest single drop waterfall – Hardraw Force. If you visit in summer you might be disappointed, but after rain, the fall makes an impressive sight, falling 100 feet from an overhanging ledge.

You can follow footpaths along the narrow gorge through ancient woodland to reach the waterfall, and for longer walks you only have to step outside the pub to get onto the Pennine Way and other trails. The waterfall has attracted famous visitors including JMW Turner, Wordsworth and Kevin Costner, who filmed scenes from Robin Hood Prince of Thieves there.

The inn's accommodation was added in the 1970s: one building has en-suite guest rooms while another has self-catering apartments for up to six people. B&B guests are provided with a hearty cooked breakfast, rounded off with toast and home-made preserves. Main meals can also be taken at the inn, which is known for its musical events, including an annual brass band contest. Q P

HAWES
White Hart Inn
Main Street, DL8 3QL

▶ On A684 between A1 at Leeming and M6 jct 37
T (01969) 667259
F (01969) 667259
W whiteharthawes.co.uk
Black Sheep Best Bitter; John Smith's Bitter; Wells Bombardier
Four double, two twin, one single room with shared facilities
£ ££
Snacks and meals at lunchtime and evening meals
Accepted

Hawes is a small market town in Upper Wensleydale at the heart of the Yorkshire Dales National Park, so the pub, which stands on the Pennine Way, is often busy with walkers and other visitors to the area. The 17th-century inn on the cobbled main street also enjoys a good local trade in its comfortable bar, warmed by an open fire where the thud of darts and click of dominoes can often be heard.

At the time of writing none of the guest rooms has private facilities but some en-suites are planned so may be available by the time you book. However, bathrobes are thoughtfully provided in the rooms, which are furnished in country style and have tea and coffee making facilities. There is a comfortable residents' lounge with television. Children are welcome and pets can be accommodated (£3 per night). The pub has secure cycle storage and drying facilities.

A hearty Yorkshire breakfast starts off with fruit, porridge or cereal followed by a traditional cooked meal, Manx kippers or free-range boiled or scrambled eggs. Local suppliers are used as far as possible and much of the pub's main menu is home cooked, including a daily casserole and fish dish.

LASTINGHAM

Blacksmith's Arms

Front Street, YO62 6TL

- Between Thirsk and Pickering, 3 miles north of A170
- T (01751) 417247
- Theakston Best Bitter; guest beers
- Two double, one twin room, all en-suite
- £ ££
- Lunchtime and evening meal
- Accepted (not Amex)

Once awarded 'Yorkshire's Perfect Pub' in a national newspaper poll, the owners of the Blacksmith's Arms make every effort to maintain this reputation by stocking a good selection of guest beers, often from local micro-breweries such as Daleside, Roosters and York, and by serving an excellent menu of good, home-cooked pub food.

The pub dates back to the 1660s and retains many original features such as exposed beams and charming nooks and crannies. An old range in the single bar is lit in winter. Opposite the pub stands the 11th-century St Mary's church – at one time the vicar and his 13 children lived here while his wife ran the hostelry. The pub is now reputed to be haunted by a ghost called Ella.

The pretty guest rooms are individually decorated in country style with low ceilings and pine furnishings; one room has a four-poster and a fold up bed is available for family use. A hospitality tray, hair dryer and TV are provided in all rooms. The breakfast menu offers a choice of a full English breakfast with black pudding, natural smoked haddock with poached egg or smoked salmon with scrambled egg.

LEYBURN

Black Swan Hotel

Market Place, DL8 5AS

▶ Off A684/A6108
T (01969) 623131
F (01677) 424265
Black Sheep Best Bitter; Caledonian Deuchars IPA; John Smith's Bitter; Taylor Landlord; guest beer
Six double/twin/family en-suite rooms; one double, three singles with shared facilities
£ £ (single room £25.95)
Lunchtime and evening meals
Not accepted

The Black Swan is a fine, ivy-clad building dating from the 1780s. As the former Corn Exchange it is centrally situated in one of the oldest market towns in the Yorkshire Dales – Leyburn is known as the 'Gateway to Wensleydale'. The busy pub is divided into a bar and dining area where you can have an excellent meal for little outlay – its Sunday carvery offers all you can eat for around a fiver. All meat is locally sourced, fresh fish delivered from Redcar and desserts are made at a local farmhouse.

The hotel offers a range of accommodation to suit all needs, all of it good value. Most of the traditionally furnished double/twin rooms have en-suite bathtub and shower, TV and tea and coffee making facilities; two of the rooms are large enough for family use. The three singles and one double have TV and shared bathroom. Breakfast is cereals followed by a full cooked meal and toast.

There is plenty to see and do around here: the Wensleydale Experience, Dales Countryside Museum, Forbidden Corner and many NT properties to discover. The area is ideal for country pursuits such as fishing, hunting and rambling.

LONG PRESTON

☆ Maypole Inn

Main Street, BD23 4PH

▶ On A65, 10 miles N of Skipton
T (01729) 840219
W maypole.co.uk
Copper Dragon BB; Moorhouses Premier; Taylor Landlord; guest beers
Two double, one twin, two family, one single room, all en-suite
£ ££
Snacks and meals daily, lunchtime and evening
Accepted

This admirable pub overlooks the village green where maypole dancing is still celebrated. A list of the landlords since 1695 is displayed in the bar, and the present incumbent has earned pride of place after nearly 25 years' service.

The immaculate bedrooms are traditionally furnished – the emphasis is on freshness and simplicity with TV, well-stocked welcome tray and good quality toiletries. There is a residents' sitting room. The reasonable room rate includes a fine cooked breakfast with excellent local Hellifield sausages and bacon, as well as kippers or roast ham and eggs. In winter the tariff is reduced if you stay two nights.

The cosy lounge has old photos of the village, and the tap room has Victorian bench seating. Guest beers are from local SIBA breweries, and the cider is Saxon Ruby Tuesday. Also known for tasty meals, the Maypole menu features steak and ale pie, Kilnsey trout with tarragon, Yorkshire ham and eggs with home-made chips, and several good veggie options.

On the doorstep is Yorkshire Dales national park, with Bolton Abbey, Skipton and the Settle-Carlisle railway close by. The Maypole has twice been awarded local CAMRA pub of the season. Q P

MALHAM
Lister Arms
Gordale Scar Road, BD23 4DB

T (01729) 830330
W listerarms.co.uk
Black Sheep Best Bitter; Caledonian Deuchars IPA; Taylor Landlord; guest beers
Five double, one twin, three family rooms, all en-suite
£ ££
Snacks and meals daily, lunchtime and evening
Accepted

Set in some of Britain's finest limestone scenery, this mellow stone coaching inn was built in the late 1600s but takes its name from Thomas Lister, first Lord of Ribblesdale, who bought it in 1723. Contemporary decor blends with original features such as an inglenook fireplace, exposed stone walls and beams. The tiled entrance opens onto a large main bar where up to four real ales are supplemented by a wide choice of foreign and British bottled beers, and a real cider or perry. Internet access is available in the bar.

The nine well-appointed letting rooms all have en-suite shower, exposed oak beams and mullioned windows, and provide TV and tea and coffee facilities. They either overlook the village green to the front or Malham Cove, Europe's largest limestone pavement, to the rear. Rates vary depending on whether you stay midweek or at the weekend. The tariff includes a full English breakfast with local sausages and free-range eggs. A wide selection of traditional and modern food is available at lunchtime and in the evening, all high quality, with local produce where possible. Guests get an automatic table reservation in the evening.

The surrounding countryside is perfect for mountain biking and bikes can be hired from the inn. It is close to Gordale Scar waterfall, with Harrogate and York near enough to visit for the day. P

MALTON
Suddaby's Crown Hotel
12 Wheelgate, YO17 7HP

In main shopping street
T (01653) 692038
F (01653) 691812
W suddabys.co.uk
Malton Double Chance, Golden Chance, After Dark Coffee Porter, Auld Bob; guest beers
Two double, three twin, three family rooms; two family rooms have en-suite facilities, the rest share bathrooms
£ £-££
Lunchtime snacks
Accepted

The Suddaby family has been running the Crown Hotel since the 1870s. The grade II listed building has some fine architectural and historic features that have been sensitively preserved. However, facilities have been brought up to date for modern customers: the former stables have been given over to car parking and a conservatory covers the old courtyard.

The hotel has long-standing connections with horse racing and brewing – one of its beers, Double Chance, was named after a horse. At present its Malton ales are brewed elsewhere but are always available on the bar. Regular beer festivals are a familiar event here. The off-licence on the premises stocks some 350 bottled beers from around the world.

Six guest rooms with shared bathrooms are in the main building: one double with Victorian brass bed and one family room on the first floor, the others on the second floor. The two en-suite family rooms are in an annexe overlooking St Leonard's Church; one sleeps three, the other is two interlinked rooms sleeping four people. All the rooms have TV and hospitality tray. A full English breakfast is served but no main meals, however there is plenty of choice in the town. P

NEWTON-UNDER-ROSEBERRY

King's Head

The Green, TS9 6QR

- ▶ A173 near Guisborough
- T (01642) 722318
- W kingsheadhotel.co.uk
- Black Sheep Best Bitter; Ring O' Bells Porkers Pride, Bodmin Boar, Sozzled Swine; guest beers
- Four double, two twin, one family, one single room, all en-suite
- £ ££-£££
- Snacks and meals daily, lunchtime and evening
- Accepted

The eight new bedrooms installed in a row of converted country cottages last year won the King's Head Best Bed and Breakfast in the North East of England. The rooms are full of character, incorporating traditional features such as inglenook fireplace, cast iron cooking range, oak beamed ceilings, and one has a four-poster bed. All mod cons are provided including en-suite bathroom, Nicam TV, CD/DVD player, phone with modem point and tea and coffee making facilities.

The room rate includes a full English breakfast which has won an award for featuring local produce. It is served in a conservatory looking out onto Roseberry Topping, the oddly-shaped mound known as 'the Matterhorn of Cleveland'.

Offering a good selection of real ales with a weekly guest beer in the bar, the Old King's Head serves a choice of meals in the 17th-century restaurant made with fresh local produce. You can eat outside on the patio in summer.

Situated on the Cleveland Way, the inn attracts guests on walking holidays, but is also within driving distance of Whitby, Hartlepool Marina, 'Heartbeat' country and North Yorkshire National Park.

SCARBOROUGH

Valley Bar

51 Valley Road, YO11 2LX

- ▶ Near bus and rail stations
- T (01723) 372593
- W valleybar.co.uk
- Jennings Sneck Lifter; Theakston Best Bitter; Wold Top Mars Magic; guest beers
- Four double, two twin, two family, two single rooms, mostly en-suite
- £ £ (room only)
- Lunchtime and evening meals
- Not accepted

The Valley offers some of the best-value accommodation in this Guide – and if you show your CAMRA membership card when you book in you will get a 15% discount. The rooms are fairly small with basic amenities, but they have been newly refurbished and if you are 'only here for the beer', more than adequate. And beer lovers will not be disappointed. The friendly basement bar's six handpumps feature guests from micro-breweries or major favourites. The pub also runs monthly beer festivals that focus on ales from a single county. No surprise that the Valley was voted Town Pub of the Year 2005 by local CAMRA members.

The pub offers a mix of rooms with en-suite or shared facilities, plus a large apartment with its own bathroom that sleeps up to seven people for £60 per night. Breakfast is charged separately so you can opt for the 'basic' – cereal, toast, porridge and egg for £3.50 – or the 'full', which is the basic plus a cooked English breakfast for just £4.50.

The hotel is a short walk from all Scarborough's attractions, the spa complex, beach and town centre.

SNAPE
Castle Arms Inn
DL8 2TB

- ▶ Village centre, off B6268, between Bedale and Masham
- T (01677) 470270
- W thecastlearms.co.uk
- Jennings Bitter, Cumberland Ale; guest beers
- Six double, three twin rooms, all en-suite; one room wheelchair accessible
- £ ££ (single occupancy £55)
- Lunchtime and evening meals
- Accepted

The inn takes its name from Snape Castle, the former home of Catherine Parr, and may date back as far as the 14th century, although the current hostelry was built in the 17th century. It has a lovely, open bar with a stone-flagged floor, exposed beams laden with brasses and a big hearth where a fire blazes in winter. To one side is a games room and on the other an excellent restaurant.

Fish is a speciality, while daily-changing blackboards show home-made dishes prepared according to the availability of local produce. Breakfasts are excellent – locally-made sausages and black pudding feature in the full English, or there is smoked haddock or kippers if you prefer.

The four diamond ETB rated accommodation is in a separate barn conversion at the rear. The en-suite rooms are decorated in country style with pine furnishings and fresh colours. TV and tea and coffee making facilities are provided. There is a pretty courtyard and garden where quoits can be played. The pub also has a small Camping and Caravanning Club site and a paddock housing tame farm animals – much loved by visiting children, who are welcome to stay, as are pets.

Q ♣ P

TAN HILL
Tan Hill Inn
DL11 6ED

- ▶ 30 minutes from A66 between Cumbria and County Durham
- T (01833) 628246
- F (01833) 628002
- W tanhillinn.com
- Black Sheep Best Bitter, Emmerdale, Riggwelter; Theakston Best Bitter, Old Peculier, XB
- Two double, two twin, one family room, all en-suite
- £ ££
- Lunchtime and evening meals
- Accepted

A former editor of CAMRA's Good Beer Guide was once the licensee at the Tan Hill Inn which, at 1,732 feet above sea level, is the highest pub in England. Neil Hanson used to regale us with tales of customers being stranded for days at the pub because of snow, but it seems not many of them ever complained! It is hard to know where the 'locals' come from as the pub stands isolated on the moors and the nearest house is more than three miles away. The pub does however lie directly on the Pennine Way, so it is a good stopover for walkers, and it is just four miles from the Coast-to-Coast trail (transport is available to and from the pub).

As well as accommodation in the pub, there is now a new four-bedroom flat available and the inn has applied for planning permission to convert a barn into a 26-bed bunkhouse, opening in 2007. For those who cannot get enough of the fresh air there is plenty of space for camping. Needless to say, a hearty walker's breakfast is provided in the morning. Special winter offers are available, including a full week's 'Chill Out'.

♣ P

THIRSK
Golden Fleece Hotel
42 Market Place, YO7 1LL

- ▶ Town centre
- T (01845) 523108
- F (01845) 523996
- W goldenfleecehotel.com
- Hambleton Bitter, Stud; Taylor Landlord
- Nineteen double, two twin, one single, one family room, all en-suite
- £ £££ (single room £65)
- Lunchtime and evening meals
- Accepted

The 'proper Yorkshire breakfast' served here is a prize winner – the hotel was awarded 'Flavours of Hambleton Best Breakfast' in 2005. To start there is fresh fruit salad, cereals or yogurt, followed by either natural smoked kipper or a full cooked meal including free-range eggs cooked to your preference, Masham sausage and Arthur Haigh black pudding. The preserves are made locally, too. All the food here is excellent quality, with most ingredients sourced locally; Sunday lunch is good value and offers interesting starters and vegetarian alternatives to the traditional roast.

The origins of this lovely old building go back to Tudor times; in its heyday as a coaching inn in the 19th century it stabled 50 or 60 horses. The spacious, split-level Paddock Bar, with its racing theme, still celebrates working animals. Thirsk is the real home of the literary vet James Herriot, popularised on television. The author's former surgery near the hotel is now a museum.

The elegant guest rooms are individually styled, some with sumptuous four-posters. Sky TV, trouser press, hair dryer and hospitality tray are provided in all rooms. Pets are permitted.

Q P

THIXENDALE
Cross Keys
YO17 9TG

- ▶ Off A166 near Malton; OS842612
- T (01377) 288272
- Jennings Bitter; Tetley Bitter; guest beers
- One double, two twin rooms, all en-suite
- £ ££
- Lunchtime and evening meals and snacks
- Accepted

The Cross Keys describes itself as 'a village pub that serves food as opposed to a restaurant that serves beer'. This single room establishment is a real old-fashioned traditional inn and does not permit children, although they are welcome in the garden. An unpretentious place, it has no games machines and the juke box plays 'old' music, which suits most of the sociable regulars.

Originally a farmhouse, the guest bedrooms are in a separate building next to the pub. The former hayloft no longer sleeps stable boys, but offers en-suite accommodation to walkers, cyclists and other travellers (no children). The rooms have facilities for making hot drinks and radio, but no TV. There is a boot room and shed for bicycles or a motorbike. Breakfast is made with local produce and guests can choose what they want for their hot meal – eggs cooked as you like them. The jam and marmalade are home made. Simple but wholesome home-cooked food is available at other meal times.

Thixendale is a picturesque village at the heart of the Wolds, not far from the coast.

♣

WASS
Wombwell Arms
YO61 4BE

- ▶ Off A170 and A19 near Thirsk, between Coxwold and Ampleforth
- T (01347) 868280
- W thewombwellarms.co.uk
- Black Sheep Best Bitter; Taylor Landlord; guest beers
- Three double, one family room, all en-suite; one room wheelchair accessible
- £ ££
- Lunchtime and evening meals
- Accepted (not Amex)

Built in the 18th century using stone from the ruined Byland Abbey nearby, the Wombwell Arms served for many years as the local estate granary and mortuary (with the inevitable resident ghost) before becoming a public house in 1924. It became an independent free house in 1971. Retaining original beams, an open fire and log burner, the central bar has a cosy area for a quiet drink, while the newly restored Poachers Bar is especially inviting.

The guest rooms, too, have all been refurbished in the last four years and offer comfortable beds, country style pine furnishings, TV and beverage tray. A full English breakfast includes bacon, sausage and black pudding along with free-range eggs, tomatoes and mushrooms, followed by toast and locally-made farmhouse preserves. Two light and airy restaurants serve freshly-cooked meals with most produce sourced from within a 25-mile radius; particular dietary requirements can be catered for.

The inn is convenient for parents visiting their offspring at Ampleforth College, and the Abbey there is also worth exploring. The pub is also a good refreshment stop for walkers on the Hambleton Hills.

Q P

YORK
Masons Arms
6 Fishergate, YO10 4AB

- ▶ A19 Fishergate/Paragon Street jct, on the Ouse
- T (01904) 646046
- W masonsarmsyork.co.uk
- John Smith's Bitter; guest beers
- Four double rooms, all en-suite
- £ ££ (room only)
- Snacks and meals daily, lunchtime and evening
- Accepted

The Masons Arms is a legend in its own lunchtime, providing gargantuan portions of wonderful home-made food at budget prices that draw university students, locals and visitors alike – think platters of freshly carved roast with seven different vegetables and home-made Yorkshire pud, fresh fish with hand-cut chips, slow roast belly pork topped with black pudding. Sadly this largesse does not extend to breakfast, the only meal not served, but many guests eat that in Wetherspoons across the road.

The bedrooms are in a separate, quiet annexe to the rear with free parking (a bonus in York). Cosy and nicely decorated, all have en-suite shower room and are immaculately clean – the landlady is very strict on that. All are equipped with TV, tea and coffee making, hair dryer and radio alarm clock.

The Masons Arms is a Tudor-style building built in 1935 as a flagship project by the local Tadcaster Tower Brewery, and has two large bars with three real fires, serving three guest beers as well as the John Smith's. Local attractions nearby include Clifford's Tower, Jorvik Viking Centre and the River Ouse.

P ⇌

South Yorkshire

BRADFIELD DALE
☆ Strines Inn
Mortimer Road, S6 6JE

- ▶ On A57 Snake Pass
- T (0114) 2851247
- F (0114) 2851247
- Bradfield Farmers Pale Ale; Jennings Cocker Hoop; Marston's Pedigree; guest beers
- Three double rooms, all en-suite
- £ ££
- Snacks and meals daily, lunchtime and evening
- Accepted

Situated high up on Snake Pass in the Peak District national park, it is hard to believe that this inn is within the environs of Sheffield. The Strines Inn stands exactly 1,000 feet above sea level in glorious walking country. It gets its name, which means 'meeting of the water', from the eight reservoirs dotted around it.

The pub itself dates back to 1275 when it was built as a manor house, although most of the present building was rebuilt and extended in the 1560s, and it did not become an inn until 1771. Inside are three rooms, each with an open fire, all containing ancient artefacts. The history of the pub is displayed on the walls. Among the regular ales is one from Bradfield Brewery nearby, brewed with pure Peak water.

The three double rooms are full of character, all with four-poster beds and patchwork quilts, beams, exposed stone and fireplaces aplenty, plus TV and tea and coffee making. The room rate includes a big English breakfast. Meat from local farms is used on the main menu that offers roast beef in a giant Yorkshire pud, fresh fish and grilled steaks.

Places to visit include the Blue John Mine and castle at Castleton, and the historic Chatsworth house at Bakewell, seen in the recent film of Pride and Prejudice.

Q P

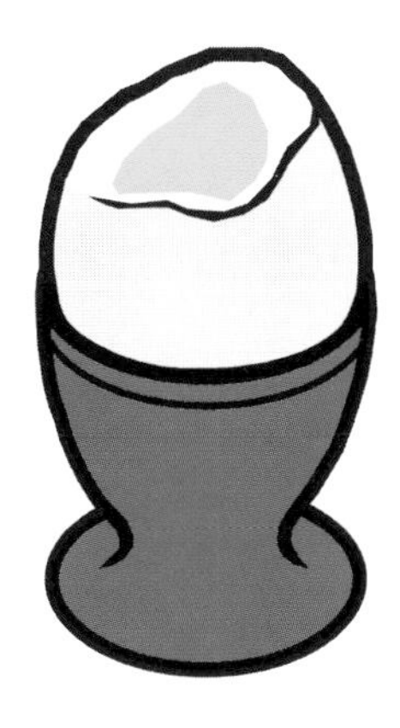

CUBLEY
Cubley Hall
Mortimer Road, S36 9DF

- ▶ Between A616 and A628, off A6102 north of Sheffield
- T (01226) 766086
- E cubley.hall@ukonline.co.uk
- Tetley Bitter, Imperial, Burton Ale; guest beers
- Eleven double, one twin room, all available as singles, all en-suite
- £ £££ (single occupancy from £60)
- Lunchtime and evening meals
- Accepted

Built in the 1700s as a moorland farmhouse, Cubley Hall was later a gentleman's residence, then a children's home for a while after the war. It became a free house in 1983, with a splendid restaurant, converted from an oak beamed barn, added in 1990. The bedrooms were opened in 1996 when the building was sympathetically extended in keeping with the original architecture. The guest rooms offer all the comforts of a country house hotel, with Sky television and tea and coffee making facilities. Children are welcome to stay and two rooms accommodate families.

The breakfast menu is more varied than most; as well as the usual continental breakfast or full English, you can also choose scrambled eggs served with mushrooms or smoked salmon, or an omelette with bacon and mushrooms or cheese and tomato. Good food ranges from gourmet pizzas in the garden conservatory to modern cuisine based on local produce in the restaurant.

At the edge of the Peak District National Park, the Hall lies near the Trans-Pennine Cycle Trail and a 16-mile waymarked walk starts from the pub car park. Nearby Sheffield and Leeds offer excellent shopping and entertainment. P

ROTHERHAM
Carlton Park Hotel
102-104 Moorgate Road, S60 2BQ

- ▶ Near M1 jct 33
- T (01709) 849955
- F (01709) 368960
- W carltonparkhotel.com
- Beer range varies
- Fifty-five double, twenty-one twin, four family rooms, all en-suite; some wheelchair accessible, one is fully adapted for disabled guests
- £ ££££ (£78 single occupancy)
- Lunchtime and evening meals
- Accepted

Right at the top of our price range, the Carlton Park Hotel has just been completely refurbished, and the guest rooms offer a high standard of decor and facilities. If you are travelling on business and want to unwind you can take advantage of the hotel's health suite, with gym, spa, sauna and solarium. As the hotel caters mainly for business clients (it has 10 conference rooms), weekend guests can take advantage of cheaper rates, or you can splash out on a 'romantic package' complete with champagne, chocolates and flowers in a suite or four-poster room.

There is a choice of a full Yorkshire breakfast or continental version. You can dine in the rather grand Regency Restaurant or the slightly less formal conservatory or have a quick lunch in the bar. The latter, furnished with leather chesterfields, offers a choice of local ales, from Acorn, Kelham Island and Rotherham's own Wentworth Brewery.
Q P

SHEFFIELD

Hillsborough Hotel

54-58 Langsett Road, S6 2UB

- ▶ Off northbound A61 dual carriageway, ½ mile from city centre
- T (0114) 232 2100
- Beer range varies
- Three double rooms (one can accommodate an extra single bed and all can be let as singles), three twin rooms, all en-suite
- £ £ (room only); single rate £35
- Lunchtime and evening meals
- Accepted

The 100-year-old Hillsborough is an unassuming building from the outside but inside is an attractive, modern bar and sunny conservatory, six guest rooms upstairs and a brewery in the cellar. The pub changed hands in 2006 but the new owners are continuing to brew Crown and Wellington beers (Wellington was the pub's former name). The eight handpumps dispense two home-brewed ales alongside six guests that change constantly; it is not uncommon for 25 or 30 different beers to be sold in a week. The well-established weekly quiz night on Tuesday and folk evening on Sunday continue to be popular.

The pub was renovated at the end of the 1990s when the upstairs accommodation was converted into six letting rooms, all with TV and facilities for making tea and coffee; an ironing board, iron and alarm clock can be provided on request. The rates charged are for room only, guests can choose either a full English breakfast for £5 or continental for £3.50.

Sheffield is noted for its real ale pubs – the Hillsborough is one of six on a recognised circuit and lies on the tram route from the city centre. Q

West Yorkshire

BRADFORD

☆ New Beehive Inn

171 Westgate, BD1 3AA

T (01274) 721784
W newbeehiveinn.co.uk
Kelham Island Best Bitter, Pale Rider; Salamander Mud Puppy; guest beers
Four double, four twin, three family, five single rooms, all en-suite
£ £ (room only)
Snacks and meals daily, lunchtime and evening
Accepted

This gas-lit pub half a mile from the city centre has a worthy place in CAMRA's national inventory for its carefully preserved, historic interior. The Edwardian inn was built in 1901 and retains virtually all its original Arts and Crafts features and oak panelling, as well as a superb mahogany back bar and pine/oak bar counters. It still has the original five drinking areas, with the addition of a cellar bar 13 years ago.

The New Beehive is at the top of a hill and the bedrooms have a fine view over the city. The rooms are all en-suite and have Sky TV, tea and coffee making, a 24-hour laundry facility, and access to a secretarial service. The budget price does not include breakfast, which is £6 for the full English. Continental can be delivered to your room for an early start. The inn has the added bonus of a large car park.

Literary societies meet here and Monday is poetry night. The National Film and Photography Museum is close by and Salts Mill with the David Hockney gallery.

Q P

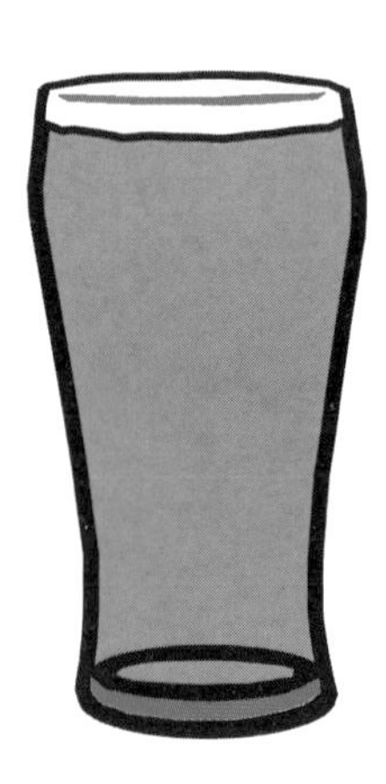

DARRINGTON

Chestnut House Hotel

Great North Road, WF8 3HR

▶ Off A1 near Ferrybridge intersection
T (01977) 600046
F (01977) 600661
W thechestnuthousehotel.co.uk
Shepherd Neame Spitfire; Timothy Taylor Golden Best, Landlord; guest beers
Fifteen double, two twin, two family rooms, all en-suite; one room adapted for disabled guests
£ ££ (single occupancy £50.95)
Lunchtime and evening meals
Accepted

The Chestnut House is a modern hotel easily accessible by road or air (Doncaster's Robin Hood Airport is a 20-minute drive) and close to Pontefract Monkhill Station. Built in the 1950s, it was recently refurbished and offers some of the facilities that are hard to find in a traditional pub building, in particular a fully-designated guest room for disabled visitors, which can be set up with a king-size or twin beds as required, with an extended desk for wheelchair access and properly-equipped bathroom. The rooms are ideal for business travellers, with modern amenities such as double glazing and individually controlled heating to ensure a good night's sleep. There is also a bridal suite with romantic four-poster bed.

Family run, the hotel has a main bar area that stocks a varied range of real ales and two restaurants offering meals based on local produce. For breakfast, the full English comes with fried, poached or scrambled eggs, accompanied by toast and yogurt or grapefruit.

There are good leisure facilities in the area including the new Xscape complex at Castleford, with a snowdome for skiing and snowboarding, rock or ice climbing and other attractions. Q ❀ ♣

HAWORTH

☆ Haworth Old Hall

8 Sun Street, BD22 8BP

T (01535) 642709
W hawortholdhall.co.uk
Jennings Bitter, Cumberland Ale, Cocker Hoop, Sneck Lifter, seasonal beer; Banks's Original; guest beers
One double, one twin room, both en-suite
£ ££
Snacks and meals daily, lunchtime and evening
Accepted

Near the home of the Brontë family but a world away from their parsonage, this imposing 16th-century Tudor manor house was named Yorkshire Tourist Board Yorkshire Pub of the Year 2006. One of the oldest buildings in the village, it was formerly known as Emmott Hall, and is entered by a formidable, studded oak front door. Inside you will find stone floors, arches, mullioned windows and a bar that looks positively baronial with its huge stone inglenook and beamed ceiling.

The Old Hall has just two letting rooms, a double and a twin, but they are quite beautiful and good value for high quality accommodation. The tariff includes breakfast – continental is served from 9.30am and the full English from 10am.

All food is freshly prepared to order using local produce where possible. A tempting menu offers a good choice of dishes including steak and Jennings ale pie, three slices of black pudding with bacon in wine and mustard sauce, a whole shoulder of lamb slow cooked in red wine, and stilton, spinach and walnut roast.

Locla attractions include the Haworth Parsonage Museum, famous main street paved with stone cobbles and lined with shops, galleries, inns and cafes, Bronte Weaving Shed, and the Keighley & Worth Valley Light Railway. ❀ P

MARSDEN

Tunnel End Inn

Waters Road, HD7 6NF

- ▶ Off B6107 between Huddersfield and Oldham
- T (01484) 844636
- W tunnelendinn.com
- Black Sheep Best Bitter; Taylor Landlord; guest beers
- Self-contained apartment that can accommodate a family, two couples, or single person
- £ ££ (room only)
- Lunchtime and evening meals
- Accepted

Bev and Gary Earnshaw are living the dream. In the spring of 2002 they were out walking in 'Summer Wine' country and fancied a pint, but the pub they came across was closed for business. So there and then they decided to buy it and turn it into the sort of place they would like to visit. They have succeeded admirably – the Tunnel End is a haven for regulars and visitors, the perfect place for a drink, meal or even to stay for a night or two.

This is not a traditional B&B pub as the accommodation is self-catering (£30 per person per night), but the Earnshaws will provide a continental breakfast if required or you can head into the village for a cooked breakfast. The apartment, with bedroom, lounge, fully equipped kitchen area, bathroom and shower has its own entrance. You can take main meals in the pub if you wish - the good, home-made food is recommended.

Marsden is surrounded by NT land and is perhaps best known for the revitalised Huddersfield Narrow Canal and Standedge Tunnel, which at three and a half miles is the longest, deepest and highest in Britain. The visitor centre is practically opposite the pub. Q

SHELLEY
Three Acres
Roydhouse, HD8 8LR

▶ Off A636 past Emley Moor mast
T (01484) 602606
F (01484) 608411
W 3acres.com
Black Sheep Best Bitter; Taylor Landlord; Tetley Bitter
Ten double, one twin, eight single rooms, one suite, all en-suite
£ ££-£££
Snacks and meals daily, lunchtime and evening
Accepted

Only 10 minutes from the M1 but set in the lush countryside of the Pennines south of Huddersfield, the Three Acres is a hundred-year-old drovers' inn renowned for fine dining. This mellow stone-built pub has two restaurants, a seafood bar and also serves meals in the bar. It incorporates a delicatessen selling a whole range of speciality foods.

Accommodation is in 20 spacious, beautifully decorated and well equipped rooms, 10 of them 'the cottages', set in their own gardens. The room rate varies depending on whether you stay midweek or at the weekend, and includes the full English with home-made sausages and black pudding, Hinchliffe's dry cure bacon and free-range eggs, Alex Spink's kippers or Arbroath smokies. Main meals might include steak, kidney and Black Sheep pie, Lunesdale duck, moorland lamb, or home-made Cumberland sausages, priced around £15.

Situated in the shadow of Emley Moor TV mast, the inn is five minutes from the National Mining Museum, Yorkshire sculpture park, and Holmfirth, famous as the setting for Last of the Summer Wine. Chatsworth House, Nostell Priory and Harewood House are all an easy drive away.

P

SILSDEN
Bridge Inn
62 Keighley Road, BD20 0EA

▶ On A6034
T (01535) 653144
E jollybusman55@msn.com
Copper Dragon Golden Pippin, Scotts 1816; Greene King IPA, Abbot; Wychwood Hobgoblin
One twin, one family, one single room, all en-suite
£ £
Lunchtime and evening meals
Not accepted

The oldest pub in town, built in 1799, the Bridge was originally known as the Spoon and Slipper. It lies alongside the Leeds-Liverpool navigation, but predates the canal and has witnessed many changes in its time. The pub's back door was originally the front entrance when the present back street was Silsden's main thoroughfare. By another quirk of its layout, the pub's pleasant canalside garden is accessed via the cellar.

This traditional old hostelry attracts walkers, cyclists and boaters but mainly caters for a local clientele; it has a pool room and darts and dominoes are also played. Major sporting events are shown on TV and at the weekend it hosts a disco.

Overnight guests do not need to worry about too much disturbance, however, as the accommodation is in a cottage next door and the rooms, all equipped with TV and hospitality tray, have separate access from the pub. Children and pets are welcome to stay. A hearty Yorkshire cooked breakfast of bacon, sausage, eggs, mushroom, hash browns, beans and tomatoes is served.

The Bridge makes an inexpensive base for exploring the Dales and Brontë country – just 20 minutes' drive away.

Q

SOWERBY BRIDGE

Alma Inn

Cotton Stones, HX6 4NS

- ▶ Off A58, between Sowerby Bridge and Ripponden
- T (01422) 823334
- F (01422) 825450
- W almainn.com
- Taylor Golden Best, Landlord; Tetley Bitter
- Three double, one twin, one family room, all en-suite
- £ ££ (single occupancy £49.50)
- Meals and snacks served all day
- Accepted

Built around the time of the Crimean War, the pub retains original features including stone-flagged floors, exposed stone walls and open hearths. As well as real ale, the bar offers a specialist menu, with tasting notes, of some 100 Belgian beers.

The restaurant is a recent addition, built in 2003. It offers a strongly Italian-influenced menu and has a proper wood-burning pizza oven, so you can be assured of the genuine article. All the food here is cooked to order and meals and snacks are available all day – good news for the many hungry walkers who stop by. The pub stands close to the 50-mile Calderdale Way and benefits from a large garden and patios.

Some of the guest bedrooms offer panoramic country views and some feature original fireplaces and exposed stone walls. All rooms are simply but attractively furnished and have TV, hospitality tray and Wifi connection. Cots are provided free of charge, under-12s sharing a parent's room are charged £9.95 for B&B, over 12s £30. Pets are welcome. A full English breakfast is provided.

Q P

Scotland

Borders

ALLANTON

Allanton Inn

Main Street, TD11 3JZ

- ▶ On B6437
- T (01890) 818260
- W allantoninn.co.uk
- Beer range varies
- Five double, one twin, one single room, all en-suite
- £ £££
- Lunchtime and evening meals and afternoon tea
- Accepted

Dating back to the first half of the 18th century, this former coaching inn stands in a small village surrounded by arable land. The Rivers Blackadder and Whiteadder (increasingly popular for game fishing) flow past a short stroll from the inn, so fishing parties often number among the guests, but walkers, cyclists, tourists and business people also visit. Paxton House, Duns, Floors and Wedderburn Castles are all nearby.

The restaurant is at the front of the hotel, serving delicious award-winning food on a daily changing menu, based very much on local produce such as lobster from St Abbs and fish from Eyemouth. Behind the restaurant, the bar always offers an interesting selection of real ales – up to three are stocked at any one time. The hotel also has a tea room.

The inn is reminiscent of a country house hotel with antique furnishings and log fires. The same style continues throughout the recently-refurbished guest rooms, offering spacious accommodation with modern amenities such as flat screen TV, DVD and CD player. A generous breakfast includes porridge or cereals and a full platter including sausage, black pudding, fried bread and mushrooms with fried or scrambled eggs.

Q P

AUCHENCROW

Craw Inn

Reston, TD14 5LS

- On B6437, follow tourist board signs from A1
- T (01890) 761253
- W thecrawinn.co.uk
- Beer range varies
- One double, one twin, one family room, all en-suite
- £ ££ (£ single room)
- Lunchtime and evening meals daily
- Accepted

In a tranquil spot with a view of the Lammermuir Hills, but just minutes from the A1, the village of Auchencrow has an interesting history and stories of witchcraft abound. The 18th-century Craw Inn is a listed building that has been completely refurbished to offer old-fashioned charm with modern facilities, including three guest rooms with private bathrooms.

Visitors come to enjoy the surrounding countryside – there is salmon fishing on the River Tweed and several golf courses in the vicinity, while horse riding, shooting and diving can also be arranged. The village is convenient for several long distance footpaths, including St Cuthbert's Way, the Southern Upland Way and the Pennine Way.

The hearty restaurant menu uses mainly local and some organically produced ingredients with flair, while bar meals range from snacks to light meals. Porridge, naturally, features on the breakfast menu. The inn caters for small parties and has a private dining room for business meetings or special dinners.

Room rates are at the top end of the price bracket, but a single can be had for £45. Special rates apply for two-day breaks.

Q P

CHIRNSIDE

Waterloo Arms Hotel

Allanton Road, TD11 3XH

- On A6105 between Berwick and Duns
- T (01890) 818034
- W waterlooarms.com
- Caledonian Deuchars IPA; Hadrian & Border Farne Island Pale Ale; guest beer (occasionally)
- Two double, one twin/double, all en-suite, two singles with shared bathroom
- £ ££
- Meals served daily from noon - 8.30pm
- Accepted

The Waterloo Arms was acquired in 2002 by an American couple who decided to abandon the rat race in the States in favour of renovating and running an inn in rural Scotland. Their decision paid off as the pub not only attracts visitors from America but is also a comfortable and popular village local. Its restaurant combines traditional Scottish fare with favourites from across the pond, such as home-made beef burgers and Cajun specials.

The good-value guest rooms vary in price according to their facilities – the singles with shared bathroom are just £25 per night and can be booked for children if parents want some privacy. Pets are welcome. Two rooms feature four-posters, one is decorated in French country style, the other has a heavy super-king-sized wooden four-poster complemented by Georgian style furnishings. This room has an attractive little sitting area and at £70 per night is the most expensive. The inn offers a choice of continental breakfast with fresh fruit and cheese, or a cooked meal with local free-range eggs.

There are many places of tourist interest to visit such as Ayton Castle and Manderston country house. Cycling, walking and fishing can all be enjoyed nearby and the owners can also organise golfing holidays. Q

CLOVENFORDS

Clovenfords Country Hotel

1 Vine Street, TD1 3LU

T (01896) 850203
W clovenfordshotel.co.uk
Greene King Old Speckled Hen
Two double, four twin-bedded rooms (one wheelchair accessible), all en-suite
£ £££
Food is served all day from noon until 9.30pm, late dinners and early breakfasts can be arranged and packed lunches provided
Accepted

Frequented by cyclists, anglers and walkers, Clovenfords lies on the Sir Walter Scott route, which is apt as the author was a regular visitor. Opened in 1750, the hotel has changed little over the years, retaining much of its original charm and offering cosy seats by a log fire or in the turreted bay windows. A conservatory restaurant has been added.

All the guest rooms have recently been refurbished to a high standard, offering colour TV, facilities for making hot drinks, trouser press and hair dryer. They all benefit from lovely views of the surrounding countryside where visitors can enjoy trout and salmon fishing, deer stalking, game shooting or horse riding. The hotel keeps plenty of tourist information on walking and cycling routes and historic houses to visit. It can also arrange a discount at most local golf clubs.

Children and pets are welcome at this friendly, family-run hotel, where the emphasis is on home-cooked food using as much local produce as possible, including fresh fish from Eyemouth. Guests with special dietary needs can always be catered for. You will be offered a full Scottish breakfast, as well as kippers and fruit.
Q P

DENHOLM

Fox & Hounds Inn

Main Street, TD9 8NU

On A698, 5 miles from Hawick and Jedburgh
T (01450) 870247
W foxandhoundsinndenholm.co.uk
Wylam Gold Tankard; guest beer
Two double, one twin room with shared bathroom
£ £
Lunchtime and evening meals and snacks
Accepted

Built in the early 18th century, this village local was the place where all the workers for surrounding farms were hired and fired. Overlooking the green, it remains an unpretentious pub with plain furnishings, but none the less cheery, especially in winter when a real fire burns in the grate of the cosy public bar. Cask ales are served through an antique fount, dating from 1925, and there are always two different beers available. Pub games including dominoes are played here and folk musicians occasionally perform. Lunches are served in the lounge and evening meals in the upstairs restaurant.

The guest rooms are in the adjacent cottage and again simplicity is the key. At present all three rooms share a bathroom, but an en-suite should be installed in one room by the time this guide is published. Children under three are free of charge and a cot can be supplied. Pets are welcome. The cottage has its own residents' lounge, with an open fire and television, a courtyard and garden; there is an outdoor play area for children. A full cooked Scottish breakfast is provided, with porridge if required, or you can simply have eggs prepared as you like them. Q P

ETTRICKBRIDGE

Cross Keys Inn

TD7 5JN

- ▶ On B7009, 6 miles from Selkirk
- T (01750) 52224
- W crosskeys-ettrickbridge.co.uk
- Beer range varies
- Three double, two family rooms, all en-suite, plus self-catering cottages
- £ ££
- Lunchtime and evening meals
- Accepted

Local CAMRA members say in the 2007 Good Beer Guide that entering this 17th-century family-run pub is like stepping into a time warp. The bar is crammed with all sorts of memorabilia from water jugs to stuffed animals, while the walls are hung with old photographs of local worthies.

The thee-star guest accommodation in the bedrooms and self-catering courtyard cottages is rustic in style, with hand-made pine furniture, but offers modern facilities such as TV, hair dryer and hospitality tray. Pets can be accommodated. In the morning you can enjoy local produce including organic free-range eggs in a full cooked Scottish breakfast or a simpler continental alternative.

Walkers, cyclists, anglers and golf fans enjoy the peaceful surroundings of this tranquil spot in the historic Ettrick Valley, where sometimes the only sound you can hear is the baa of sheep. Tourists can head off to sites such as Traquair House, the oldest inhabited house in Scotland, with its own brewery, or Bowhill house and country park noted for its collection of paintings, and Abbotsford, home of novelist Sir Walter Scott.

Q P

LAUDER

Black Bull

13-15 Market Place, TD2 6SR

- ▶ On A68, 28 miles south of Edinburgh
- T (01578) 722208
- F (01578) 722419
- W blackbull-lauder.com
- Broughton Brewery ales; guest beers
- Four double, two twin, two family rooms, all en-suite
- £ £££
- Lunchtime and evening meals
- Accepted

If you've just come off the Southern Upland Way or been out in the fresh air all day, fishing or game shooting, then what better way to recover than with a pint of Broughton ale or a fine malt by the fire in the Black Bull's wonderful traditional bar?

This 18th-century inn offers every modern comfort but retains its period character in all areas, including the richly-decorated Georgian dining room and the eight individually-styled guest rooms. The spacious rooms are furnished with antiques and original artworks; hospitality tray, TV, hair dryer and luxurious toiletries are supplied and Internet access is available. Children are welcome and pets can be accommodated.

A good choice is offered to start your day: a variety of cereals, porridge, fruit and yogurt followed by a full Scottish breakfast, scrambled eggs (plain or with smoked salmon), boiled free-range eggs or a continental plate with cheese, salami and prosciutto. This award-winning pub also serves an imaginative menu in the bar and restaurant, using local beef and lamb, and game in season, with daily specials.

Surrounded by the Lammermuir Hills and within easy reach of the capital, Lauder has much to offer visitors.

Q P

MELROSE

☆ Burts Hotel

Market Square, TD6 9PL

- ▶ Town centre
- T (01896) 822285
- F (01896) 822870
- W burtshotel.co.uk
- Caledonian Deuchars IPA, 80/-; Taylor Landlord
- Four double, nine twin, seven single rooms, all en-suite
- £ ££££
- Lunch and evening meals daily
- Accepted

This elegant hotel was built in 1722 and has been run by the Hendersons for over 35 years. Many of its visitors are corporate clients using the conference facilities or shooting parties; prices for the rooms and in the restaurant reflect this (the set price for a three-course evening meal is around £32). The food, much of it sourced locally, is excellent and the less formal bar/bistro offers cheaper options that may appeal to families. Children are welcome.

There is plenty of choice on the breakfast menu. The buffet offers fresh fruit or fruit compôte, cereals, rolls, oatcakes and yogurt, while the cooked menu includes porridge and grilled kippers, eggs prepared as you like them, potato scones, tomato and mushrooms. You will also be offered bacon, sausages and black pudding from Ramsay's of Carluke.

The charming guest rooms are all individually decorated and well appointed with all you need for a comfortable stay. There are plenty of leisure amenities locally and Melrose is famous for rugby – the hotel gets extremely busy during Melrose Sevens week and real ale may not be available then, although you will always find a choice of some 80 plus malt whiskies.

Q P

SELKIRK

Heatherlie House Hotel

7 Heatherlie Park, TD7 5AL

▶ Half a mile west of Selkirk centre
T (01750) 721200
F (01750) 720005
W heatherlie.freeserve.co.uk
Broughton Brewery ales; guest beer
Seven double/twin rooms including two family, all en-suite
£ £££
Lunchtime and evening meals
Accepted (not Amex)

Scotland is said to be the cradle of golf, and nowhere is that more evident than in Selkirk – over 20 golf courses are within striking distance of this hotel, so it is no surprise that golfing breaks are a feature here. The proprietors can also organise clay pigeon shooting and fishing permits in advance of your arrival by arrangement. Friendly service is the hallmark of this small family-run hotel. Packed lunches can be provided for guests embarking on a day's walking, cycling or other outdoor pursuit.

Originally a Victorian villa, the Heatherlie stands in two acres of peaceful wooded grounds. The bar and lounge have recently been refurbished but without losing any sense of grandeur; note the intricate hand-carved fireplace depicting owls.

The en-suite guest rooms have TV, hair dryer and tea and coffee making facilities. Two rooms are large enough for children to stay and a cot can be provided. A varied menu is offered at breakfast – you choose what you wish from a list of cooked ingredients, accompanied by fruit juice, cereal or yogurt. Local produce is used as far as possible in all meals. The bar always stocks a Broughton ale, supplemented by a guest in summer.

P

SWINTON
Wheatsheaf
Main Street, TD11 3JJ

- ▶ Off A6112 between Duns and Coldstream
- T (01890) 860257
- W wheatsheaf-swinton.co.uk
- Caledonian Deuchars IPA; guest beer
- Eight double, one twin, one family room, all en-suite; one room wheelchair accessible
- £ ££££
- Lunchtime and evening meals
- Accepted (not Amex)

Featuring in CAMRA's Good Pub Food guide, the Wheatsheaf's award-winning kitchen is renowned for its food; the inn describes itself as a 'restaurant with rooms'. A member of the Scottish Beef Club, all its beef comes from prime Scottish animals, fruit and vegetables come from local growers and other fine ingredients are sourced from around the world. The menus are complemented by an excellent wine list and real ales from Scottish breweries, such as Broughton.

With these credentials it is no surprise that the breakfast here is something special. Freshly-squeezed orange juice is accompanied by a compôte of stewed fruits or fresh grapefruit, followed by a full Scottish breakfast, or fish such as kippers, smoked salmon with free-range scrambled eggs or lightly-poached smoked haddock with poached egg.

The guest rooms, graded four star by the Scottish Tourist Board, have superior bathroom fittings, TV and hospitality tray. Three new executive rooms feature king-sized beds, plasma screen TV with Freeview and DVD player.

With many guests at the Wheatsheaf visiting the Borders to enjoy the country pursuits nearby – fishing, walking, golf and cycling – the inn provides a rod room, drying room and cycle shelter. Q P

TOWN YETHOLM
Plough Hotel
Main Street, TD5 8RF

- ▶ On main road between Kelso and Coldstream
- T (01573) 420215
- F (01890) 882830
- W ploughhotelyetholm.co.uk
- Theakston Best Bitter; guest beer
- Three double, two twin rooms, mostly en-suite
- £ ££ (single occupancy £35)
- Lunchtime and evening meals and snacks
- Accepted

An ideal stopover for walkers, the Plough stands on St Cuthbert's Way between Melrose and Lindisfarne and is at the northern end of the Pennine Way. In 1999 Yetholm was established as the terminal point of the ambitious E2 footpath that will extend across mainland Europe.

After a hard day's trek walkers will appreciate a proper soak in the bathtub in the spacious en-suite bathrooms attached to most of the rooms here (one double and one twin, let as a family room, share facilities). The rooms themselves are large and airy, recently refurbished to a high standard and equipped with TV and hospitality tray. Before setting off again in the morning you can fuel up with a full and hearty Scottish breakfast; French toast with maple syrup is a lighter alternative. Children are welcome and pets can be accommodated by prior arrangement.

The pub itself is a friendly village local with a public bar, games room and pleasant dining room where you can enjoy home-cooked fare. Town Yetholm lies just a mile across the border from England and is separated from Kirk Yetholm by Bowmount Water. ♣ P

Central

DOLLAR

Castle Campbell Hotel

11 Bridge Street, FK14 7DE

- ▶ Follow the A91 into Dollar town centre; the hotel is by the bridge
- T (01259) 742519
- F (01259) 743742
- W castle-campbell.co.uk
- Harviestoun Bitter & Twisted; guest beer
- Four double, three twin, one single room; one room can accommodate a family, all en-suite
- £ £££
- Lunch and evening meals
- Accepted (not Diners Club)

If you enjoy the regional produce served at the Castle Campbell Hotel, the proprietors will happily provide you with information about their suppliers, including Iain Mellis cheeses, Mackies ice cream and Campbell Brothers meat. The most local supplier is Harviestoun Brewery in Alva, whose Bitter & Twisted was voted Best Beer in Britain in 2003. Also on the bar you will find a selection of over 70 single malt whiskies supplied by Gordon & McPhail of Elgin.

At breakfast you can sample some of Scotland's finest ingredients, including Loch Fyne kippers, award-winning haggis and black pudding from Cockburns in Dingwall. The comprehensive breakfast menu also offers home-made yogurt, porridge and cream, grills, smoked haddock with poached egg or smoked salmon with scrambled egg. At other mealtimes, a varied menu caters for all tastes, including vegetarians and children.

This early 19th-century coaching inn has eight attractive rooms, all with en-suite facilities. Ideally located within an hour of Edinburgh, Glasgow, Stirling, Perth and St Andrews, from here you can explore the Ochil Hills and Dollar Glen with its spectacular gorges and waterfalls. Castle Campbell, the Wallace Monument, Stirling Castle and Falkirk Wheel are all within a half-hour drive.

Q P

Winnock Hotel, Drymen, Central

DRYMEN
Winnock Hotel
The Square, G63 0BL

▶ Off A811 at village centre
T (01360) 660245
W winnockhotel.com
Caledonian Deuchars IPA, 80/; guest beers
Twenty-four double, nineteen twin, fifteen family, five single rooms, all en-suite; two rooms wheelchair accessible
£ ££££
Meals and snacks served all day
Accepted

This lovely old coaching inn stands on the pretty village green on the eastern side of Loch Lomond. It has recently been the subject of complete refurbishment and modernisation by the Best Western group to provide guest rooms of individual character; many of them are spacious enough to accommodate families and two are adapted for disabled visitors. Some are designated 'superior' and have a private balcony or terrace.

Care has also been taken in the public rooms to retain the original features of the 18th-century building, with tartan carpets and hunting trophies ensuring a highland flavour. Scottish flavours abound, too, on the menu in the Highlander restaurant with local beef, lamb and venison offered alongside fish caught in the loch or sea and cooked to order. Meals and snacks are also served in the bar. A full Scottish breakfast or continental version is offered to overnight guests. The Oak Room and Garden Room are frequently booked for corporate or other events. Murder Mystery weekends are an established feature here.

Situated on the West Highland Way, and an ideal venue for a rural break, the hotel has been recognised by the Green Tourism Scheme for its excellent environmental practice.

DUNBLANE
Dunblane Hotel
10 Stirling Road, FK15 9EP

▶ Next to railway station
T (01786) 822178
E mcleandunblanehotel@ecosse.net
Greene King Abbot; Kelburn Dark Moor; Taylor Landlord; guest beers
Two double, two twin, two family rooms, all en-suite
£ ££
Lunchtime and evening meals
Accepted

This small family-run hotel was built in the late 18th century as a coaching inn on the main route from the north of England to Glasgow and Edinburgh. It remains easily accessible from both these cities either by road or train – the station is right next to the hotel and journey times are just over an hour to Edinburgh and under 50 minutes to Glasgow.

The pub is a popular stop off for commuters on their way home. The comfortable bar, decorated with old brewery mirrors, frequently stocks guests from Scottish micro-breweries such as Houston, Fyne and Tryst. Sky Sports can be viewed in the bar while the lounge offers a more peaceful panorama of the River Allan. In the dining area you can enjoy traditional pub food based on local produce, with daily specials. The pub also has a sheltered garden.

The guest rooms all have en-suite facilities and children and pets can be accommodated. In the morning cereals and fruit juice are followed by a traditional 'English' breakfast. The River Allan is good for salmon and trout fishing and the hotel can arrange fishing or golfing breaks.

KIPPEN

Cross Keys Hotel

Main Street, FK8 3DN

- ▶ Off A811, 10 miles west of Stirling
- T (01786) 870293
- E crosskeys@kippen70.fsnet.co.uk
- Harviestoun Bitter & Twisted; guest beers
- Two twin rooms, one en-suite
- £ ££
- Lunchtime and evening meals
- Accepted (not Amex)

This 300-year-old inn has maintained a tradition of welcoming travellers since its coaching days. A comfortable, olde-worlde hostelry at the centre of the village, with stone walls, wood panelling and coal fires, it is popular with locals and visitors. Dogs are welcome in the public bar and can be accommodated overnight. The Harviestoun ale is occasionally supplemented by a Belhaven or Caledonian brew.

The guest rooms are sited away from the bar, so you are assured of a peaceful night's rest. The en-suite room is the larger of the two (£10 per night more); the second room has a private bathroom. Both have TV and hospitality tray; children are welcome to stay. The breakfast menu offers freshly squeezed orange juice, cereals or porridge followed by a full cooked meal with choice of eggs, poached smoked haddock or scrambled eggs with smoked salmon. The kitchen sources much of its produce locally – the butcher is in Kippen – and provides an inviting main menu of mostly home-made dishes that changes regularly.

On the road to Loch Lomond, this area has many places of tourist interest, including Stirling Castle and the Wallace Monument.

Q P

STIRLING

Portcullis

Castle Wynd, FK8 1EG

- ▶ Last building on left on approach to Stirling Castle
- T (01786) 472290
- W theportcullishotel.com
- Isle of Skye Red Cuillin; Orkney Dark Island; guest beer
- One double, two twin, one single room, all en-suite
- £ £££
- Lunchtime and evening meals
- Accepted

Originally built in 1787 as a boys' school, this small, friendly, family-run hostelry was renovated ten years ago with care taken to preserve its character. The interior has exposed stone walls, log fire and traditional furnishings; outside is a pretty walled garden where drinks and meals can be taken in good weather. Next to Stirling Castle, the pub can get busy at weekends and during the tourist season.

The guest accommodation is on the second floor and most of the rooms afford impressive views over the town to the Ochil Hills. The rooms are furnished and equipped to a high standard. You can choose between a hearty breakfast of two eggs, bacon, sausage, black pudding, tomato and mushrooms or a lighter meal of smoked salmon and scrambled eggs. Children are welcome and pets can be accommodated by arrangement.

Stirling is well placed for touring Scotland by road or rail, with regular services to both Edinburgh and Glasgow, and the town itself has plenty to offer, not least the castle where Mary Queen of Scots spent her childhood, the Wallace Monument that dominates the town, the Old Jail and Argyll's Lodging. P

Dumfries

DALRY

Clachan Inn

10 Main Street, DG7 3UW

- ▶ On A713 at the village centre
- T (01644) 430241
- F (01644) 430681
- W theclachaninn.com
- Caledonian Deuchars IPA; Greene King Abbot
- Four twin, one family, one single room, all en-suite
- £ ££
- Lunchtime and evening meals and snacks
- Accepted

This popular village inn was taken over in July 2006 by chef/proprietor Jill Lawrie who is maintaining its winning formula. The pub lies on the Southern Upland Way and attracts followers of all kinds of rural pursuits, including trout fishing on a four-acre loch at the edge of town, shooting and cycling.

All the guest bedrooms have secure gun cabinets and space for drying wet clothes; the inn offers a laundry service and a separate drying room. The bedrooms are spacious, with tea and coffee making facilities and TV. The family room has two singles and a bunk bed. Pets can be accommodated by arrangement. A self-catering cottage is also available. There is a reduced accommodation rate for walkers available all year round.

You can enjoy a lie in as Jill thoughtfully serves breakfast from 7.30am until almost lunchtime. Food is good here – the full Scottish, including haggis, can be substituted for poached haddock, grilled kippers or eggs as you like them. At lunch and in the evening a varied home-cooked menu and good daily specials are served in the busy Bothy Restaurant, where you can sample local produce including venison and Garroch pheasant in season, organic lamb and freshly caught Glencree salmon.

Q

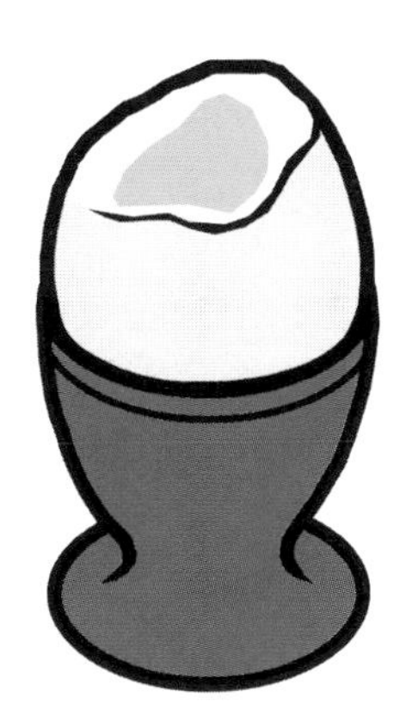

ISLE OF WHITHORN
Steam Packet Inn
Harbour Row, DG8 8LL

▶ Off A75 at Newton Stewart
T (01988) 500334
W steampacketinn.com
Theakston Best Bitter; guest beers
Five double, one twin, one family room, all en-suite
£ ££ (£ Nov-Mar)
Lunchtime and evening meals and snacks
Accepted

The hotel stands on the quayside in a picturesque fishing village on the southernmost tip of the Machars Peninsula, which has a long history of seafaring and trade, going right back to the Vikings. The harbour now attracts fishermen and leisure sailors whose comings and goings can be observed from the hotel's picture windows. The restaurant specialises in fish and seafood as well as other fresh Scottish produce; specials are chalked up twice a day on blackboards.

The hotel's public areas are free from piped music and games machines; dominoes is a popular activity in the flagstoned public bar, while the back bar houses a pool table. The guest rooms are either standard or deluxe (£10 per night more). Deluxe rooms have power shower, luxury handmade bed and a seating area by the large windows to make the most of the harbour views. All rooms have television and hospitality tray. Children are welcome at a reduced rate.

For breakfast, porridge will be cooked to order or there are cereals or yogurt to start. You can then tuck into the full 'Galloway' breakfast: bacon, sausage, egg, tattie scone, haggis and tomato, or perhaps Manx kippers or croissants with Galloway preserve or local honey. Q

KIRKCOLM
Blue Peter Hotel
23 Main Street, DG9 0NL

▶ On A718, 5 miles north of Stranraer
T (01776) 853221
W thebluepeterhotel.co.uk
Beer range varies
One double, two twin rooms, all en-suite
£ £ (single occupancy £35)
Weekend lunches and evening meals daily
Accepted

The Blue Peter has been a hotel since 1844 but the building itself dates back to 1704. The property changed hands in 2005 and has since undergone a major refurbishment of a high standard. The interior is full of interesting artefacts and antiques, with plenty of beer memorabilia in the nautically-themed public and lounge bars. The inn is a true find for beer lovers, in an area that is a real ale desert, with a choice of beers that changes as often as three times a week. The pub also stocks over 80 malt whiskies.

This traditional family-run hotel has three simply-furnished guest rooms with television and hospitality tray; the double can be adapted to suit a family and children are welcome. CAMRA members are offered special deals on accommodation. The cooked breakfast is 'the full monty'. Fresh local produce is used in all meals and any particular dietary requirements can be catered for.

Close to Loch Ryan and the hidden coves of this interesting coastline, the hotel is popular with birdwatchers, anglers, walkers and cyclists. The garden is home to red squirrels, while buzzards and a peregrine falcon can often be spotted overhead.
Q ♣ P

MOFFAT

Black Bull Hotel

Churchgate, DG10 9EG

- ▶ Off M74 jct 15, 1½ miles from A74
- T (01683) 220206
- F (01683) 220483
- W blackbullmoffat.co.uk
- Caledonian Deuchars IPA, McEwan's 80/-; Theakston Best Bitter; guest beers
- Eight double, two twin, one family, two single rooms, all en-suite; three rooms wheelchair accessible
- £ ££
- Lunchtime and evening meals
- Accepted

This 16th-century inn has a fascinating history. In the 1680s Graham of Claverhouse was based here before being sent by the English King to put down religious rebels on the border. He built the stables that now house the public bar. Known as the Railway Bar, it is full of memorabilia, particularly of the Caledonian Railway.

Across the courtyard is the main building where you will find the Claverhouse Restaurant and the Burns room – dedicated to the poet who is said to have penned his 'epigram to a scrimpit nature' while drinking at the inn. The bedrooms are also in the main hotel, three on the ground floor are wheelchair accessible. Decorated in traditional style, they all have hospitality tray and TV.

The chef obviously has a sense of humour – you might find a 'sporran' of black pudding on the recommended menu. At breakfast the full Scottish offering includes Ayrshire bacon and potato scone along with eggs, tomato, mushrooms and sausage. Porridge and cereals are also available.

The hotel has no car park but there is ample public parking nearby and bicycles can be hired, with cycling routes nearby.

NEW GALLOWAY

Cross Keys Hotel

High Street, DG7 3RN

- ▶ On A713, east of Dumfries
- T (01644) 420494
- W crosskeys-newgalloway.co.uk
- Beer range varies
- Six double, three twin rooms, all en-suite
- £ ££
- Lunchtime and evening meals
- Accepted

Exposed beams, stone walls, flagged floors and a big open fire are just some of the reasons why this pub is popular with locals and visitors alike. It usually stocks at least two real ales, predominantly from Houston. The snug was once the police station, now it houses the whisky bar with a fine selection of malts from all over Scotland, while the lounge, converted from the old police cells,

is used for bar meals – children are welcome here until 9pm. Children may also stay overnight; one double room can take a cot and another either a single or bunk beds.

Recently refurbished, the bedrooms are attractively decorated, but the Sheriff's Room is the biggest and the best with period furniture and a leather sofa. All rooms have TV, hospitality tray, complimentary mineral water and 'honesty' bar; each room has a safe for valuables. In the morning, guests can tuck into a full Scottish breakfast, complete with haggis; fainthearts can opt for the continental or smoked haddock.

New Galloway, Scotland's smallest Royal Burgh, stands at the northern end of Loch Ken and the southern edge of the Galloway National Forest.

NEW LUCE

Kenmuir Arms

31 Main Street, DG8 0AJ

▶ Overlooking River Luce off A75 near Stranraer
T (01581) 600218
W kenmuirarmsnewluce.co.uk
Houston Brewery beer, guest beer
Two double, three twin, two family rooms; three en-suite, three shared bathrooms
£ £
Snacks and meals 9am-9pm
Accepted

Overlooking the Crosswaters of Luce, this whitewashed free house in the south-west of Scotland, not far from Luce Bay, is a marvellous place for outdoor types – walking, golfing, angling, horse riding and shooting are all popular activities. The hotel has a gun locker, small workshop for essential repairs, safe storage for mountain bikes and laundry facilities. A baggage transfer service is available for walkers at a small extra charge. On the Southern Upland Way and serving food all day, the bar is often very busy with ramblers at lunchtime enjoying food made with local produce.

The rooms are a bargain, from £20 per person per night, very clean and comfortable with a pleasant guest lounge. The price includes a real Scottish breakfast – both haggis and black pudding on your plate along with bacon, sausage, eggs, fried bread, mushrooms, tomatoes and beans.

A midge buster machine in the riverside garden helps keep the wee beasties at bay while you enjoy a pint from Houston brewery, or a guest beer that might come from anywhere around the UK. The hotel is situated close to Stranraer, Kennedy Castle and Black Loch, Laggangairn standing stones, and a lovely little drive (or long hike) down the peninsula to the Mull of Galloway.

Q ❀ ♿ ♣ P

THORNHILL

Buccleuch & Queensberry Hotel

112 Drumlanrig Street, DG3 5LU

▶ On the A76 at Thornhill Cross
T (01848) 330125
F (01848) 330125
W buccleuchhotel.co.uk
Caledonian Deuchars IPA, McEwan's 80/-; Greene King Old Speckled Hen
Three double, six twin, three family rooms, all en-suite
£ ££
Lunchtime and evening meals
Accepted

Close to Drumlanrig Castle, seat of the Duke of Buccleuch, the hotel was built by the Duke in 1851 as a coaching inn. Now owned and run by the Spencer family, it continues to serve locals and travellers, and caters for those enjoying outdoor pursuits such as shooting, cycling and fishing – the River Nith nearby is famous for its salmon. The traditional bar is popular with local drinkers for its fine cask ale.

The twelve en-suite bedrooms have recently been refurbished and decorated to a three-star standard. They are fully equipped with colour TV, radio and hospitality tray. At breakfast you can help yourself to fruit juice, cereals, fresh fruit, yogurt and oatcakes and choose from a varied cooked menu of naturally-smoked haddock or oak-smoked kippers, free range eggs – including a choice of omelettes – porridge and croissants with savoury fillings such as mushroom and bacon.

The meals offered in the lounge bar and restaurant are all freshly cooked by the hotel chefs from premium Scottish products, sourced locally. Home-made bread and pastas are prepared on a daily basis.

Drumlanrig Castle is well worth a visit, noted for its beautiful gardens and art collection.

Q ❀ ♿ ♣ P

Grampian

ABERDEEN

Atholl Hotel

54 King's Gate, AB15 4YN

- ▶ West end of city, off Anderson Drive
- T (01224) 323505
- F (01224) 321555
- W atholl-aberdeen.com
- Draught Bass; Taylor Landlord
- Fourteen double, twelve twin, one family, nine single rooms, all en-suite
- £ £££
- Lunchtime and evening meals and snacks
- Accepted

This four-star privately-owned hotel lies off Anderson Drive, the city's main north-south thoroughfare to the west of the city centre. It is a few minutes by taxi from the station and five miles from Aberdeen airport. Popular with business travellers, tourists can take advantage of weekend break rates and other special offers. The rooms are comfortable and attractively furnished, with an emphasis on tartan. They are well equipped with satellite TV, trouser press, hair dryer and hospitality tray and benefit from free Internet broadband access.

The hotel restaurant is listed in CAMRA's Good Pub Food guide for its tempting dishes prepared to order with fresh local produce. The main menu changes monthly but favourites such as deep-fried haddock, 'Mince 'n' Skirlie', Moray scampi and roast rib of Scottish beef are always available. The Scottish cheeseboard is very good. For overnight guests, a full Scottish breakfast is provided.

The hotel is well situated for discovering all that Aberdeen has to offer – shopping, galleries and gardens, not forgetting the wealth of Good Beer Guide listed pubs in the city - eight in the 2007 edition. Further afield are castles to visit, Cairngorms National Park and, of course, several golf courses.

Q P

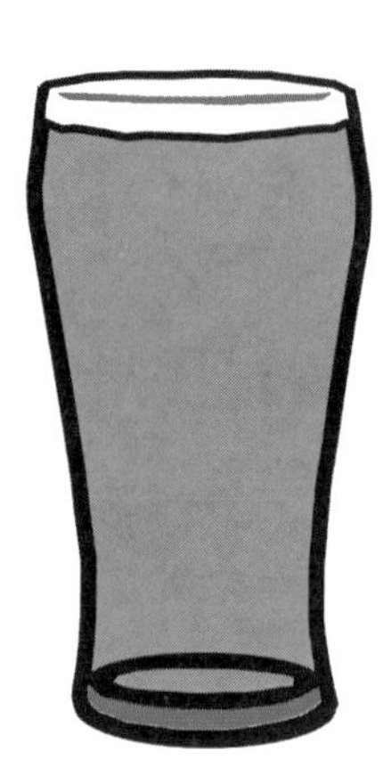

ABERDEEN

Carriages Brentwood Hotel

101 Crown Street, AB11 6HH

- ▶ Just off Union Street in city centre
- T (01224) 595440
- F (01224) 571593
- W brentwood-hotel.co.uk
- Caledonian Deuchars IPA; Courage Directors; Flowers Original; guest beers
- Thirty-one double, twenty-three single, three twin, eight family rooms, all en-suite
- £ £££ (££ weekend)
- Lunchtime and evening meals
- Accepted

Situated five minutes' walk from the rail and bus stations and a 30-minute drive from the airport, the three-star rated Brentwood Hotel is an ideal choice for both business travellers and tourists – weekend visitors can take advantage of heavily discounted rates.

The guest rooms have all been refurbished in modern style with good facilities including TV, trouser press and dataport. Two executive suites are available, both with two double beds and an adjoining lounge area. The family rooms have a double and single bed; an additional Z-bed or cot can be provided. You can help yourself to cereal, fruit juice and more at the breakfast buffet and hot items are cooked to order.

The basement bar of the hotel, Carriages, is popular with residents and locals. With ten handpumps dispensing a changing range of beers, it offers the best choice of ales in the city as well as a good selection of malt whiskies. Unlike many hotel bars it has a relaxed, friendly atmosphere and is a frequent local CAMRA award winner. The adjoining restaurant serves buffet lunches and excellent evening meals.

The Brentwood is convenient for Aberdeen's attractions: the Maritime Museum, Art Gallery, Concert Hall and shops. P

ABERLOUR

Mash Tun

Broomfield Square, AB38 9QP

- T (01340) 881771
- W mashtun-aberlour.com
- Cairngorm Trade Winds, Black Gold, seasonal beer; Houston Peter's Well, seasonal beer; guest beers
- Three double, one twin, one family room, all en-suite
- £ £££
- Snacks and meals daily, lunchtime and evening
- Accepted

This unusual curve-fronted mellow stone building was originally built for Thomas Campbell in 1896 (his initials are over the front door) by a marine architect who designed it in the shape of a boat. This handsome whisky bar also serves excellent ales from Cairngorm and Houston breweries, with other Scottish micros among the guests. The interior is made from old wood taken from local distilleries – the floor was an old wash back, the bar oregon pine taken from casks.

The five en-suite rooms, named after local distilleries Glenfiddich, Glenfarclas, Aberlour, Macallan and Glenlivet, are all comfortably furnished and decorated in the colours of the different distilleries' bottles. The room tariff includes a full Scottish breakfast with local sausages, smoked salmon with scrambled eggs, or kippers.

All meals are served in the bar, freshly prepared with locally sourced ingredients. The chef here is passionate about Scottish contemporary cooking and on the menu you might find haggis, neeps and tatties with whisky sauce, venison sausages with mash, and Aberdeen Angus rump steak with hand cut chips, prices around £10.

There is fishing and walking on the River Spey, distilleries to visit and, of course, a wee dram to finish the night. P

BANCHORY
Douglas Arms Hotel
22 High Street, AB31 5SR

- ▶ On the main street, 18 miles west of Aberdeen
- T (01330) 822547
- F (01330) 825989
- W douglasarms.co.uk
- Beer range varies
- Five double, one twin, two family rooms, all en-suite
- £ ££
- Lunchtime and evening meals
- Accepted

The beer range at the Douglas Arms changes weekly; there is usually a choice of three ales with one from a Scottish micro-brewery. You can enjoy your pint in the well preserved, classic long bar and admire the etched glass windows and vintage mirrors, or the comfortable lounge, with its leather chesterfields and warming large fireplace. The hotel also has a function room and a restaurant that serves excellent food made with local produce.

The eight guest rooms are simply furnished and equipped with hospitality tray, trouser press, hair dryer and TV. The hotel is popular with fishing and shooting parties and golfers, all of whom need a solid start to the day, so a full cooked breakfast is provided, with bacon, sausage and black pudding, or a vegetarian alternative.

The village of Banchory sits amidst some of the most spectacular scenery in Scotland. Ancient pine forests and the highest mountain range in Britain are all nearby. The hotel makes a good base for exploring this part of Scotland, with its many whisky distilleries and castles, such as Crathes nearby, while the 'granite city', Aberdeen, is just a short drive away.

♣ P

CRAIGELLACHIE
Highlander Inn
Victoria Street, AB38 9SR

- ▶ Off A95/A941 midway between Inverness and Aberdeen
- T (01340) 881446
- W whiskyinn.com
- Cairngorm Trade Winds; guest beers
- Two double, two twin, one family room, all en-suite; one room wheelchair accessible
- £ ££
- Lunchtime and evening meals
- Accepted

Situated on the Speyside Whisky Trail, the Highlander's cosy cellar bar naturally offers a fine selection of some 150 single malts, but it is also recognised as a fine pub for real ale – over 100 different guest beers have been offered here over the course of a year and tasting sessions are a regular event.

The inn changed hands in 2005 and has been undergoing a planned programme of renovation work. First, the bar, lounge and restaurant were refreshed and now all the bedrooms have been updated, too. Individually designed and well appointed, they now have 'great showers' according to the owners; one room can accommodate a wheelchair. Pets are permitted in the bedrooms.

The restaurant only seats 20 diners but meals can also be taken in the bar. Food here is good, with local produce to the fore; vegetarian and gluten-free diets can be accommodated. For breakfast there is a choice of cereal or fruit compôte, followed by free-range eggs accompanied by black pudding, bacon, sausages, mushrooms and tomatoes.

The River Spey and the Speyside walking route both run through the village, offering excellent opportunities for outdoor pursuits.

♣ P

FINDHORN
Crown & Anchor Inn
IV36 3YF

- T (01309) 690243
- F (01309) 690243
- W crownandanchorinn.co.uk
- Cairngorm Tradewinds; Taylor Landlord; guest beers
- Five double, two twin, one family room, all en-suite
- £ ££
- Lunchtime and evening meals
- Accepted

There is just one road to Findhorn, and the Crown and Anchor is the only hotel in the village, but it is well worth the journey. The village has become internationally famous for the Findhorn Foundation, which started out as a spiritual community in 1962 on a caravan site. It now has an eco-village, education centre and shop that sells an excellent range of organic bottled beers from near and far.

Findhorn offers safe water for dinghy sailors, windsurfers and waterskiers and is a haven for twitchers and wildlife lovers, not to mention the golden sands that stretch for seven miles.

The inn, recognisable by its crow-step gables, has a lovely, old-fashioned bar warmed by a wood-burning stove. By contrast, its newly updated conservatory restaurant is bistro style with modern furnishings. The guest rooms, some of which afford views of the bay, also have a contemporary look and are equipped with TV and facilities for making hot drinks. One room has a king-sized bed. A full Scottish breakfast is served, complete with porridge or cereal as well as toast and fruit juice. Locally sourced produce is used as far as possible in all the menus. ❀ ♣ P

GLENKINDIE
Glenkindie Arms Hotel
AB33 8SX

- ▶ On A97, east of Glenkindie
- T (019756) 41288
- W theglenkindiearmshotel.com
- Beer range varies
- One double, two twin/double rooms, all en-suite; one room for family use
- £ £
- Food served all day summer, evening meals only winter
- Accepted (not Amex)

This 400-year-old former drovers' inn, once a Masonic Lodge, is popular with farmers, forestry workers and locals who enjoy its cosy atmosphere and regularly-changing real ales.

With a mile of fishing rights on the River Don it is an excellent hotel for anglers, and offers fishing packages of four or six nights in season; it can even provide the services of a ghillie if notice is given. Set in beautiful scenery on the edge of the Cairngorm National Park, the hotel also attracts walkers and is close enough to the Lecht Ski Centre to be an inexpensive option for winter sports enthusiasts.

The Glenkindie has just three bedrooms and pets are welcome. Guests can choose what they want for breakfast, from the full Scottish to kippers, for £5 per person. The only hotel in the Glen to serve food all day during the tourist season, all meals here are good value; the cooked high tea at £6.95 a head is particularly popular.
Q ❀ ♿ P

LOSSIEMOUTH

Skerry Brae

Stotfield Road, IV31 6QS

- ▶ Eight miles from Elgin
- T (01343) 812040
- W skerrybrae.co.uk
- Beer range varies
- Six single, five double, four twin (one wheelchair accessible), four family rooms, most en-suite
- £ £££
- Lunchtime and evening meals, afternoon snacks
- Accepted (not Amex)

Perched above the Moray Firth and the 18th fairway of the Old Moray Golf Course, the Skerry Brae is in a wonderful location with fantastic views. Most of the bedrooms overlook the coastline and all are bright and comfortably furnished, with en-suite facilities. Ten rooms situated in the Golf Links Annex are particularly spacious and have digital TV set and broadband Internet facilities; one has been purpose built to accommodate wheelchair users.

Golf is a major attraction in this area, but visitors can also enjoy sailing, fishing, clay pigeon shooting and even dolphin watching. There are amenities for more modern outdoor pursuits, too, such as off-road driving, quad biking and paintball games.

A full Scottish breakfast is served in the conservatory, prepared from local produce including Lossiemouth smoked haddock and black pudding. Your eggs will be cooked as you like them. The hotel specialises in steaks and seafood. Meals can be taken in the dining room, conservatory, out on the terrace or in the lounge bar. The pub attracts a varied clientele from holiday makers to local RAF personnel, all enjoying the three real ales that change frequently.

P

MINTLAW

Country Park Inn

Station Road, AB42 5EB

- ▶ On A950
- T (01771) 624538
- F (01771) 623833
- Courage Directors; Theakston Old Peculier; guest beer
- One twin, two family rooms, all en-suite
- £ £ (single occupancy £35)
- Lunchtime and evening meals
- Accepted

The Country Park Inn was originally built as a station hotel for the long-gone line from the fishing port of nearby Peterhead to Aberdeen. The railway line has now been converted to a long-distance footpath, the Buchan Walkway, covering some 36 miles to the outskirts of Aberdeen, and the hotel is a popular night stop for walkers. The attractively-decorated rooms, where children are welcome to stay, all have en-suite facilities and are equipped with a hospitality tray. A full Scottish breakfast is served.

This area is something of a beer desert, so real ale lovers travel quite a distance to enjoy a pint here in the comfortable bar, while the restaurant is popular with families. Local produce features on the menu and seafood is something of a speciality here. The spacious hotel also has a function room.

This traditional country inn is convenient for Aden Country Park, just to the west of the village. Here you can explore 230 acres of woodland, wildlife and nature reserves as well as a heritage centre and displays of agricultural life in the 1940s and 50s.

P

OLDMELDRUM
Redgarth
Kirk Brae, AB51 0DJ

- ▶ Off A947, towards golf course
- T (01651) 872353
- F (01651) 873763
- W redgarth.com
- Beer range varies
- Two double, one twin, all en-suite
- £ £££
- Lunchtime and evening meals and snacks
- Accepted

Considering that the Redgarth was not licensed until 1980, served time as a cocktail bar, and only became an inn offering cask-conditioned ale in 1994, its reputation now with beer lovers is quite remarkable. Indeed the pub's motto (if I've translated it correctly from the Latin) is something like 'life's too short to drink bad beer'. A regular local CAMRA award winner, it stocks real ale from Scottish breweries - Inveralmond, Isle of Skye, Houston, Orkney, Cairngorm and many others.

Redgarth was built in 1928 as a private home. The four-star rated guest rooms are of generous proportions, with elegant furnishings and all the usual amenities. Two benefit from panoramic views of the splendid Grampian landscape.

A continental breakfast is delivered to the room with the morning paper. Fresh fruit cocktail and freshly-squeezed orange juice are followed by croissants, brioches, toast, Aberdeenshire rolls and preserves.

Oldmeldrum is a medieval market town of narrow streets and interesting old houses. Three popular tourist trails are close by - the Castle Trail, Coastal Trail and Whisky Trail. Museums in the vicinity are dedicated to lighthouses, agriculture and transport. Surrounded by wonderful walking country, golf courses are also plentiful. ❀ ♿ ♣ P

TOMINTOUL
Glen Avon Hotel
The Square, AB37 9ET

- T (01807) 580218
- F (01807) 580733
- W glenavon-hotel.co.uk
- Cairngorm Trade Winds
- Two double, three family en-suite rooms; one twin-bedded with separate facilities
- £ £-££
- Lunchtime and evening meals plus snacks
- Accepted

Situated in the highest village in the Highlands, this small family-run hotel overlooks the village square. The route to the hotel over the A939 from Cockbridge tends to be one of the first to be blocked during winter snowfalls, however an alternative route via Dufftown is usually accessible. In winter this family-run hotel is popular with visitors to the nearby Lecht Ski Centre, with its downhill and Nordic ski runs. In summer an extensive network of mountain bike trails is a major attraction here. Less energetic visitors can discover the Speyside distilleries and the Glenlivet Estate, visit the battlefields of Culloden or take a ride on a steam railway.

The hotel offers warm, comfortable accommodation with Sky TV and tea and coffee making facilities. The tariff includes breakfast, which is a hearty cooked meal guaranteed to set you up for the day's activities. The lunch and evening menus offer a selection of hearty home-cooked favourites made with fresh local produce wherever possible, such as steak pie or chicken curry, as well as vegetarian choices and typical pub fare for children. The large bar has a friendly atmosphere with plasma TV, juke box, pool table and dartboard. ❀ P

Highlands

DRUMNADROCHIT

Benleva Hotel

IV63 6UH

- ▶ Just off A82, ½ mile from the village
- T centre
- F (01456) 450080
- W benleva.co.uk
- Beers change daily, always one from the Isle of Skye Brewery
- Three double, two twin, one family room, all en-suite
- £ ££
- Lunchtime and evening meals
- Accepted

Popular with local CAMRA members who voted it their Pub of the Year in 2003 and 2005, the Benleva Hotel is an ideal choice for those in search of the Loch Ness monster – there are two visitor centres in Drumnadrochit dedicated to Nessie.

Situated on the Great Glen Way, the hotel is a former manse dating back 300 years set in an acre of grounds - look out for the 400-year-old Spanish chestnut, a former hanging tree. The present owners acquired the hotel in 2001 and after extensive refurbishment quickly established a reputation for their excellent cuisine based on local produce such as venison, lamb, beef and seafood. All food is freshly prepared so meals can be adapted to suit particular requirements. Local free-range eggs are used in the full Scottish breakfast menu. The pleasant guest rooms include tea and coffee making facilities, a TV and hairdryer.

Local attractions include Urquhart Castle a mile away. You can go Nessie hunting on the loch or, if you want to see real wildlife rather than the legendary variety, explore the beautiful Glen Affric where there are red deer, golden eagles and otters, or visit Chanonry Point to spot dolphins and porpoises; both sites are within half an hour of the hotel. Q P

FORTROSE

☆ Anderson

Union Street, IV10 8TD

- ▶ Eight miles from A9, 15 miles from Inverness Airport
- T (01381) 620236
- F (01381) 620236
- W theanderson.co.uk
- Beer range varies
- Seven double, two twin rooms, all en-suite
- £ ££ (single occupancy £45)
- Lunch served at weekends, evening meals every day
- Accepted (except Amex)

A mecca for real ale lovers, the Anderson is owned and run by American beer writer Jim Anderson who serves a changing range of cask ales including Scottish micros, over 80 Belgian bottled beers and 200-plus single malts. This 19th-century building successfully encompasses a cosy bar where locals mix with guests from around the world, an award-winning restaurant and nine-bedroom hotel. The en-suite guest rooms are all individually decorated, featuring a mix of modern and antique furniture. Nice touches are luxurious toiletries and fair-trade tea and coffee; one room has a four-poster and deluxe bathroom.

Food is exceptional: guests can opt for a full Scottish, English or American breakfast or choose from an à la carte menu. Free-range, organic eggs come from two local farms, sausages, black and hogs pudding from nearby butchers, muesli, marmalade and jams are home-made. Anne Anderson, a New Orleans chef, now cooks an ever-changing menu using local produce such as sika venison and wild mushrooms, sometimes home-smoked fish, always interesting Scottish cheeses. Two courses are around £15.

Pristine beaches, bird and dolphin watching, hill walking and golf are available close by. From October 1-March 31 CAMRA members can stay two nights for the price of one.

P

GAIRLOCH
Old Inn
Flowerdale Glen, IV21 2BD

- ▶ Via A832, the inn stands opposite Gairloch Harbour
- T (01445) 712006
- F (01445) 712044
- W theoldinn.net
- Cairngorm Trade Winds; Caledonian IPA; Greene King Abbot; Isle of Skye Red Cuillin
- Five double, seven twin, two single, three family rooms, all en-suite; one adapted for disabled guests
- £ ££
- Lunchtime and evening meals
- Accepted

The Old Inn is one of the few entries in this guide that properly caters for guests with mobility problems. Three rooms are on the ground floor and one, with a wet room, is designed to accommodate a wheelchair. The inn's family rooms can sleep up to five people. The hotel has broadband connection. One room has a balcony overlooking picturesque Flowerdale Valley and stream, while on the other side the harbour has far-reaching views across to Skye.

Not surprisingly, the inn attracts walkers, cyclists and nature lovers to Beinn Eighe Nature Reserve, Inverewe Gardens and unspoilt sandy beaches. There are sailing facilities at the harbour and a pony trekking centre within walking distance. Wildlife cruises leave Gairloch pier several times a day during the summer – you may see whales, dolphins, otters and rare seabirds.

An hour's walk to Flowerdale Waterfall and back should give you an appetite for a wonderful dinner such as local venison cassoulet or 'fish kettle' mixing scallops, squid, mussels, squat lobster and fish. At breakfast, help yourself from a splendid hot buffet including Scottish potato pancakes as well as local sausages, bacon, and black pudding, with eggs poached or fried as you watch.

P

GLENCOE
Clachaig Inn
PH49 4HX

- ▶ Off A82, 2 miles south of Glencoe village on old riverside road
- T (01855) 811252
- F (01855) 812030
- W clachaig.com
- Beer range varies
- Ten double, seven twin, one single, five family rooms, all en-suite, plus self-catering chalets
- £ ££
- Meals and snacks served all day
- Accepted

Glencoe offers some of the most challenging walks in Scotland, however you do not have to be an experienced hiker to make the most of the beautiful surroundings as there are several trails that take no more than a couple of hours at an easy pace – one leads to Signal Rock and the monument commemorating the Glencoe Massacre of 1692. The Clachaig is an excellent base for anyone wanting an extreme outdoor experience whether it be climbing, mountain biking, sailing or skiing. The inn has a large drying room and packed lunches can be prepared to order.

The CAMRA award-winning, fairly spartan stone-floored bar (ideal for walking boots) offers a good range of beers from Scottish micro-breweries such as Atlas and Williams (try their heather ale where you can really taste the flowers) and holds regular beer festivals showcasing up to 15 different ales. Meals are served all day in this bar and two more comfortable drinking areas.

The attractive, recently refurbished bedrooms offer all the modern comforts and guests can enjoy a traditional Scottish breakfast (with optional haggis), or a vegetarian version, as well as cereals or porridge, yogurt and fruit.

P

GLENSHIEL
Kintail Lodge Hotel
IV40 8HL

- ▶ On A87, 15 miles south of Kyle of Lochalsh
- T (01599) 511275
- F (01599) 511226
- W kintaillodgehotel.co.uk
- Isle of Skye Red Cuillin
- Seven double, two twin, two single, one family room, all en-suite
- £ ££-£££ (pets £3 per night)
- Lunchtime and evening meals
- Accepted

'Munro bagging' is just one of the outdoor pursuits on offer at the Kintail – there are over 30 Munros (separate hills over 3,000 ft) within striking distance of the hotel, so enthusiasts can up their score here quite easily. The hotel enjoys an enviable position at the foot of the Five Sisters of Kintail on the shore of Loch Duich. Pony trekking, fishing and guided walks are all available locally. Nearby is Eilean Donan – possibly the most romantic castle in Scotland.

The Kintail combines a good traditional pub where you can enjoy bar meals and Scottish music (played live on Thursday evenings through the summer) with modern hotel facilities. The guest rooms have recently been updated to a high standard, with TV, hair dryer and hospitality tray and all benefit from views of either the loch or mountains. Inexpensive bunkhouse accommodation is also available for walkers.

You can dine in either the bright conservatory that looks out onto the garden and loch, or the more formal restaurant. A varied menu is offered at breakfast: highland muesli and fresh fruit followed by scrambled egg and smoked salmon or Scottish grill of tattie scone, sausage, bacon, tomato, fried egg and the famous Cockburns black pudding.

♣ P

LOCHCARRON
Rockvilla Hotel
IV54 8YB

- ▶ Centre of village, on A896
- T (01520) 722379
- W rockvilla-hotel.co.uk
- Beer range varies
- One double, one twin, one family room, en-suite or private facilities
- £ ££
- Snacks and meals daily, lunchtime and evening (in summer)
- Accepted (Visa and Mastercard)

On the shore of lovely Lochcarron in the centre of a charming village, the Rockvilla has spectacular views over the loch and nearby mountains. The lounge bar provides a range of ales, generally one from Isle of Skye Brewery, serving three real ales in summer, two in winter, a wide range from Scottish micro-breweries. In winter (November to March) the bar is closed to non-residents on Sunday afternoon, Monday and Tuesday.

All three letting rooms overlook the loch, two with double aspect views. The family room sleeps four and has an en-suite bathroom, the two other rooms each have private WC and shower. Rates vary depending on the room and include a full Scottish breakfast with local sausages and black pudding, eggs as you like them, grilled kippers as available, and locally smoked salmon with scrambled eggs. The yoghurt is organic.

Tempting main meals include local langoustine and squat lobster, venison and vegetable casserole, cullen skink and a large local haddock in real ale batter.
An excellent base for exploring the Western Highlands, the hotel hosts an unofficial tourist information area. Guests can be collected from the station three miles away.
Q ❀ ⊟ ♿ ♣ P

PLOCKTON
Plockton Inn
Innes Street, IV52 8TW

- ▶ 50 yards from the seafront
- T (01599) 544222
- F (01599) 544487
- W plocktoninn.co.uk
- Caledonian 80/-; Fuller's London Pride; Greene King Abbot; guest beers
- Five double, three twin, four family, two single rooms, all en-suite
- £ £££
- Lunchtime and evening meals
- Accepted

Not to be confused with the Plockton Hotel on nearby Harbour Street, which also offers accommodation and sells real ale, the Plockton Inn is situated by the harbour. Winner of Scotland's Seafood Pub of the Year award in 2004, the menus offer a wonderful variety of local langoustines, scallops and locally-landed fish. At breakfast you can choose between the inn's own smoked haddock with poached egg, smoked salmon with scrambled eggs or kippers. Alternatively, there is the full traditional cooked breakfast with eggs of your choice, bacon, sausage, black pudding and tomato. Porridge, cereal, fruit and yogurt are also served.

Plockton lays claim to being one of Scotland's most beautiful villages and the sea, warmed by the Gulf Stream, is 50 metres from the door of the hotel. The airy, modern en-suite rooms have TV and tea making facilities, and some rooms offers breathtaking sea views. The village is served by a station on the Inverness to Kyle railway, within easy reach of Eilean Donan Castle and the Isle of Skye. The inn is also known for its live, traditional music that is staged on two evenings a week, when the audience is welcome to join in.
⛫ ❀ ⊟ ♿ ♣ P ≹

SUTHERLAND

Scourie Hotel

Scourie, IV27 4SX

- ▶ In the village centre, on the A894
- T (01971) 502396
- F (01971) 502423
- W scourie-hotel.co.uk
- Black Isle Yellowhammer, Red Kite; Cairngorm Trade Winds, Black Gold, Nessies Monster Mash; Isle of Skye Red Cuillin
- Six double, six twin, two family, six single rooms, most en-suite
- £ ££ (low season) £££ (high season)
- Lunchtime and evening meals
- Accepted

A haven for game fishers and nature lovers, it is no surprise to discover that the famous Scottish naturalist Charles St John stayed here in the 1840s. With access to 25,000 acres of lochs, rivers and hill lochs, the hotel has 36 fishing beats held exclusively for its guests and a further three beats on Loch Stack and Loch More for sea trout and salmon. Also nearby is Handa Island, a haunt of ornithologists, Assynts rock desert, a mecca for geologists, and Britain's highest waterfall.

Built in the 1640s as a fortified house, the Scourie has since been extended to provide comfortable, well-appointed guest rooms, mostly benefiting from views over the bay or the distant peaks of Ben Stack, Foinaven and Arkle. All the rooms have facilities for hot drinks and hair dryer, but no TV. A fisherman's chalet is also available with two bedrooms, a bathroom and sitting room.

A full Scottish breakfast is provided and an inventive menu, using local produce as available, changes frequently. The set price of £25 for dinner is considerably reduced for guests taking the dinner, bed and breakfast option. Packed lunches can be provided. Q P

STROMNESS

Ferry Inn

10 John Street, KW16 3AD

- ▶ Orkney, off A965
- T (01856) 850280
- W ferryinn.com
- Highland Scapa Special, St Magnus Ale; Orkney Red MacGregor, Dark Island
- Three double, six twin, two family, one single room; seven rooms en-suite, three with shower, two share shower and WC
- £ £-££ according to facilities
- Snacks and meals at lunchtime; evening meals
- Accepted

Set right beside the ferry terminal, the inn is a particularly welcoming sight after a rough crossing from Scrabster. Its location makes it attractive to groups of divers as many dive boats are berthed nearby. It is also convenient for tourists who can hire bicycles or a car locally to explore the island. Places of interest in the vicinity include Skara Brae, a Viking settlement dating back more than 5,000 years, the Pier Arts Centre and Stromness Museum.

The inn's lively, sea-faring themed bar is popular with both locals and visitors and is known for its live entertainment at weekends and traditional music performed midweek in summer. If you want to be sure of a quiet night, ask for one of the rooms in the annexe opposite, which also has a large TV lounge.

In the morning breakfast is served in the recently-refurbished dining room where you will find locally-produced sausages, black pudding and haggis accompanied by free-range eggs. A vegetarian option is available and the kitchen can also cater for special dietary needs. The lunch and evening menus offer local seafood and Orkney beef from an award-winning butcher. Look out for the daily specials. P

Stein Inn, Waternish, Highlands

WATERNISH

Stein Inn

IV55 8GA

- ▶ Isle of Skye, north of Dunvegan at the end of B886
- T (01470) 592362
- W steininn.co.uk
- Beer range varies
- Four double/twin (two family), one single room, all en-suite
- £ £-££
- Lunchtime and evening meals
- Accepted

The long and winding road that leads to the sea also brings you to the oldest inn on the Isle of Skye. The family-run Stein Inn benefits from a wonderful setting on the shore of Loch Bay in a tiny hamlet. Officially designated a 'Whisky Embassy' for its stock of around 100 single malts, it also does a fair job of promoting local ales, with beers from Skye and Cairngorm often featuring on the bar. Scottish produce, particularly fish and seafood, forms the basis of the main menus that change according to what is available.

Stone walls, low ceilings, exposed beams and open fires characterise the public rooms, while the bedrooms, individually furnished, are bright and cheerful with lovely sea views. Two rooms are large enough for a family; pets are also welcome. There is also an attractive one bedroom self-catering apartment to let that has its own entrance. The breakfast menu offers a long list of options including venison sausages, organic oatmeal porridge, free range eggs cooked as you like them, and a selection of cheeses, smoked salmon or ham. If you fancy the peat-smoked kippers you have to remember to order them the night before. P

WORMADALE

Westings Inn

ZE2 9LJ

- ▶ Shetland Isles, turn right out of Lerwick ferry terminal, on A971 8 miles
- T (01595) 840242
- F (01595) 840546
- W westings.shetland.co.uk
- Fuller's London Pride or Taylor Landlord; guest beers
- One double, two twin, three single beds
- £ ££
- Lunchtime and evening meals
- Accepted

Perched on the side of Wormadale Hill, benefiting from unparalleled views, the Westings was built in 1947. The comfortable bar offers regularly changing guest ales, often from Shetland's own Valhalla Brewery – the most northerly in Britain.

The bar leads to a spacious games room with pool, darts and Sky TV, where regular customers will often invite visitors to join their games. There is no juke box or noisy games machine; the TV and music are only switched on by request. The pub also has a lounge bar where breakfast, cooked to order with local free range eggs, is served. Local kippers or smoked fish are sometimes available. No other food is served, but evening meals are provided by arrangement.

The simply decorated bedrooms are compact. Children are usually given a single room (at a reduced rate) where a foldaway bed can (just) be fitted in, adjoining parents' double or twin room. The rooms have modern pine furnishings, TV, tea and coffee making facilities and hair dryer. They all offer a beautiful view over Whiteness Voe. It also has its own campsite. Pets can stay.
Q P

Lothians

GIFFORD

Goblin Ha' Hotel

Main Street, EH41 49H

- ▶ 5 miles south of Haddington via B6369
- T (01620) 810244
- W goblinha.com
- Caledonian Deuchars IPA; Greene King Abbot; Hop Back Summer Lightning; guest beers
- Four double, four twin rooms, all en suite; two family rooms with shared facilities
- £ ££
- Lunchtime and evening meals
- Accepted

This village pub and country hotel has earned an excellent reputation for its food, earning it a place in CAMRA's Good Pub Food guide. An inventive menu, based on fresh local produce, is varied enough to suit all tastes. A continental breakfast is included in the room rate for B&B guests – but do not be disheartened if you yearn for the full Scottish, you may have one for a supplementary charge.

Much of the pub, including the smart lounge bar and the conservatories, is given over to food service, however the smaller, rustic public bar, with its wood panelled and stone walls, tends to be the choice of ale drinkers (and their dogs). The bar opens on to a games room. In summer the attractive garden comes into its own.

The accommodation attracts walkers, cyclists and golfers - all these activities can be enjoyed locally and packed lunches are available for those wishing to make a day of it. The hotel also caters for business visitors and families. Most of the comfortable rooms have en-suite facilities. Pets are welcome.

The pub gets its name from an underground chamber beneath Yester Castle near Gifford, said to be built by fairies and goblins – the Goblin Ha. Q P

LASSWADE

Laird & Dog Hotel

5 High Street, EH18 1NA

- On A768 near the river
- T (0131) 663 9219
- W lairdanddog.btinternet.co.uk
- Beer range varies
- Three double, three twin, two family, two single rooms, all en-suite
- £ ££
- Lunchtime and evening meals and snacks
- Accepted

This country village inn near the River Esk caters for all-comers, locals as well as visitors. An olde-worlde bar contrasts with the new conservatory restaurant. An unusual feature of the refurbished lounge is an old bottle-shaped well, uncovered during renovations, that was briefly used for brewing ale in the 1780s. Today the two regularly-changing real ales usually come from small breweries nationwide; the bar also keeps a good selection of malt whiskies. Food is served all day, with the menu supplemented by daily specials and snacks.

The guest rooms are fairly small and the decor slightly old-fashioned, but they are comfortable with superior beds, TV and hospitality tray. Children are welcome and pets can be accommodated. A full Scottish breakfast is served in the morning.

Situated just seven miles south of Edinburgh, the pub is a convenient base for exploring the area, with golf courses and scenic walks in abundance. Buses from the capital stop outside the pub. There is a ski slope nearby for winter sports enthusiasts to prepare for the winter season, while Da Vinci Code fans can make a beeline for the Rosslyn Chapel.

Q P

LOTHIANBRIDGE

Sun Inn

EH22 4TR

- On A7, south of Dalkeith, 20 mins from Edinburgh Airport
- T (0131) 663 2456
- F (0131) 663 5800
- Caledonian Deuchars IPA; guest beer
- Three twin, one family, one single room, all en-suite
- £ ££
- Lunchtime and evening meals daily
- Accepted

A quick look at the Sun's visitors' book to read all the favourable comments (particularly about the breakfasts) helps to explain why so many guests return again and again. Families appreciate the landscaped grounds that include a children's play area and the woodland walks nearby. Situated in a convenient location just seven miles from the centre of Edinburgh and handy for the airport, the inn is also close to beaches, the Scottish Mining Museum, a butterfly farm and Midlothian Ski Centre. There are 25 golf courses within a 10-mile radius, you can watch the racing at Musselburgh or go fishing 20 minutes' drive away. Rosslyn Chapel is now a very popular attraction, too.

The accommodation here is well appointed with a full Scottish breakfast included in the tariff. All the rooms have tea and coffee making facilities, hair dryers and colour TV. The en-suite bathrooms have bathtubs and showers.

The extensive home-cooked menu is supplemented by daily specials. You can eat in the comfortable bar or the dining room; from Friday to Sunday main meals are served all day from noon. This friendly establishment was built in 1837 and stands in the shadow of the disused but still impressive Waverley viaduct. P

NORTH BERWICK
Nether Abbey Hotel
20 Dirleton Avenue, EH39 4BQ

▶ On A198, ½ mile west of town centre
T (01620) 895298
F (01620) 895298
W netherabbey.co.uk
Caledonian Deuchars IPA; guest beers
Three double, nine twin, one single room, all en-suite
£ £££
Lunchtime and evening meals; served all day Friday to Sunday
Accepted

Since 2004 the Nether Abbey has been undergoing a planned programme of refurbishment. The open-plan public areas, all light wood and steel, now have a cool contemporary feel. The bar area can be extended outside, under cover of a retractable canvas roof. The marble-topped bar counter features gleaming modern chrome fonts dispensing three guest ales.

The upgrading of the guest rooms will have been completed by the time this guide appears. Furnished in individual style and equipped to a high standard, rooms include two junior suites with Sky Movies, one aimed at honeymooners. All the rooms have TV, hair dryer and hospitality tray. Children are welcome and pets can be accommodated.

A good choice is provided at breakfast: fresh grapefruit, prunes, apricots and cereals, cheese and cold meats or smoked haddock with poached eggs are all offered as an alternative to the usual eggs and bacon. The Fly Half Bar and Grill is open for other meals, presenting a seasonal menu.

There is plenty to see and do around the charming seaside town of North Berwick, including boat trips and the new Scottish Seabird Centre at the harbour. ❀ P

UPHALL
Oatridge Hotel
2-4 East Main Street, EH52 5DA

▶ Jct A899/B8046
T (01506) 856465
F (01506) 855801
Beer range varies
Two double, two twin, one family, two single rooms; four en-suite, two with shower, one shared bathroom
£ ££
Snacks and meals daily, lunchtime and evening
Accepted

Built around 1830, the Oatridge was originally a coaching inn and popular stop over for stagecoaches on the Glasgow to Edinburgh run. Today the friendly hotel, run by the same family since 1973, attracts locals and visitors alike.

Real ale is dispensed in the stylish public bar which has an art deco feel, featuring a large mirror etched with a scene depicting life from a bygone era. Up to three real ales are served, often including Caledonian Deuchars IPA, and beers from Scottish micros. TV sports are popular at the weekend, and there is a pool table.

The larger, newly decorated, en-suite bedrooms are on the first floor; the remaining four smaller rooms are on the top floor. The tariff includes a full cooked breakfast of sausage, bacon, egg, beans or tomatoes, while the restaurant operates mainly as a steak house serving fine Scottish beef from local farms.

Attracting local workers during the week, tourists at weekends, the Oatridge is also a popular wedding venue, and has a garden area. Just off the M8, it is well placed for visiting Edinburgh, and is within a mile of a railway station.

❀ ♣ P

Strathclyde

CASTLECARY

Castlecary House Hotel

Castlecary Road, G68 0HD

- ▶ On B816, just off A80, north of Glasgow towards Stirling
- T (01324) 840233
- F (01324) 841608
- W castlecaryhotel.com
- Beer range varies
- Forty double, seven twin, three family rooms, all en-suite (one room adapted for disabled use); five single rooms with shared facilities
- £ ££-£££
- Meals available all day
- Accepted

Most of the guest rooms in this privately owned hotel are in cottage-style buildings set in the grounds, with just a few in the main building. Some are accessible for wheelchair users and one has been adapted to accommodate disabled guests. For families there is a choice of interconnecting rooms or two-bedroom family apartments. The rates vary according to the rooms – from standard to executive (with Wifi Internet access). All but the single rooms have en-suite bathroom, trouser press, hospitality tray, TV and sitting area. Pets are welcome.

The full Scottish breakfast, complete with porridge, cereal or yogurt and fresh fruit, is described as 'thumping'; a vegetarian

option is also available and a continental breakfast can be arranged for groups. Bar meals can be enjoyed at any time in the traditional Poachers Lounge, while the modern Camerons Restaurant offers a weekly-changing menu. Up to three real ales, mostly Scottish, also change weekly.

The village lies close to the newly restored Forth and Clyde Canal where the Falkirk Wheel – the world's only rotating boat lift – is a must-see. Stirling, Glasgow and the Roman fort on the Antonine Wall are also nearby. The nearest station is Cumbernauld two miles away. P

CLACHAN OF GLENDARUEL

Glendaruel Hotel

PA22 3AA

- Off A886, 15 miles south of Strachur
- T (01369) 820274
- F (01369) 820317
- Fyne Highlander; guest beers
- Two double, three twin, one family, one single room, all en-suite
- £ £££-££££
- Lunchtime and evening meals
- Accepted

The hotel dates back to the 17th century and has seen a fair number of changes over the years, yet it remains a comfortable, traditional hostelry. The small, bare-boarded public bar, warmed by a log fire, houses a pool table watched over by a mounted stag's head. Shooting for pheasants and clay pigeon remains a popular pursuit in these parts and the hotel can arrange shooting permits and will kennel your dog (domestic pets can stay in the guest rooms by arrangement). Fishing permits can also be obtained.

The bar is a meeting place for members of the local farming community but there is also a larger lounge/dining area where good food is served, based on local produce. The breakfast here will certainly set you up for a day enjoying country pursuits; the cooked meal includes local bacon, sausage and black pudding, free-range eggs and all the trimmings. In the main tourist season you will also be offered a choice of porridge, smoked haddock and kippers.

Rated two star by the Scottish tourist board, the individually decorated guest rooms are equipped with TV, hospitality tray and hair dryer; an iron and ironing board can be provided.

P

CLACHAN SEIL
Tigh-an-Truish Inn
Isle of Seil by Oban, PA34 4QZ

▶ Off B844, by the Atlantic Bridge
T (01852) 300242
W tigh-an-truish.co.uk
Beer range varies
One double, one twin room, both en-suite
£ £
Lunchtime and evening meals
Not accepted

Although the address of the inn is the Isle of Seil, there is some debate about whether the delightful Seil can truly be designated an island - since 1793 it has been connected to the mainland by the Atlantic Bridge (and it is only a short bridge at that). The inn, situated next to the bridge, was named Tigh-an-Truish (the 'house of trousers' in Gaelic) following the Battle of Culloden in 1746, when the kilt was outlawed and any transgressors were sure to be executed. The islanders continued to wear the kilt but used the inn to change into their 'trews' before going to the mainland.

Today, kilts and most other forms of dress are welcome at the inn where you can enjoy ales from several Scottish micro-breweries, including Fyne, Atlas and Orkney. The beers are usually served in rotation in summer, when the pub is open all day for food and drink. The local seafood is recommended here.

The guest accommodation is in two small apartments, each with its own kitchen and bathroom. They enjoy a peaceful situation overlooking Clachan Sound and the bridge. A continental breakfast is served in the apartment.
Q P

GIRVAN
Royal Hotel
36 Montgomery Street, KA26 9HE

▶ Residential area off A77
T (01465) 714203
W royalhotelgirvan.com
Beer range varies
Two double, two twin, two family, one single room; five en-suite, two sharing bathroom
£ £-££
Snacks and meals daily, lunchtime and evening
Accepted

Five minutes' walk from the harbour, this small, homely white-painted hotel is situated in an attractive Clyde coastal resort still clinging to fishing and tourism. The clean, welcoming rooms are all decorated in different colours and named accordingly – Mellow Yellow and Palace Brown, for example – with views over the town across the Firth of Clyde to Arran, the Mull of Kintyre and Ailsa Craig (or Paddy's Milestone). All rooms have TV and tea and coffee facilities. The room rate includes a full cooked breakfast with eggs cooked as you like them and a tattie scone.

The traditional public bar attracts locals, anglers, walkers and cyclists enjoying the regular ale from Houston brewery and guest – mainly in summer – from another Scottish micro, or bottled beer from an interesting collection. Simple bar meals include haggis, neeps and tatties with Drambuie and cream sauce, traditional steak pie, sirloin steak and freshly-made soup.

In an area of outstanding natural beauty, close to clean, sandy beaches, the Royal is only five miles from world-renowned Turnberry golf course. It is near Culzean Castle, the ruins of Crossraguel Abbey and Burns National Heritage Park. Q ♣ P

GLASGOW
Babbity Bowster
16-18 Blackfriars Street, Merchant City, G1 1PE

T (0141) 552 5055
Caledonian Deuchars IPA; Houston Peter's Well; guest beer
Three double, two twin, one single room, all en-suite
£ ££
Snacks and meals daily, lunchtime and evening
Accepted

A period house in a pedestrian paved area, the pub gets its name from a lewd 18th-century dance. Now converted to a beautiful pub, restaurant and small hotel, the Babbity, designed by Robert Adam, features a splendid bar with high ceilings and a peat fire.

Excellent food prepared by longstanding French chef Jean-Claude earned the hotel a star in CAMRA's Good Pub Food guide. The menu is split between French and traditional Scottish with the best cullen skink (smoked haddock and potato soup) in Glasgow, west coast mussels, haggis, neeps and tatties and home-made gravadlax of herrings marinated in Scotch malt whisky, alongside duck confit and croque monsieur, with more sophisticated choices in an intimate restaurant upstairs.

The en-suite bedrooms, all on the first floor, have a fresh, rustic French ambience and are simply furnished, without TV. Breakfast is not served here but is easily available close by.

Mainly Scottish beers are served and, unusually for central Glasgow, the pub has a garden where in summer there are barbecues and boules. Handy for the centre of Glasgow, buses and trains, the pub is a regular meeting place for locals, business folk and visitors. Q P

INVERKIP
Inverkip Hotel
Main Street, PA16 0AS

▶ Off A78
T (01475) 521478
W inverkip.co.uk
Caledonian Deuchars IPA
Three double, one twin, one family room, all en-suite
£ ££ (single occupancy £45)
Lunchtime and evening meals
Accepted

This early 18th-century hostelry keeps just one real ale (although additional guest beers sometimes arrive by boat during the busy summer season), but the public bar does stock a fine selection of malt whiskies. A friendly little hotel, it is situated right next to the yachting marina in a small conservation village on the Clyde coast.

Inverkip makes an ideal base for island hopping as ferries berth just five minutes' drive from the hotel and Island Rover tickets are available at good rates if booked in advance. You can also take excursions to the popular resort of Largs (a calling point for the Waverley paddle steamer) or to Glasgow – a short train ride or 40 minutes in the car.

The hotel bedrooms are rated three stars by the Scottish Tourist Board; all have TV, welcome tray and hair dryer. The family room can sleep up to four people. A full Scottish breakfast is served in the private dining room, known as the Rogue's Room – so-named because of the display of photographs of local characters taken by the late Holmes Gilmour. Food is good here, locally sourced as far as possible. Highland game is available in season and the salmon and smoked trout are recommended.
Q P

KILMICHAEL GLASSARY

Horseshoe Inn

PA31 8QA

- ▶ On A816 towards Oban, 3 miles north of Lochgilphead
- T (01546) 606369
- W horseshoeinn.biz
- Caledonian Deuchars IPA; guest beers
- Two double, two twin, one family room; four rooms en-suite, one with private bathroom
- £ £ (room only)
- Weekend lunches, evening meals daily
- Accepted

This welcoming country inn in a small village just north of Lochgilphead in the atmospheric Kilmartin Glen provides an inexpensive base for exploring the historic surroundings, including stone circles, a fort where legend has it the first Scottish kings were crowned, and other archaeological sites that date back some 5,000 years. The spacious inn does not, however, rely entirely on tourist trade – locals as well as visitors enjoy its garden, games room with pool and darts, and good food that comes in generous portions. The pub hosts a regular Friday quiz and occasional live entertainment. One of Houston Brewery's beers is often stocked as a guest on the bar.

Children are welcome to stay here, under-fives free of charge, five to 14-year-olds £12.50 per night - half the adult rate. Pets are also permitted. Breakfast is not included in the room rate as experience has shown that many people plan a breakfast stop in their day's activities. However you can opt for a substantial full cooked breakfast for £6.95 or a lighter meal of toast and cereal for £3.95. The inn also has a self-catering flat available.

Q P

LOCH ECK

Coylet Inn

PA23 8SG

- ▶ On A815, 9 miles north of Dunoon
- T (01369) 840426
- F (01369) 840426
- W coylet-locheck.co.uk
- Caledonian Deuchars IPA; Fyne Highlander; guest beer (summer)
- Three double, one twin room; all en-suite
- £ ££
- Lunchtime and evening meals
- Accepted

The Coylet Inn, in a delightful location on the shore of one of Scotland's prettiest lochs, offers boat hire as well as B&B. For just £5 you can enjoy an hour's rowing around the loch or, for a reasonable £40 (including fuel and fishing permits), you can hire a motor boat for the day and explore the lovely sandy beaches to your heart's content. When you have satisfied your Swallows and Amazons yearnings, relax in the comfort of the inn's cosy bar before enjoying an excellent dinner in the restaurant.

The 17th-century inn was restored six years ago, preserving its original character with exposed beams and three log fires. Meals here rely on local seasonal produce including game and fish. The bar offers Fyne ales from Argyll and a choice of over 30 malt whiskies.

The bedrooms are reached via an original spiral staircase and have tea and coffee facilities, but no TV. Some rooms have panoramic views over the loch and one double room boasts a bath big enough for two set in a bay window overlooking the loch. A full Scottish breakfast is offered, or eggs on toast, local Loch Fyne kippers or ham and cheese croissants. Children are welcome. Q P

STAIR

Stair Inn

KA5 5HW

- ▶ On B730, 7 miles from Ayr
- T (01292) 591650
- W stairinn.co.uk
- Beer range varies
- Two double, two twin, one single, one family room, all en-suite
- £ ££
- Lunchtime and evening meals
- Accepted

Just seven miles from Prestwick Airport, at the heart of Burns Country, you will find the delightful stone-built Stair Inn, which has been looking after travellers and locals alike since the beginning of the 18th century. The family-run inn nestles at the foot of the glen near the historic Stair Bridge on the River Ayr, leading to the Source to Sea footpath.

The pub has recently been refurbished with some style. The bar, warmed by an open fire, is furnished with bespoke hand-made pieces, as are the bedrooms, giving a real sense of individuality. The beer range changes, but you are likely to find Caledonian Deuchars IPA and Houston Killellan on handpump, while the dining room offers good food with lovely country views during the day, candlelight by night.

The guest accommodation has a quirky, rustic charm with hand-made furnishings including headboards fashioned from uneven wooden planks. All the usual modern facilities are provided as well as toiletries and fluffy white towels. For breakfast you can choose from a list of favourites including black pudding and tattie scone, or tuck into a pair (or half) of kippers or oak-smoked haddie with poached egg. Children are welcome.

P

TROON

Ardneil Hotel

51 St Meddans Street, KA10 6NU

- ▶ Next to the station in Troon
- T (01292) 311611
- F (01292) 318111
- E ardneilhotel@btconnect.com
- Caledonian Deuchars IPA; guest beers
- Two double, five twin, two family rooms, all en-suite
- £ £-££
- Lunchtime and evening meals
- Accepted

Situated on Scotland's 'golf coast' and close to Troon's municipal golf courses, it is no surprise that the Ardneil attracts many fans of the game. However, there is always a good mix of customers including locals.

The premises underwent a complete makeover during 2006, but the bar has remained largely traditional, maintaining its Scottish theme and original carved wooden ceilings. It has a pool table and dartboard in a lower seating area. Two guest beers are always available. The dining room is smart and modern.

Guest rooms are all individually designed,

decorated in attractive, pale colours to give a light, airy feel, and equipped with tea and coffee making facilities and TV. Children are welcome – a cot and z-bed are available – and the rooms can be let for single occupancy. The breakfast is a full Scottish affair, or you can choose kippers, cereal and fresh fruit. The kitchen can cater for most dietary requirements as all meals are prepared from fresh ingredients, with fish, meat and dairy produce purchased daily from local suppliers.

WHITING BAY

Eden Lodge Hotel

Isle of Arran, KA27 8QH

▶ Edge of village, 8 miles south of Brodick ferry terminal
T (01770) 700357
W edenlodgehotel.co.uk
Caledonian Deuchars IPA; guest beer (summer)
Four double rooms and one bunk room; two doubles have en-suite facilities
£ ££
Meals served all day in summer and winter weekends; evening meals winter weekdays
Accepted

In fine weather you can sit in the hotel garden and admire the view of Whiting Bay or watch a game of bowls on the green next door. A short stroll from the village shops, the hotel is also convenient for the local 18-hole golf course five minutes' walk away. The hotel attracts walkers and cyclists and has bicycle storage.

The bright, open bar, with clear views across to Holy Island, is furnished with plain wooden tables and chairs. A new games room is planned in the basement for the 2007 season. Summer visitors will always find a guest beer, maybe from Arran's own brewery at Brodick, but just the Deuchars is stocked in winter.

The guest accommodation has recently been updated and upgraded to feature attractive modern furniture and fittings. Two of the double rooms have en-suite facilities, the other rooms have wash basins; they all have TV and hospitality tray. A full Scottish breakfast includes haggis and black pudding, but a vegetarian option is available. Unusually, guests make take breakfast at any time between 9am and noon. During the season the main menu, featuring home-cooked meals with meat sourced locally, is served all day until 9pm. Q P

Tayside & Fife

ABERDOUR

Aberdour Hotel

38 High Sreet, KY3 0SW

▶ Five miles from M90 jct 1 via A921
T (01383) 860325
F (01383) 860808
W aberdourhotel.co.uk
Caledonian Deuchars IPA; guest beer
Six double, six twin, four family rooms, all en-suite; two wheelchair accessible
£ ££-£££
Evening meals
Accepted

This small, friendly hotel in a picturesque village started out as a staging post for coaches, but the stables have now been converted to provide additional accommodation, with five guest rooms, two on the ground floor wheelchair accessible. All the rooms have recently been refurbished; those in main building have a slightly more traditional look, but they all have satellite TV, tea and coffee making facilities and free Internet access.

For breakfast there is a choice of a full Scottish affair, vegetarian alternative or simply eggs prepared to your taste. Breakfast and evening meals are served in Mortimer's Deep Restaurant – the unusual name is taken from the deep channel that lies between the village and the Isle of Inchcolm. Guests can stroll down to the shore to admire the view across to this lovely island and Edinburgh beyond. Sightings of seals are common here. Serious walkers can follow the Fife Coastal Path that passes through Aberdour.

Just 17 miles from Edinburgh with direct rail connection, and 15 minutes' drive from the airport, Aberdour is a good location for those reliant on public transport.

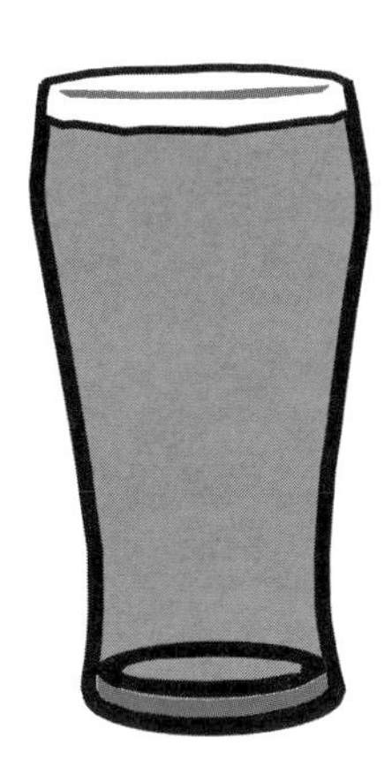

ABERNETHY

Crees Inn

Main Street, PH2 9LA

▶ 5 miles from M90 jct 9 via A912
T (01738) 850714
W creesinn.co.uk
Beer range varies
One double, one twin, one family, one single room, all en-suite
£ ££
Lunchtime and evening meals
Accepted

A former CAMRA Tayside Pub of the Year and regular entry in the Good Beer Guide, the bar offers a range of five hand-pulled Scottish and English brews that changes weekly. For whisky drinkers there is a choice of 40 malts.

The stone-built, listed building, once a farm, dates back to the 18th century. It lies within sight of Abernethy's historic Pictish watch tower – one of only two remaining in Scotland and a relic from the time when the village was the southern Pictish capital of Scotland. The village itself is now a conservation area and the inn is just one of several buildings to have been renovated to a high standard – it was refurbished in 2000.

The en-suite rooms are good value, equipped with TV, tea and coffee making facilities and a hair dryer. A full cooked breakfast is provided and special requirements, such as vegan or gluten-free meals, can be catered for with notice. A tempting dinner menu mixes Scottish fare, such as haggis and chicken terrine, with pub favourites including fish and chips and steak and ale pie, supplemented by a seafood dish of the day.

Q P

BROUGHTY FERRY

☆ Fisherman's Tavern Hotel

10-16 Fort Street, DD5 2AD

T (01382) 775941
W fishermans-tavern-hotel.co.uk
Beer range varies
Ten twin, one family room; nine en-suite, two rooms share private facilities
£ ££
Lunchtime and evening meals and snacks
Accepted

The Fisherman's Tavern, converted from seaside cottages, still maintains a traditional public bar and there are three further rooms for drinking and dining, plus a walled garden. A favourite with local CAMRA members, the 'Fish' stocks the largest range of real ales in the Dundee area and regularly offers beers from local micro-breweries Inveralmond and Moulin – the choice can change on a daily basis.

The attractive, comfortable guest rooms are fairly new and have been graded 'one' for accessibility by Visit Scotland. All but two have en-suite facilities. Children are welcome (as are pets by arrangement). A guest lounge is provided for hotel residents. The Fisherman's offers a full cooked Scottish breakfast or a continental option served in the breakfast room. Local produce, particularly haddock and grass-fed Scottish beef, is used as far as possible in all the menus.

Once dubbed the richest square mile in Europe, where the jute barons of Dundee took their ease, Broughty Ferry with its fine esplanade and extensive sandy beaches still has much to offer visitors. In the town centre Broughty Castle houses a good museum, while other fine castles such as Glamis are nearby. Famous golf courses St Andrews, Carnoustie and Gleneagles are within easy reach. Q

DUNKELD
Taybank
Tay Terrace, PH8 0HY

▶ On A984
T (01350) 727340
F (01350) 727979
W thetaybank.com
Inveralmond Ossian's Ale
One double, one twin, one single, two family rooms, shared facilities
£ £
Meals served all day
Accepted (not Amex)

Renowned as 'Scotland's musical meeting place', once owned by Scottish folk singer Dougie Maclean, the Taybank is a magnet for lovers of traditional music. Regular concerts and other musical events are staged here; there is a weekly Acoustic Music Club on Friday and spontaneous sessions frequently take place. Visiting musicians are welcome to borrow an instrument in the bar and join in. If you want to learn to play you can even sign up to regular classes here.

The accommodation is fresh and bright, but not grand. Guests share two large bathrooms, but each room has its own hand basin. For families, one room has a double and single bed, or there are two adjoining rooms with one double and two single beds. The price of accommodation includes continental breakfast; children are charged £10, under-twos are free but you have to bring your own cot. Pets are welcome. Breakfast, served in the music room, consists of cereals, toast, muffins and fruit juice. The limited but inventive restaurant menu changes monthly.

The hotel looks across to Birnam Hill, immortalised in Macbeth, and its lovely garden offers a fine view of the River Tay. Q P

GLENDEVON
Tormaukin Country Inn
FK14 7JY

▶ On A823
T (01259) 781252
F (01259) 781526
W tormaukin.co.uk
Beer range varies
One double, six twin/double, two twin, two family, one single room, all en-suite; four rooms wheelchair accessible
£ £££
Lunchtime and evening meals
Accepted

The Tormaukin is a country inn dating from 1720 and its guest rooms certainly have a charming rustic feel, albeit with up-to-the-minute facilities including satellite TV and modern en-suite bathroom. There are twelve comfortable rooms in the hotel itself, with four on the ground floor that are wheelchair accessible. The hotel also has a spacious, well-equipped cottage with three double bedrooms and a smaller self-catering lodge. Pets can be accommodated in some rooms. The generous breakfast includes a range of cooked items from eggs as you like them, black pudding, haggis, fried bread or potato scones to porridge or kippers.

Situated on a quiet country road that cuts through the Glen, the Tormaukin, surrounded by the Ochil Hills, is an ideal choice for lovers of outdoor pursuits, and is particularly popular with golfers as it is just a few miles from Gleneagles and other courses. The romantic setting is just right for a weekend a deux – the hotel offers packages for couples, as well as golfing and other breaks. Two comfortable lounge bars stock up to three real ales and an extensive menu offers Scottish and international dishes. Q P

KIRKMICHAEL

Strathardle Inn

PH10 7NS

- East end of village, on A924
- T (01250) 881224
- W strathardleinn.co.uk
- Beer range varies
- Three double, one twin, two family rooms, all en-suite
- ££
- Lunchtime and evening meals
- Accepted

This fine Victorian inn with a history dating back to the 17th century was once reputed to have been visited by Queen Victoria herself. Set in over four acres of wooded grounds, the inn owns a stretch of the River Ardle, where hotel residents can fish for trout free of charge. The Cataran Trail passes right in front of the inn; cyclists can store bikes and equipment in outbuildings and make use of a drying room. Golf is another popular activity and golf passes for three or five days for nine or 18-hole courses can be arranged by the inn.

The smart, spacious guest rooms all have either a power shower or bath, as well as facilities including hair dryer, TV and hospitality tray. A cot can be provided and pets accommodated by prior arrangement. Two cottages can be booked for self-catering holidays. Children aged three to ten are charged £10, under-threes free.

For breakfast there is a choice of a full cooked Scottish meal or a varied continental selection with ham, sausage, cheeses and oatcakes as well as cereals and unlimited supplies of toast. Seasonal produce, including local game, is served in the candlelit restaurant, while the bar promotes Scottish micro-breweries' beers.

KIRKTON OF GLENISLA

Glenisla Hotel

PH11 8PH

- On B954, 10 miles north of Alyth
- T (01575) 582223
- W glenisla-hotel.com
- Beer range varies
- Three double, three twin rooms, all en-suite
- ££
- Lunchtime and evening meals
- Accepted

Dating from the 17th century, this former coaching inn has a lovely beamed bar warmed by an open fire where a variety of Scottish ales are stocked from breweries such as Houston, Inveralmond and Kelburn. Hearty lunches and suppers can be enjoyed at the oak and pine tables. There is also an elegant dining room and a drawing room where comfortable seating invites you to settle down with a book.

Close to the Cateran Trail, the hotel attracts walkers and those interested in outdoor pursuits. There are 40 golf courses in the vicinity and facilities for cross-country skiing, angling and horse riding. Glamis Castle, Scone Palace and various local whisky distilleries can be visited.

The guest rooms are all on the first floor, affording views over the glen. They have recently been refurbished to offer simple but comfortable accommodation with a hospitality tray. Cots can be provided or a third bed for an older child. Pets are welcome. A good choice of food in the morning ranges from a full Scottish breakfast to smoked haddock with poached eggs. The main menu majors on local produce such as venison, wild salmon and hill-reared lamb.

MEIGLE
Belmont Arms Hotel
PH12 8TJ

- ▶ Off A94 between Dundee and Alyth, ½ mile south of Meigle
- T (01828) 640232
- F (01828) 640726
- W belmontarms.co.uk
- Caledonian Deuchars IPA; Inveralmond Thrappledouser; guest beers
- One twin, three double, one family room, all en-suite
- £ ££ (single occupancy £45)
- Lunchtime and evening meals and high teas
- Accepted (not Amex)

This small hotel was first licensed in 1831 to accommodate guests from nearby Belmont Castle, then served as a coaching inn and later as a railway hotel for nearby Alyth junction. Recently renovated, its guests today are more likely to be lovers of the great outdoors. Set in the beautiful Strathmore Valley, the hotel has easy access to the Angus glens and Perthshire hills. There are numerous golf courses to choose from, including St Andrews and Gleneagles, while Auchterhouse Country Sports, 10 minutes' drive, offers facilities for activities such as quad biking, off-road driving, clay pigeon shooting and archery. For guests whose interests are of a more cultural nature, a visit to nearby Glamis Castle is recommended.

The attractive guest rooms are airy, spacious and comfortable with TV and hospitality tray. Simply furnished and decorated, one has a four-poster bed. Children are welcome and the enclosed garden has a play area. If you are not up to the full Scottish breakfast, you can choose poached, boiled or scrambled eggs with toast or soda bread. Local produce is used in the kitchen and the hotel offers a traditional high tea.

P

MEIKLEOUR
Meikleour Hotel
PH2 6EB

- ▶ Off A93, 5 miles south of Blairgowrie
- T (01250) 883206
- F (01250) 883406
- W meikleourhotel.co.uk
- Beer range varies
- One double, one twin, three twin/double rooms, all en-suite; three on the ground floor are wheelchair accessible
- £ ££
- Lunchtime and evening meals
- Accepted (not Amex)

This four-star inn stands behind the world's largest beech hedge – planted in 1745 and listed in the Guinness Book of Records – in a conservation village. The stone-flagged bar and comfortable lounge both stock one or two real ales from Inveralmond, Fyne, Orkney or Houston breweries; you can take your pint into the delightful garden.

Three traditionally-styled guest rooms have twin beds that convert to king-sized doubles; z-beds can be provided for children under 16 and cots are available. Three ground-floor rooms are accessible to guests with mobility problems.

Pets are not forgotten either; the Sportsman Room is used for feeding dogs and drying outdoor clothes and equipment. The hotel also has a rod room for safe storage of fishing tackle (and even a freezer to store your catch). Even if you do not fish you will find plenty to do here – Scone Palace and Glamis Castle are just two of the popular attractions nearby.

Breakfast is something to look forward to. The hotel makes its own sausages, jam and marmalade and serves locally-baked bread. A full cooked meal includes Stornoway black pudding and local bacon. The same care is taken with renowned main meals, where steaks are from the hotel's beef herd, a mix of Aberdeen Angus and Highland cows, and the salmon is local. Q P

PERTH

Cherrybank Inn

210 Glasgow Road, PH2 0NA

- ▶ Off A9
- T (01738) 624349
- F (01738) 444962
- W cherrybankinn.co.uk
- Inveralmond Independence, Ossian's Ale; guest beer
- One double, six twin rooms, all en-suite; one room wheelchair accessible
- £ £
- Lunchtime and evening meals
- Accepted

Situated just off the main road from Glasgow on the western fringe of Perth, this former drovers' inn has been a popular stop for travellers for more than 200 years – horse-drawn carriages needed to take a break here to rest and water their horses before tackling the hard climb ahead. One of the oldest pubs in the town, it is popular with local residents for its varied food menu and real ale. The pub stocks up to four beers from Perth's own Inveralmond Brewery, as well as guests from other Scottish micro-brewers. The small public bar is flanked by two adjacent rooms, with the lounge doubling as a dining room serving lunches and evening meals.

Good-value accommodation is in bright en-suite rooms with modern pine furnishings, TV and tea and coffee making facilities. One room has been especially adapted for wheelchair use. The room rate includes a continental breakfast served in your room, or for a supplement of £3.50 you can tuck into a full cooked meal.

The inn is popular with golfing parties and the staff can make tee bookings on your behalf. The pub is convenient for the amenities of the town including the new concert hall, and Huntingtower Castle and Black Watch Regimental Museum nearby.

Q P

PITLOCHRY

Moulin Hotel

11-13 Kirkmichael Road, PH16 5EH

- ▶ On A924, ½ mile from Pitlochry
- T (01796) 472196
- F (01796) 474098
- W moulinhotel.co.uk
- Moulin Light Ale, Braveheart, Ale of Atholl, Old Remedial
- Six double, six twin, three family, one single room, all en-suite
- £ ££
- Meals served all day, afternoon snacks
- Accepted

The Moulin is a former coaching inn dating from 1695 that has retained its character and warm and welcoming atmosphere, with old stone walls, wood beams and two log fires. There is no background music, but it does have an antique fruit machine and a bar billiards table. The Moulin Brewery opened in 1995 in a converted stable to coincide with the hotel's 300th anniversary and its four real ales are much appreciated by locals and visitors. You can also sample them in the Moulin's sister hotel, the Atholl Arms in Blair Atholl. Tours of the brewery can be arranged.

Most of the guest accommodation is in the newer part of the building – albeit added over 100 years ago. The comfortable bedrooms are individually styled and well equipped. Children are welcome and pets can be accommodated for a small charge. In the morning you can order what you want from an extensive breakfast menu that includes a cooked vegetarian option of poached egg, tomato, mushrooms, fruit pudding and potato scone. A little patience is required for freshly prepared porridge, but while you wait you can admire the view of the garden and burn from the restaurant. An appetising menu is served throughout the day featuring some local produce.

Q ♣ P

Wales

Glamorgan

BRIDGEND

Wyndham Arms

Dunraven Place, CF31 1JE

T (01656) 673500
W jdwetherspoonlodges.co.uk
Brains SA; Marston's Burton Bitter, Pedigree; guest beers
Fifteen double rooms, nine twins, two singles, all en-suite
£ £ (room only)
Snacks and meals throughout opening hours
Accepted

The Wyndham is an 18th-century coaching inn, though the foundations are possibly medieval. Now a Wetherspoon pub, 26 rooms on the first and second floors were converted to Wetherlodge accommodation five years ago. The age of the building is reflected in the room proportions, though all offer spotless, modern facilities including en-suite bathroom, tea and coffee facilities and TV. A lift goes as far as the first floor providing wheelchair access, and one room has been converted for disabled use. Prices really are bargain basement and two nights for the price of one deals are often available. This does not include breakfast, an extra £1.99 for either a full English or vegetarian version. Some double rooms are also available for family use.

In the pub itself, different areas add to the friendly atmosphere of this old hostelry, with the history of Bridgend displayed on the walls.

Midway between Swansea and Cardiff, the Wyndham Arms is well placed for visiting the Brecon Beacons, Black Mountains and Vale of Glamorgan.

CARDIFF

Cayo Arms

36 Cathedral Road, CF11 9LL

- ▶ On A4119
- T (02920) 391910
- Brains Rev James; Tomos Watkin Brewery Bitter, OSB; guest beers
- One double, two twin, one family, one single room, all en-suite
- £ ££ (room only)
- Lunchtime and evening meals
- Accepted

Named after the leader of the Free Wales Army, William Cayo-Evans who died in 1995, this splendid double-fronted building, originally a pair of private houses, is near the river in the Pontcanna area of the city. It is less than a mile from Cathays Station and just over a mile from Cardiff Central.

The pub gets busy on match days; for major sporting events a marquee is erected in the car park to cater for fans. The pub has a large lounge but the bar is more homely, popular with locals, visitors and ale enthusiasts. The Cayo offers a good beer range and often stocks the award-winning Son of a Bitch from Cardiff's Bullmastiff Brewery.

The guest rooms on the first floor are decorated in pale colours and simply furnished with modern pine beds and furniture. Children are welcome to stay. Rates are for the room only; CAMRA members are offered a 10% discount on production of a current membership card. Breakfast is around £5 per person.

Cardiff has been completely revitalised in recent years and the Cayo, with its large car park, makes an ideal base for exploring the city.

P

GODREAMAN

Falcon Inn

1 Incline Row, CF44 6LU

- ▶ On road to Cwmaman, 2 miles south of Aberdare
- T (01685) 873758
- W thefalcon.co.uk
- Beer range varies
- Four double, four twin/family rooms, all en-suite
- £ ££
- Bar snacks available on request
- Not accepted

The Falcon opened in 1988 in a former ale house and goes from strength to strength. As a free house it stocks a changing range of cask beer 'from any brewery with good ale', with four on handpump at any one time, usually including something Welsh from Brains or Felinfoel.

The guest accommodation is in an attractive adjoining stone building, with four rooms on the ground floor that may suit less mobile guests, and four on the first floor. Children are welcome and the twin rooms can be adapted to suit a family. The pub has a pitch for touring caravans.

Breakfast is made using locally sourced ingredients. A plate of egg, sausage, bacon and beans or tomatoes is served – those with especially healthy appetites are welcome to ask for more! At other times a freshly-made bar snack can be rustled up on request and other meals can be provided by prior arrangement.

Although slightly isolated outside the village of Cwmaman, the Falcon gets busy in summer as the large conservatory and patio right beside the River Aman attract locals and visitors.

P P

TREHERBERT

Baglan Hotel

30 Baglan Street, CF42 5AW

- ▶ At top end of Rhondda Valley on A4061
- T (01443) 776111
- F (01443) 771601
- Brains SA, seasonal beers; guest beer
- Two double, three twin, one family room, all en-suite
- £ £
- By arrangement
- Accepted

The Baglan was built in the 1850s to cater for the local colliery and, apart from a few years in the early nineties, has been run by the same family since 1947. Its trade now comes from mountain walkers and cyclists, sports fans visiting the Millennium Stadium and locals who relish the opportunity of enjoying a decent pint. This area suffers from a lack of real ale – indeed the Good Beer Guide describes the Baglan as an oasis in a 'veritable desert'. The pub always stocks at least one guest beer.

The accommodation is good value – the basic B&B rate is discounted for multiple occupancy or long stays. The family room has a double bed, two singles and a cot, while both double rooms also have a single bed. All have TV and tea and coffee making facilities. A full cooked breakfast is provided – the sausages and rashers can be swapped for vegetarian alternatives if required. Other meals can be provided by prior arrangement.

The pub benefits from a large garden and four patios. There are mountain walks to be enjoyed all around, while Dare Valley Country Park, Dan-yr-Ogof Caves and the Heritage Park Museum are all well worth a visit.

Q

Gwent

ABERGAVENNY

☆ Angel Hotel

15 Cross Street, NP7 5EN

- ▶ In town centre, take A4042 from M4 jct 26
- T (01873) 857121
- F (01873) 858059
- W angelhotelabergavenny.com
- Brains Rev James; Fuller's London Pride; guest beer
- Sixteen double, ten twin, two family, two single rooms, all en-suite
- £ £££
- Lunchtime and evening meals and afternoon teas
- Accepted

This smart but friendly town-centre hotel offers a good range of accommodation, all well furnished and equipped, from standard rooms through to the deluxe, with extras including a separate sitting area with comfy armchair, flat screen TV and DVD player, and recently refitted Villeroy and Boch bathroom. One room has a four-poster bed. Families can book either a double room with cot or Z-bed for children under twelve or two interconnecting standard twin rooms.

A recent acquisition for the hotel is The Lodge at the entrance to Abergavenny Castle a few hundred yards away, offering independent accommodation, with a charming sitting room, bathroom and small kitchen on the ground floor and two double bedrooms upstairs. The apartment costs £220 per night for four people, including breakfast. Dogs are permitted for £10 per night.

With award-winning cuisine based on local and organic produce, breakfast in the hotel is something to be savoured – the choice is yours from the full cooked English to poached eggs on toast, scrambled eggs (with or without Black Mountain smoked salmon), free range boiled hen or ducks eggs, buttered kippers or smoked haddock and egg.

Q P

CLYTHA

☆ Clytha Arms

NP7 9BW

- ▶ Off A40, on the B4598 old Abergavenny to Raglan road
- T (01873) 840206
- W clytha-arms.com
- Beer range varies
- Four double rooms, all en-suite; children welcome
- £ £££
- Lunchtime (not Mon) and evening meals (not Sun)
- Accepted

The former dower house of the Clytha Estate, this delightful pub stands in its own grounds near the River Usk. It has won local CAMRA's Pub of the Year award more often than any other hostelry and has received numerous other awards, particularly for its food, so you can be assured of a good breakfast. This meal offers far more variety than the usual 'full English'; the 'full Welsh' includes wild boar sausage, black pudding, laverbread and cockles alongside the eggs and bacon. There is a vegetarian alternative, too, with laverbread rissole, marmite fritter, tomato, mushrooms and egg. Fish lovers could opt for kippers or eggs with smoked salmon or smoked haddock.

With a wonderful array of bar snacks and imaginative main menu (just under £20 for three courses) you might find it hard to leave the pub at all, however you should take time out to visit Raglan's 15th-century castle, while Cardiff is a 40-minute drive away.

The guest rooms are spacious and individually styled – one has a four-poster bed and leather armchairs, another has a Mackintosh theme of plum and cream roses. All have TV and hot drinks facilities (including specialist tisanes).

Q P

LLANGATTOCK LINGOED

Hunters Moon Inn

NP7 8RR

- ▶ Two miles off B4521 at Llanvetherine
- T (01873) 821499
- W hunters-moon-inn.co.uk
- Wye Valley Hereford Pale Ale; guest beers
- Three double, one twin room, all en-suite
- £ ££
- Lunchtime and evening meals
- Accepted

This traditional pub, dating back to the 13th century, is popular with walkers due to its proximity to Offa's Dyke footpath which runs through the yard of the neighbouring church. You will be assured of a peaceful night's rest in this inn in the tiny hamlet of Llangattock in the lee of the Skirrid Mountain, surrounded by wonderful countryside. The pub's large garden has a waterfall, stream and ponds (the ducks might provide the eggs for your breakfast).

The small bar offers the regular Wye Valley beer on handpump, while guest ales are dispensed straight from the casks behind the bar. Accommodation is in four comfortable rooms which have recently been refurbished and equipped to three-star standard, with king-sized beds, but have retained attractive original features such as exposed stone walls.

A full cooked breakfast is accompanied by fresh fruit, yogurt and cereals. Main meals are served in the candle-lit, beamed dining room, warmed by an open fire. The food here is recommended, based on home-cooked local produce. Food lovers may want to visit Abergavenny, which has a thriving market and in September hosts an annual food festival.

Q P

LLANTHONY

Half Moon Hotel

NP7 7NN

▶ Six miles from A465 at Llanfihangel Crucorney
T (01873) 890611
E halfmoon@llanthony.wanadoo.co.uk
Bullmastiff Welsh Red, Son of a Bitch; guest beer
Five double, three twin, one family, two single rooms, with shared facilities
£ £
Lunchtime and evening meals
Not accepted

This unpretentious, friendly pub lies in an unspoilt valley between Abergavenny and Hereford. It is close to Offa's Dyke and the new Beacons Way is just a 10-minute walk from the pub, while National Cycle Route 42 also passes through Llanthony. The scenery around here is stunning – Hay Buff nearby offers a view over six counties. The area is also popular for pony trekking and the hotel can organise a day's trek or a full week's riding holiday. Horses (and dogs) are welcome at the hotel.

Accommodation here is not fancy and none of the rooms has en-suite facilities, but this is reflected in the reasonable rates. Included in the price is a hearty cooked breakfast with free-range eggs and sausages from a local farm, or a vegetarian alternative. Bar meals and daily specials are available at lunchtime and in the evening; all day on Saturday and Sunday.

The evocative ruins of Llanthony Priory are a must-visit, while avid readers will want to head for Hay-on-Wye, now famous for its bookshops and literary festival in May.
Q P

MONMOUTH

King's Head

8 Agincourt Square, NP25 3DY

▶ Opposite town hall
T (01600) 710500
W jdwetherspoonlodges.co.uk
Brains Dark; Greene King Abbot Ale, Old Speckled Hen; guest beer
Eight double, eight twin, six family, two single rooms, all en-suite
£ £ (room only)
Snacks and meals during opening hours, from 8am
Accepted

Charles II is reputed to have been a guest at this white-fronted 16th-century coaching inn with olde-worlde rooms, ornamental fireplaces and local history on the walls. Now a Wetherspoon pub, the King's Head is one of a small number that features Wetherlodge accommodation, situated on the two floors above. In 2006 the rooms were upgraded to three star by the Welsh Tourist Authority – yet you can stay here at bargain basement prices, with room rates even cheaper at the weekend. It is worth checking the website for special deals, for example two nights for the price of one. Rooms are en-suite with TV, tea and coffee making facilities and hairdryer. One bedroom has disabled access. Breakfast is not included in the room rate but is available for just £1.99 for a full English served in the pub below.

Busy with tourists in summer, the interior includes a large bar with additional smaller rooms creating a cosy atmosphere, as well as two family areas. Monmouth, ancient county town and birthplace of Henry V, is entered via a spectacular 13th-century bridge gate, and is close to Tintern Abbey and Forest of Dean. Q P

TINTERN
☆ Cherry Tree Inn
Forge Road, NP16 6TH

▶ Take A466 to Tintern from M4/M48
T (01291) 689292
W thecherry.co.uk
Hancock's HB; Wye Valley Butty Bach; guest beers
Three double rooms, all en-suite
£ ££
Lunchtime and evening meals
Accepted

The Cherry Tree is held in high regard by CAMRA members and is the only pub in Wales to have appeared in every edition of the Good Beer Guide. Its wonderful food has earned it a listing in CAMRA's Good Pub Food guide, too. The pub offers a good choice of real ales (up to six at any one time in summer). This 16th-century former cider house lies in good walking country, near the Wye Valley Walk, Offa's Dyke and Symonds Yat, and you will barely get into your stride to reach Tintern Abbey, just five minutes on foot.

The Cherry Tree is much more than just a pub as it also encompasses the village shop and post office. Each guest room has its own character: the Rambler features a four-poster and chintz, while the Agrarian is more masculine in style; for a romantic break the owners recommend the Cherish with its hand-made bed and country views.

The breakfast menu offers a full English or interesting alternatives such as hot croissants with cold meats and cheese, omelettes or maybe kippers as available. Meals are freshly prepared on the premises using local and organic produce as much as possible.
Q P

TINTERN
Wye Valley Hotel
NP16 6SQ

▶ On A466 at north end of Tintern
T (01291) 689441
W wyevalleyhotel.co.uk
Wye Valley Bitter, Butty Bach; guest beer
Six double, two twin, one family room, all en-suite
£ ££
Lunchtime and evening meals
Accepted

Originally a small ale house built in 1835, the building was extended in 1930 when it was given its current name. Attractive from the outside, with its cascades of flowers, and inside, with its well laid out bar and beamed restaurant, the hotel is well situated for tourists, between Monmouth and Chepstow and within walking distance of the beautifully preserved ruins of Tintern Abbey. Wye, described by Wordsworth as 'the most romantic valley in Wales' has great charm and much to offer visitors, including canoeing, golf, cycling, angling and horse racing at Chepstow. The hotel can arrange baggage transfers for walkers on Offa's Dyke and overnight storage for bicycles; it also has drying facilities for wet gear.

Whether you have been on a demanding day's trek or exploring the area at leisure, you will appreciate the comfort and amenities of the hotel's spacious guest rooms. One has a four-poster bed, all have television and tea and coffee making facilities. You can dine here in the bar or restaurant – good quality food is made using produce sourced locally as far as possible – and in the morning enjoy a full cooked breakfast. Take time to linger over a pint in the hotel bar to admire the display of celebration ales. P

ABOVE: Wye Valley Hotel, Tintern

TRELLECH
Lion Inn
NP25 4PA

- ▶ Off B4293
- T (01600) 860322
- W lioninn.co.uk
- Beer range varies
- One double/family room in self-contained cottage
- £ ££ (low season) £££ (high season)
- Lunchtime (not Mon) and evening meals
- Accepted (not American Express or Diners)

Visitors to this multi-award-winning pub were so keen to stay that the owners were eventually persuaded to convert a derelict Elizabethan pig cot into guest accommodation. After nine months' work, completed in the autumn of 2003, the cottage is now a charming self-contained annexe.

The open-plan layout houses a double bed and a double sofa bed so it can sleep a family of four, with a shower, television, table and chairs and a compact kitchen area. It backs onto open fields and benefits from a small private patio that is a suntrap in summer. The cottage can be booked for overnight B&B or a self-catering stay of a minimum of four nights (from £210 a week low season, £300 high season). A laundry service is available and packed lunches can be provided at a reasonable cost. Dogs may be accepted.

This busy, 16th-century pub is highly regarded for its real ales and usually offers four beers from independent breweries. Food is superb; Hungarian cuisine is a speciality and vegetarians are well catered for. B&B guests can enjoy a full cooked breakfast with local butcher's sausages along with cereals, toast and fruit juice.

P

TRELLECH GRANGE
Fountain Inn
NP16 6QW

- T (01291) 689303
- W fountaininn-tintern.com
- Beer range varies
- Two double, one twin room
- £ £
- Lunchtime and evening meals
- Accepted

Tucked away in the Wye Valley, the inn is close to Tintern Abbey but far enough from the major tourist routes to offer a peaceful retreat. Walkers join regulars in the small flagstoned bar of this 17th-century inn to sup ales that are mostly brewed locally. Two well-known walking routes start from the pub; bicycle hire can be arranged for those who prefer to explore on two wheels.

The Fountain changed hands in 2004 and, according to local CAMRA members, has gone from strength to strength since then. It provides simple but good value B&B accommodation in rooms looking over the gardens and surrounding fields. The two double rooms both have a shower and all rooms have their own separate WC. Tea and coffee making facilities and TV are provided. For breakfast there is a choice of a full cooked meal or continental version. Main meals are served in dining areas off the bar. The popular menu changes frequently depending on the availability of local produce.

Sports fans have a 20-minute drive to Chepstow racecourse and there is easy access to the Millennium Stadium in Cardiff. Trout fishing can also be enjoyed nearby. The pub also has a camping area.

P

UPPER LLANOVER
Goose & Cuckoo Inn
NP7 9ER

- Off A4042 between Abergavenny and Newport OS291073
- T (01873) 880277
- W gooseandcuckoo.com
- Beer range varies
- One en-suite twin room, plus self-contained cottage
- £ ££
- Lunchtime and evening meals and snacks
- Not accepted

You are advised to consult an OS map when visiting this old drovers' inn for the first time. In the Brecon National Park, two miles up a country lane above Llanover, it is certainly worth the trek, not just for the pub itself, but for the outstanding views stretching 40 miles across to the Malvern Hills (if you forget your field glasses the landlord keeps a pair behind the bar for birdwatching). A real retreat, Gwent CAMRA Pub of the Year 2005 is free from TV, games machines or juke box, but you can listen to the clock ticking and warm yourself by the wood-burning stove. The pub benefits from a large garden inhabited by ducks and goats.

The food here is all home made – even the bread and desserts – and cooked in the pub's Aga. Overnight guests can enjoy a full English breakfast. The pub has just one room (children and pets are welcome), but a self-catering cottage that will sleep six is due to be completed by January 2007.

Nearby attractions include Sugar Loaf and Skirrid Mountains and the Blaenavon Ironworks or Big Pit (National Mining Museum of Wales). Q P

Mid Wales

ABERCRAVE

Copper Beech Inn

133 Heol Tawe, SA9 1XS

- Off A4067 between Swansea and Brecon
- T (01839) 730269
- Beer range varies
- Three double, one twin room (all available as singles), all en-suite
- £ ££ (single occupancy £35)
- Lunchtime and evening meals
- Accepted

Just outside the Brecon Beacons National Park, the inn makes an ideal base for visiting the first Geopark in Wales. The Fforest Fawr (Great Forest) that covers the whole of the western half of the national park was designated a Geopark by UNESCO in 2005 because of its stunning natural attractions and geologically interesting landscape. Another big attraction, the Dan-y-Ogof Showcaves, lies two miles from the pub. A long-time favourite with caver, the pub hosts meetings of the local caving club and raises money for Cave Rescue. It is also busy with motorcycle and four-wheel-drive off roaders.

This friendly village inn was built in the 1870s as the home of a colliery owner. It retains many original architectural features and benefits from spacious grounds. The large bar offers a range of Welsh ales, and there is a games room and function room.

The varied menu is excellent and curries are particularly recommended – there is usually a list of 10 of varying strengths to choose from. The kitchen aims to cater for all dietary needs and this applies to breakfast, too, with a choice of full English or continental meal. The en-suite guest rooms can accommodate families or singles.

Q P

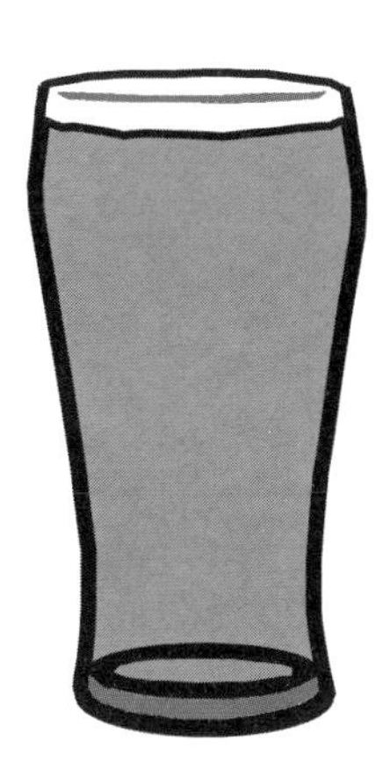

ABEREDW
Seven Stars
LD2 3UW

- ▶ Off B4567, near Builth Wells
- T (01982) 560494
- F (01982) 560494
- W sevenstarsinn.7p.org.uk
- Wadworth 6X; Wood Shropshire Lad; guest beer
- Two double, one twin room, all en-suite
- £ ££
- Lunchtime and evening meals
- Accepted

Though little known, the Edw Valley has been described as one of the most beautiful valleys in Britain. This delightful inn is nestled in an enchanting village at the head of the valley. Lovers of outdoor pursuits, whether horse riding, canoeing, paragliding, or simply hiking and cycling, will not be disappointed. The area is historically linked with Prince Llewellyn – said to be the last true Welsh prince. Prince Llewellyn's Cave can be visited nearby; legend has it he spent his last night there before being beheaded in nearby Cilmery.

The Seven Stars makes an ideal base for visitors to this wonderful part of Wales. B&B visitors check into the reception area in the little side bar before being shown to the charming guest rooms. The double rooms feature original beams and stonework, and all have hospitality tray. Children (and pets) are welcome to stay.

Breakfast is served in the spacious, rustic dining room – the usual full English can be substituted for a veggie version, or various alternatives – the hosts aim to cater for all requests. Main meals can be taken in the dining room or traditional bar with exposed stone walls.

Q P

BUILTH WELLS
Greyhound Hotel
3 Garth Road, LD2 3AR

- T (01982) 553255
- W thegreyhoundhotel.co.uk
- Fuller's London Pride; Greene King Abbot; guest beer
- Eight double/twin, two single, one family room, all en-suite
- £ ££
- Lunchtime and evening meals and snacks
- Accepted

Recently refurbished, the Greyhound is a smart but unpretentious hotel that enjoys a good reputation for its food, and features in CAMRA's Good Pub Food guide. A fairly straightforward menu of pub favourites – steak, cottage pie, lasagne – is complemented by two specials boards. One offers no fewer than 12 curries, while the other is dedicated to fish, with a choice of around six dishes. Some of the produce comes from local farms. The same quality is evident at the breakfast table, where a full cooked meal can be supplemented with porridge, or kippers ordered as an alternative. The hotel keeps a good wine list and its guest ale changes weekly.

The Greyhound has good conference facilities for business guests, but also attracts golfers, walkers, cyclists and other tourists. Elan Valley Dams and Brecon Beacons National Park are nearby, while the Royal Welsh Showground is within walking distance - the pub hosts a beer festival during the week leading up to the annual show.

Guest accommodation is provided in unfussy but comfortably furnished rooms with TV and tea and coffee making facilities. The room prices are reduced by £10 per night in winter. Children are welcome.

P

BWLCH
New Inn
LD3 7RQ

- ▶ On A40 between Brecon and Crickhowell
- T (01874) 730215
- W starbunkhouse.com/NewInn.htm
- Brains Rev James; guest beers
- One double, two twin rooms, all en-suite
- £ £
- Lunchtime and evening meals and snacks
- Not accepted

At the heart of the Brecon National Park, near the recently established Beacons Way, this pub is ideally located for all sorts of outdoor activities, from the traditional such as canoeing, cycling, riding and fishing to the more modern pursuits of hang-gliding, paragliding, gorge walking and paintballing. All are available in the environs of the National Park, which also hosts a programme of events including the Royal Welsh Show in July, the Brecon Jazz Festival and Pontardawe Folk Festival, both in August.

Originally a coaching inn dating back to the 15th century, the New Inn is a lively pub at the centre of picturesque Bwlch, with stunning views of the Usk Valley. Here you can enjoy a variety of real ales, a choice of 30 malt whiskies and good food in the traditional surroundings of its bar with exposed stone walls and crackling log fire.

The three guest bedrooms have recently been refurbished to a high standard; the double room has a four-poster bed. Accommodation is excellent value, with a full cooked breakfast included, served any time between 7am and 10am. Excellent home-cooked meals and bar snacks are made using local produce where possible.

Local attractions include Llangorse Lake, the Brecon-Monmouthshire canal and Big Pit coal museum at Blaenavon.

Q P

LLANWRTYD WELLS
Neuadd Arms Hotel
The Square, LD5 4RB

- ▶ On A483, between Builth Wells and Llandovery
- T (01591) 610236
- F (01591) 610610
- W neuaddarmshotel.co.uk
- Brains SA; Felinfoel Double Dragon; guest beer
- Eight double, eight twin, five single rooms, all en-suite
- £ ££
- Food served all day
- Accepted

The refurbishment of the hotel's 21 bedrooms over the past four years has meant that its next project – the conversion of derelict stables into a brewhouse – has had to take a back seat, but brewing should be underway by the time you check in. The enterprising family that owns this hotel also organises guided walking and mountain biking holidays and short breaks, under the banner of the Red Kite Activity Centre.

The Victorian hotel is full of character with a public bar housing an original 1970s juke box that plays seven inch vinyls, a games room and restaurant. There is also a TV lounge and launderette for the exclusive use of hotel residents. No two bedrooms are alike, but all offer comfortable, homely accommodation with TV and hospitality tray. A hearty full Welsh breakfast is served with copious toast, tea and coffee or your choice of boiled or scrambled eggs.

Llanwrtyd Wells lies in a remote area of the Cambrian Mountains, often called the Welsh Lake District, noted for its birds of prey such as the red kite and peregrine falcon. Despite its small size, the town hosts many events including the now famous bogsnorkelling triathlon.

Q P

LLANYMYNECH
Cross Keys
North Road, SY22 6EA

- ▶ On A483 between Oswestry and Welshpool
- T (01691) 831585
- F (01691) 831669
- W crosskeyshotel.info
- Beer range varies
- Two double, three twin, one family room; four rooms en-suite, two share a bathroom
- £ £
- Lunchtime and evening meals
- Accepted (not Amex)

Situated by Offa's Dke path, the Cross Keys offers an excellent service for walkers: good value accommodation, packed lunches and a luggage transfer facility. And there's always a well-earned beer after a day's hiking – usually two real ales from a varying range, often including a brew from Offa's Dyke Brewery near Oswestry.

The pub, a listed building built in the late 1700s, has been completely refurbished in the last few years, but maintains its character and open fires. The bar with dartboard and Sky sports on TV leads through an archway to a pool area. The attractive restaurant serves traditional pub food based on local produce. Live music is featured most Fridays in the summer. The pub has wireless Internet connection.

The simply furnished guest rooms have tea and coffee making facilities and TV. Children are welcome (the family room has bunk beds) and pets can stay. One dormitory room sleeps six. A full cooked breakfast is provided, along with cereals and toast.

Waterfalls, lakes and mountains are all a short drive away. Llanymynech Wharf was an important transhipment point in the heyday of the canals; a visitor centre there offers summer boat trips. Q P

NEWBRIDGE-ON-WYE

New Inn

LD1 6HY

- ▶ On A470, five miles from Llandrindod Wells
- T (01597) 860211
- E dave@pigsfolly.fsnet.co.uk
- Breconshire and Wye Valley brewery ranges; guest beers
- Five double, three twin, one family room, all en-suite
- £ £
- Lunchtime and evening meals
- Accepted

The New Inn, with its good value accommodation, is an excellent base for a walking holiday. Collection can be arranged from either Llandrindod Station or Builth Road Halt on the Mid Wales line. This single track railway runs from Swansea to Shrewsbury through some wonderful scenery; arriving by train would make a great start to any rural holiday. The pub, in the delightful Upper Wye Valley, has easy access to the Elan Valley and west coast beaches. National cycle route no. 8 passes nearby and the pub offers secure storage for bikes.

The black and white stone pub was built 200 years ago on an old drovers' route. The guest accommodation has recently been renovated to a high standard and features solid pine furniture. All the rooms have TV and tea making facilities. A hearty, full Welsh breakfast will set you up for a day's rambling or sight-seeing. Sausages and potato cakes are home-made here, served with home-cured bacon, free-range eggs, mushrooms and locally baked bread. The kitchen can cater for special dietary requirements. Most of the produce served on the menu in the lounge-cum-restaurant is sourced locally.

❀ ♣ P

PEN-Y-CAE

Ancient Briton

Brecon Road, SA9 1YY

- ▶ On A4067 in Brecon Beacons National Park
- T (01639) 730273
- F (01639) 730273
- E gerald.james@btconnect.com
- Beer range varies
- Two double, one twin, one family room, all en-suite
- £ ££ (single occupancy £40)
- Lunchtime and evening meals
- Accepted

The Ancient Briton is expanding. Five additional rooms are to be added as well as a campsite in the meadow at the rear to cater for the increasing number of people who want to stay at this popular pub in the Brecon Beacons National Park.

The hostelry, dating from 1836, was voted Swansea CAMRA Pub of the Year in 2006. It has an attractive open-plan interior divided into lounge and bar, dining area and games section. The garden has a play area. Seven handpumps offer a constantly changing range of real ales and the good quality home-cooked food is recommended – particularly the curries. The four guest rooms available at the moment have been refurbished; the family room can sleep two adults and two children under 11, and rooms can be booked as singles. A full breakfast is provided, with fresh local eggs.

The River Tawe flows opposite the pub and is renowned for its salmon, sewin and trout fishing (angling permits can be obtained at the pub). The area is well known for caving and the National Showcaves Centre for Wales at Dan-yr-ogof nearby offers a fascinating day out. Other outdoor activities are available here, including cycling and off-road vehicle trails.

Q ❀ ♣ P

RHAYADER

Crown Inn

North Street, LD6 5BT

- ▶ In town centre off A470
- T (01597) 811099
- W thecrownrhayader.co.uk
- Brains Dark, Bitter, Rev James, seasonal beers; guest beers
- Three twin rooms, shared shower room
- £ £ (£25 single occupancy)
- Lunchtime and evening meals (all day Sat and Sun summer)
- Accepted

This 16th-century pub was much altered internally during the 1970s but retains a lot of charm and character with many original features preserved. The heavily beamed open-plan interior is crammed with local memorabilia and provides a photographic history of the town – look out for the item referring to a former owner, Major Stanscombe. At the rear of the building is an attractive walled garden terrace with seating for alfresco drinking and dining. This Brains pub is a rare outlet for its mild (Dark) and is notable for stocking its seasonal ales and commemorative brews.

The food here is excellent value. All the meat is sourced locally and fresh fish comes from the indoor market in Cardiff. You are assured of a good breakfast – the full cooked meal can be substituted for something simpler such as poached or scrambled eggs if preferred.

In a quiet spot in the town centre, the accommodation is simple but comfortable. Three rooms each have TV and hospitality tray and share a shower room between them. Rhayader is at the heart of Wales, surrounded by moors and lakes, so wildlife abounds and there are dozens of nature reserves in the flooded Elan Valley.

Q P

TALYBONT ON USK

Star Inn

LD3 7YX

- ▶ Just off A40 between Crickhowell and Brecon
- T (01874) 676635
- Beer range varies
- One double, one twin room, both en-suite
- £ £ (£30 single occupancy)
- Lunchtime and evening meals
- Accepted

A CAMRA award-winner, this traditional inn is a lively pub popular with ramblers, cyclists and fans of outdoor pursuits. The surrounding National Park offers facilities for all kinds of activities including guided hill walking, cave diving and canoeing. After an active day, visitors can gather in the hospitable bar where live bands play on Wednesday evening, or enjoy the evening sun in the garden and watch the craft pass by on the Brecon-Monmouth Canal.

As can be seen from the array of pump clips, the Star sells a vast range of real ales that changes all the time, often sourced from Welsh and border breweries such as Breconshire, Felinfoel and Wye Valley. The pub was built around 1770 and remains unmodernised, with three rooms around a central servery, full of bric a brac and warmed by a fire in the inglenook.

The guest rooms are spacious, both have an extra single bed, so are suitable for a family (no charge for a young child sharing a parent's room) or three friends sharing. The furniture is simple, with TV and tea and coffee making facilities. A hearty breakfast is provided and good meals at lunchtime and in the evening are based on local produce as available.

Q

North East Wales

LLANASA

Red Lion Inn

CH8 9NE

- ▶ Between A5151 and A548, 4 miles from Prestatyn
- T (01745) 854291
- F (01745) 888605
- Courage Directors; Webster's Yorkshire Bitter; guest beers
- Four double, one twin room, all en-suite
- £ £ (room only)
- Lunchtime and evening meals
- Accepted

A huge stone fireplace dominates the bar of this typical Welsh country inn, adding warmth to the friendly atmosphere that you will encounter here. The pub also has a games area with pool table and darts and a popular restaurant. Good, home-made fare is produced by members of the family team that runs the Red Lion.

The light, bright guest bedrooms are well furnished and equipped with colour TV and refreshment tray. Children are welcome to stay. Prices are charged for the room only and breakfast is provided for £4.50 per person – the full English (or should that be Welsh?) along with cereals, toast and preserves.

The inn stands at the heart of Llanasa, a pretty conservation village in the gentle rolling countryside of the Clwydian range. It is just six miles from the traditional family seaside resort of Rhyl, from where there is a cycle route to Prestatyn, with its good beaches. Other places of interest nearby include St Winifred's Chapel at Holywell, a place of pilgrimage since the 12th century, 17th-century Bodrhyddan Hall, owned by Lord Langford, and Bodelwyddan Castle, an outpost of the National Portrait Gallery.

♣ P

LLANGOLLEN

Wynnstay Arms

Bridge Street, LL20 8PF

- ▶ Centre of town
- T (01978) 860710
- W wynnstay-arms.co.uk
- Greene King IPA, Abbot; Tetley Burton Ale; guest beers
- Two double, one twin, one family room, all en-suite, plus three bunkhouses
- £ £
- Lunchtime and evening meals
- Accepted

This popular town-centre pub is a former coaching inn, largely unaltered. The steps at the front originally served as a platform for mounting your horse (though there is level access via the courtyard and rear door). The walls of the inn are lined with original tack from the canal horses and a log fire burns in the main bar. The games room is served via a hatch. Further rooms to the back are used by families for a quiet drink, and diners.

The en-suite bedrooms are in the main building; some are on the ground floor so are accessible to wheelchair users. They have tea and coffee making facilities and TV. The three bunkhouses off the stable yard can each accommodate up to six people. They are basic but good value for walkers and travellers on a budget. Children are welcome and so are pets.

A full cooked breakfast will set you up for the day whatever your plans and you can enjoy bar meals at lunchtime and a good home-cooked meal in the evening. Local places of interest include Dinas Bran Castle and Valle Crucis Abbey, as well as the Llangollen Canal and Railway. Outdoor pursuits are catered for too, from golf to pot-holing, kayaking and climbing.

Q P

LLANGYNHAFAL

Golden Lion Inn

LL16 4LN

- ▶ Off A494 between Mold and Ruthin
- T (01824) 790451
- W thegoldenlioninn.com
- Coach House Gunpowder Mild; Holt Bitter; guest beer
- Two twin en-suite rooms
- £ ££
- Evening meals
- Not accepted

A charming, 18th-century creeper-clad pub in an area of outstanding natural beauty, the Golden Lion nestles at the foot of the Clwydian Hills, close to Offa's Dyke path. Llangynhafal is one of the most peaceful, and certainly one of the smallest, hamlets in the Vale of Clwyd – ideal for a relaxing break – and you are assured of a quiet night's rest.

The pub attracts walkers and cyclists to its quiet country lanes and often receives groups of visitors from the local gliding club. This is the only free house in Wales serving Joseph Holt beers; the landlord collects the ales himself from the brewery.

The pub has just two guest suites – the Clwydian is the smaller of the two with en-suite shower, while the Carnea has a jacuzzi bath and shower. Recently refurbished, the rooms have TV and hospitality tray. The inn's accommodation is not suitable for children. Behind the pub garden is a paddock for campers.

Breakfast is usually a full cooked meal but lighter alternatives can be ordered such as scrambled eggs with smoked salmon or kippers. Local eggs and meat are used in the kitchen, which also offers a good and varied menu in the evening.

Q P

MARCHWIEL

Cross Lanes Hotel (Kagan's Brasserie)

Bangor Road, LL13 0TF

▶ On A525 between Wrexham and Whitchurch
T (01978) 870555
F (01978) 780568
W crosslanes.co.uk
Plassey Bitter; guest beer
Eight double, four twin, four single rooms, all en-suite
£ £££-££££
Lunchtime and evening meals
Accepted

Set in six acres of grounds, the Cross Lane Hotel was built as a private residence during Victoria's reign. However, the magnificent oak panelling in the front hall is Jacobean, rescued from Emral Hall at Worthenbury during the 1930s. The house was converted to a hotel in 1959 and now belongs to the Best Western group.

Original Victorian features and a homely ambience have been carefully preserved – the bar and Kagan's Brasserie, with slate floors, solid oak tables and wonderful open fires, offer a warm, friendly atmosphere in which to enjoy the local Plassey Bitter or an informal meal. In summer you can sit out on the patio and admire the beautiful gardens.

The first-floor bedrooms are individually designed in country style, with digital TV, high speed Internet access, trouser press, hair dryer and hospitality tray. A Celebration Break in the four-poster room includes flowers, chocolates and champagne. Children are welcome; under 16s sharing a parent's room are charged only for breakfast. An extensive buffet with warm rolls, fruit and yogurt is followed by a full Welsh breakfast with eggs cooked as you like them, poached smoked haddock or home-baked ham with cheese.
Q P

NORTHOP

☆ Soughton Hall & Stables Bar

CH7 6AB

▶ Take A5119 turn off of A55, through Northop village
T (01352) 840577
F (01352) 840372
W soughtonhall.co.uk
Beer range varies
Eleven double, two twin, three family rooms, all en-suite; two wheelchair accessible
£ ££££
Lunchtime and evening meals
Accepted

This beautiful country house hotel was built as a bishop's palace in 1714 and was home to the Wynne-Bankes family. William John Bankes, a great traveller, added the stylish touches such as mullioned windows and Islamic turrets that characterise the house. The building had fallen into a poor state of repair before being restored in 1986 and returned to its former glory, creating a splendid hotel.

Accommodation here is high-priced, but for a special occasion the location and facilities are well worth the expense, and a two-night mid-week break with breakfast and dinner is offered at a reduced rate. The spacious guest rooms are all decorated in individual style and some have four-posters. Fresh fruit, mineral water, hot drinks facilities, television and trouser press are provided. Some rooms have wireless Broadband access or you can use the service in the library.

In the morning the full Welsh breakfast includes local eggs and sausages, or there is haddock, kippers, cheeses and ham, fresh and dried fruits. Real ales from Plassey and Coach House are served in the delightful Stables bar and restaurant that has been converted with flair, retaining the original cobbled floors, stalls and roof timbers. Evening meals are served in the Hayloft. Q P

North West Wales

ABERDYFI

Penhelig Arms

LL35 0LT

- ▶ On the coast road (A493), 10 miles from Machynlleth
- T (01654) 767215
- F (01654) 767690
- W penheligarms.com
- Hancock's HB; guest beers
- Two double, nine twin, one family, four single rooms, all en-suite, two rooms wheelchair accessible
- £ £££-££££
- Lunchtime and evening meals and snacks
- Accepted

The Penhelig Arms has an outstanding, award-winning wine list and its brasserie-style restaurant has also won national recognition (Rick Stein praises the seafood). Beer lovers are not forgotten, either; the two guest ales served in the Fisherman's Bar change every fortnight. Set in a wonderful seaside location in Snowdonia National Park and offering luxurious accommodation, this hotel is unmissable.

Converted from a row of 18th-century cottages, the hotel offers 10 individually designed bedrooms, most with sea views. In addition there are four spacious suites in a separate building, Bodhelig, with balconies providing stunning views of the mountains, estuary and the sea. Two of these suites are adapted for disabled guests. The hotel's latest addition, offering the height of luxury, is Penhelig House: a suite with upmarket contemporary furnishings on two levels with two bathrooms.

Breakfast is taken seriously here – a wonderful spread. There is the usual cooked affair with sausage, bacon, black pudding and eggs prepared as you like, or home-baked ham with Snowdonia cheddar, grilled kipper or poached naturally smoked haddock, along with yogurt, fruit compote, fresh fruit and cereals. Q P

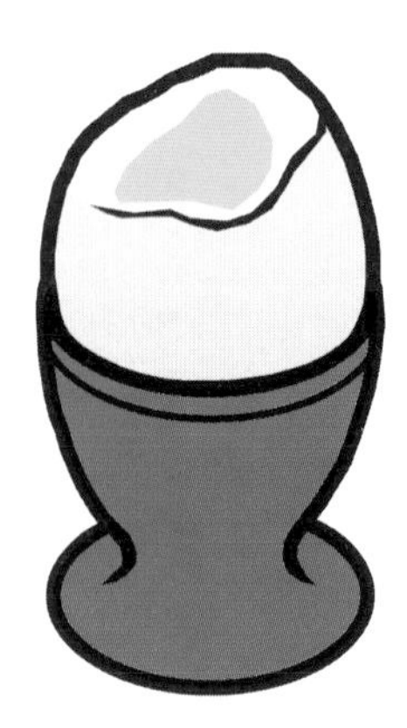

BANGOR
Boatyard Inn
Garth Road, LL7 2SF

▶ Take A55 to Bangor, turn right just after Dickie's Boatyard
T (01248) 362462
W boatyardinn.co.uk
Marston's Burton Bitter; guest beers
One double, one twin, one family room with shared bathroom
£ £ (£25 single occupancy)
Lunchtime and evening meals
Not accepted

After a recent extensive refurbishment the pub now has a fresh coat of paint throughout and a new name (it was previously called the Union Tavern and is listed in CAMRA's 2007 Good Beer Guide as such), and is back in business. A friendly pub with a warm welcome, the Union was always known for its character and the original, eclectic style has been retained. The bar is full of fascinating artefacts, particularly of a nautical nature, and one room is dedicated to the landlord's interest in horse racing.

The guest bedrooms have also been freshened up. Each room has a hand basin, TV and facilities for making hot drinks. With a full breakfast of eggs, bacon, sausage, black pudding, tomato and mushrooms included, the rate for a night's B&B is a bargain. Local produce features on the main menu, with fish from the Menai Straits.

The pub garden benefits from a view over Hirael bay with sailing boats and Bangor Pier is five minutes' walk. Anglesey, Snowdonia and Portmeirion are all within striking distance.
Q ❀ ♿ P ⇌ 🚌

BETWS-YN-RHOS
Wheatsheaf Inn
LL22 8AW

▶ From A55 Expressway, take A548 1 mile towards Llanrwst then B5381
T (01492) 680218
W thewheatsheafinn.org.uk
Black Sheep Best Bitter; Courage Directors
Two double, one family, one single room, all en-suite
£ £
Lunchtime and evening meals and snacks
Accepted

The Wheatsheaf enjoys an enviable setting in a village that was voted 'Best in Wales' in 2003, opposite the church of St Michael, which is notable for its twin towers. Built in the 13th century as an ale house, it was licensed as a coaching inn during the 17th century to serve the mail route between Chester and Conwy. Many of the building's original features remain, including the solid oak beams (now covered with brasses), the stone pillars and old hayloft ladder. The guest rooms are two-star rated by the Welsh tourist board and all have TV and facilities for making hot drinks.

At breakfast you will be offered scrambled, poached or boiled eggs or a full cooked breakfast. The pub kitchen uses local produce as much as possible and can cater for special requirements such as vegetarian, vegan and gluten-free diets. Light meals and snacks are served in the lounge bar and garden, while an à la carte menu is served in the restaurant.

Tennis, golf and bowls can all be played in this pretty village, while short excursions will take you to Bodnant Gardens, Conway Castle and the Victorian resort of Llandudno. ❀ ♿ ♣ P

CONWY
Groes Inn
LL32 8TN

▶ Take B5106 from Conwy
T (01492) 650545
W groesinn.com
Great Orme Best; Tetley Bitter, Burton Ale; guest beers
Fourteen double/single en-suite rooms; includes one family room, one with disabled access
£ £££
Lunchtime and evening meals
Accepted

Groes Inn (pronounced Grois as in voice) is a fine old hostelry, dating from around the 16th century, reputed to be the first licensed house in Wales. To say it has character would be an understatement; its rambling rooms all have their own style, while nooks and crannies hide all sorts of artefacts, from old cooking utensils to Victorian portraits, even stone cats in the lounge fireplace. The owners' efforts to retain the hotel's traditional character throughout the accommodation have earned them a Civic Society award.

The 14 bedrooms are individually styled, but mostly with a traditional look. They are spacious and airy with comfortable seating, television, hairdryer and refreshment tray. Some have a private balcony or terrace and all benefit from splendid views of the foothills of Snowdonia or Conwy Valley. The hotel also offers the High Cabin, a luxurious, self-catering hideaway for two people which is completely private. It boasts an outdoor hot tub where you can soak in the water and soak up the scenery at the same time.

With meals based on fresh local ingredients you can dine at the inn in style in the restaurant or enjoy an informal bar meal. The breakfast menu offers all you could want from porridge to kippers.

Q P

GWYTHERIN
Lion Inn
LL22 8UU

▶ Off B5348, just outside the Gwytherin village
T (01745) 860123
W thelioninn.net
Hanson's Mild; Marston's Burton Bitter; guest beer
Two double, one twin, one family, one single room; all en-suite
£ £££
Lunchtime (not Mon-Fri) and evening meals
Accepted

In Gwytherin they say, 'the peace is extreme'. You can't pick up a mobile phone signal in this deeply rural location and in the morning you will be awakened by birdsong rather than traffic. The traditional whitewashed Lion Inn is over 300 years old and stands opposite St Winifred's Church. The two bars and restaurant are uncluttered, with leather seating, and are free from intrusions such as television; music is only played on request.

The guest rooms are equally relaxing, complementing the character of the inn, in pale colours with good quality, modern fixtures and fittings. All the rooms have a DVD player and DVDs are available free from the pub's library. One room has a balcony where you can sit and watch the hares playing in the field and the red kites wheeling overhead. The family room has a double bed, with two singles and a cot in an adjoining annexe; a baby monitor is available. Pets can be accommodated.

A full cooked breakfast is provided, and the owners will cater for individual requests as far as possible; if you ask for porridge and boiled eggs or salmon and scrambled eggs they will always try to oblige.

Q P

ISLE OF ANGLESEY

Auckland Arms

Water Street, Menai Bridge, LL59 5DD

- Turn right over Menai Suspension Bridge, off A545
- T (01248) 712545
- W aucklandarms.co.uk
- Greene King IPA; guest beers
- Five double, one twin, two family rooms, all en-suite; two rooms are wheelchair accessible
- £ £
- Evening meals
- Accepted

Built at the end of the 19th century, this used to be one of a run of 'spit and sawdust' pubs on Water Street, leading down to the slipway. Now thoroughly respectable and a fairly recent convert to real ale, it retains a real pub character and great atmosphere. It is popular with customers from all walks of life, including divers, walkers and students. Pool and table football are played and it has a pretty garden and sunny terrace.

The guest rooms come in two categories: standard with television and hot drinks facilities and superior, with Freeview TV channels, DVD player, a sofa or armchair and stylish, modern fittings. There is also a separate Coach House with double, twin and single rooms and bathroom. This can be rented for £120 per night based on five adults sharing; cots and extra beds are available on request.

A good continental breakfast is served in your room: cereals, yogurts, bagels, ham, cheese, preserves and cereals are available. Evening meals can be taken in the pub and barbecues are a feature in summer. Close to the pier, the pub is well situated for exploring the town and Anglesey.

ISLE OF ANGLESEY

☆ Ye Olde Bull's Head Inn

Castle Street, Beaumaris, LL58 8AP

- Take Britannia road bridge to Anglesey, then A545 to Beaumaris
- T (01248) 810329
- W bullsheadinn.co.uk
- Draught Bass; Hancock's HB; guest beer
- Nine double, four twin rooms, all en-suite
- £ £££
- Lunchtime and evening meals and snacks
- Accepted

The Bull is a marvellous old inn with a fascinating history. Built over 500 years ago, it is one of the oldest of the Quaker meeting houses on the island. Cromwell's General Mytton commandeered the inn for his headquarters in 1645 during his siege of Beaumaris Castle. Other famous guests include Dr Samuel Johnson and Charles Dickens – some of the hotel's guest rooms are named after his characters.

And what rooms. All are individually styled with high quality furnishings and well equipped; many have exposed roof timbers incorporated into the design. The impressive Mr Pickwick has a romantic carved oak four-poster, the General Mytton suite boasts a splendid bathroom with underfloor heating, and the Lofthouse suite in the rear courtyard has subtle, modern decor, a king-sized bed and widescreen TV. Children are welcome to stay.

Breakfast ranges from a full Welsh that comes complete with laverbread and black pudding if required, or there are kippers, cold ham, smoked salmon or eggs cooked as you like them. The hotel has an elegant restaurant under the eaves of the oldest part of the building as well as an informal brasserie.

ISLE OF ANGLESEY

Victoria Hotel

Telford Road, Menai Bridge, LL59 5DR

▶ Turn right over Menai Suspension Bridge, on A545
T (01248) 712309
E vicmenai@barbox.net
Draught Bass; guest beers
Six double, seven twin, seven family, one single room, all en-suite; one room adapted for disabled guests
£ ££
Lunchtime and evening meals
Accepted

This grade II listed stone hotel first became popular when Liverpool pleasure steamers used to dock in Menai Bridge and continues to be an ideal choice for tourists. In a picturesque setting overlooking the Strait and Snowdonia, seven bedrooms enjoy stunning views as far as the Great Orme in Llandudno, and the delightful garden has the same panorama. The hotel is just three miles from the university town of Bangor with its good shopping facilities, while Beaumaris Castle and Anglesey's unspoilt beaches are just some of the attractions on the island itself.

The hotel's guest rooms offer comfortable accommodation with facilities including a TV and hospitality tray, as well as a hair dryer and ironing board. Families are welcome (seven double bedrooms have an additional single or bunk bed) and the hotel has a play area for children. One ground floor room is adapted for wheelchair users, but most rooms are on the first floor. The hotel is licensed for weddings.

A good choice is served at breakfast time: cereals and fruit juices, a full cooked breakfast, kippers or smoked haddock as well as toast and preserves. Special dietary requirements can usually be met on request. Q P

LLANBEDR

Ty-Mawr Hotel

LL45 2NH

▶ Off A496 Barmouth-Harlech road
T (01341) 241440
W tymawrhotel.org.uk
Beer range varies
Six double, two twin, one family, one single room, all en-suite
£ ££
Lunchtime and evening meals
Accepted

Originally a farmstead dating back to the 16th-century, a pub was added to the hotel in 1982 by the Smith family, who still own and run Ty-Mawr. The pub quickly grew in popularity and, free of tie, it stocks a constantly changing range of real ales, mostly from Welsh breweries such as Conwy and Purple Moose. The modern lounge bar features a slate-flagged floor and a wood-burning stove, and is decorated with unusual flying memorabilia, an indication of its connections to a local airfield. French windows open onto an attractive garden.

The guest rooms are individually styled, spacious and comfortable. They all have television and hospitality tray. The generous breakfast menu includes local bacon and free-range eggs. Main meals, also featuring local produce, can be taken in the bar or restaurant, with changing special dishes listed on the blackboard. Morning coffee and afternoon tea are served in the residents' lounge. Pets are permitted at the hotel.

The River Artro, noted for its salmon fishing, passes opposite the hotel gates. Uncrowded beaches, riding and golf can all be enjoyed nearby in the surrounding Snowdonia National Park.
P

LLANDWROG

Harp Inn

LL54 5SY

- ▶ Off A499, 6 miles from Caernarfon
- T (01286) 831071
- W welcome.to/theharp
- Beer range varies
- One double en-suite, two twin and one single room with private bath or shower
- £ £-££
- Lunchtime and evening meals
- Accepted

If you want to practise speaking Welsh, this is the place to stay as staff here are bilingual. Maybe a pint of ale from a Welsh brewery, such as Purple Moose, Snowdonia or Evan Evans might help to loosen your tongue.

This lovely old inn, close to the sea and the mountain, is hidden away on a back road in a quaint village. It offers country-style accommodation and children are welcome. If the weather turns against you the pub has a supply of newspapers and magazines, while the games room has plenty of board games for adults and children as well as a pool table and fruit machines. The pub, home to Dylan the parrot, benefits from a peaceful garden, cosy snug and a restaurant.

The kitchen makes use of local produce as far as possible, including Welsh lamb, beef and sausages. At breakfast you can choose between cereals and porridge followed by a full cooked meal or eggs prepared to your preference.

For active pursuits this area has much to offer; among the more unusual opportunities are rock climbing, pleasure flights at Caernarfon Airport and scuba diving in quarries or the sea, while steam enthusiasts can take a ride on the Welsh Highland steam railway. P

ST GEORGE

☆ Kinmel Arms

The Village, LL22 9BP

- ▶ Signed from A55 westbound
- T (01745) 832207
- F (01745) 822044
- W thekinmelarms.co.uk
- Tetley Bitter; guest beers
- Four double rooms, all en-suite, one wheelchair accessible
- £ ££££
- Lunchtime and evening meals; closed Monday except bank holidays
- Accepted

This former coaching inn is far from an average pub – described as a restaurant with rooms, it is a very stylish destination, with prices to match. Lynn and Tim Watson both knew the Kinmel Arms from their childhood. When they acquired the property in 2001 they set about transforming it into the kind of place they liked to visit themselves. Now an award-winning dining venue, it has been completely refurbished to give an L-shaped bar for drinking and dining and a spacious conservatory, mostly used for dining.

The four luxury guest suites have elegant, contemporary decor influenced by Tim's paintings. The Eryr (Eagle) suite on the ground floor can accommodate a wheelchair. The rooms feature super king-sized beds, a sofa and lounge table, wireless broadband connection, television and DVD player, fridge and hospitality tray. The bathrooms are equally luxurious and each room has a private balcony or patio. Breakfasts are imaginative: platters of fresh fruit, local cheese and ham, Welsh yogurts and home-made bread and preserves. There is tea and coffee of course, but also fruit smoothies.

Q P

West Wales

GOGINAN
Druid Inn
High Street, SY23 3NT

- On A44, 7 miles east of Aberystwth
- T (01970) 880650
- W goginan.com/druid
- Banks's Bitter; Draught Bass; Brains SA; guest beers
- Two double, one twin, one family room with shared facilities
- £ £
- Lunchtime and evening meals
- Not accepted

A former Ceredigion CAMRA Pub of the Year, the Druid is a focus for village life and is very popular with locals and visitors alike. The pub accommodation is convenient for those attending courses at the Old Garage Stained Glass Studio just 50 yards away.

The guest rooms, a fairly recent venture, are in a newly furnished and decorated cottage next to the pub. Each room has its own television and tea and coffee making facilities and a hand basin, but they share a bathroom. One room is on the ground floor; pets are welcome. Some rooms benefit from magical views across the Melindwr Valley. Good value, the tariff includes a hearty cooked breakfast with fresh fruit and yogurt available on request. Home-cooked lunches and evening meals can be enjoyed in the bar or restaurant of this friendly pub.

The cottage provides secure covered storage for cycles and other equipment. The nearby Nant y Arian forest – famous for its Red Kites – offers excellent mountain bike trails at all levels through spectacular scenery. Other attractions include the Llewernog silver mine, the Rheidol Railway and the Centre for Alternative Technology at Machynlleth.

Q P

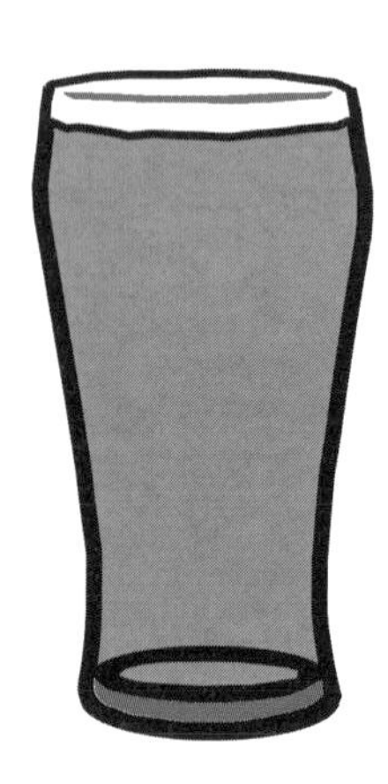

LLANELLI

Waun Wyllt Inn

Horeb Road, Five Roads, SA15 5AQ

▶ Three miles north of Llanelli on B4309
T (01269) 860209
W waunwyllt.com
Beer range varies
Three double, one twin room, all en-suite; rooms are wheelchair accessible and may be let as singles
£ ££ (£42 single occupancy)
Lunchtime meals and snacks, evening meals and afternoon teas
Accepted

Dating in part to the 1700s, the term waun wyllt means wild moor or wild meadow, derived from the inn's location nestled in the Sylen hills. The building has recently been sympathetically refurbished. The main bar retains its olde-worlde charm – warmed by a log fire and furnished with comfy leather chairs and sofas, it is free from juke box and games. A free house, the bar usually offers four real ales, including Welsh brews from Evan Evans and Felinfoel.

The guest rooms are in a detached chalet-style lodge and this, too, has been updated to a high standard with an attractive patio outside. Rooms are light and airy, with television and hospitality tray. Two rooms have showers and two have baths with showers. Children are welcome to stay.

Food here is good; the restaurant specialises in Welsh black beef and fish, which varies daily according to what is delivered and what the chef has caught! Breakfasts are generous with a full cooked meal served, including eggs cooked to your preference, as well as yogurts, fresh fruit, toast and preserves. A good ramble is recommended to walk it off, which is fine as the pub is situated 100 yards from the coastal path. It is also handy for the National Cycle network. Q P

NEW QUAY

Cambrian Hotel

New Road, SA45 9SE

▶ Take B4342 from A487 between Cardigan and Aberystwyth
T (01545) 560295
Archers Village; Brains Buckley's Best Bitter; Felinfoel Double Dragon; guest beer
Three double, one twin room, all en-suite, also available as singles
£ ££
Lunchtime and evening meals
Accepted

Built around a hundred years ago as a private house, this small, family-run hotel benefits from a peaceful setting on the outskirts of New Quay and affords panoramic views of Cardigan Bay. Open all year to residents and non-residents, the cosy bar is recommended by local CAMRA members for its real ale, which includes a guest, often from a local micro-brewery, during the summer season and at other busy times. Its annual beer festival, usually held in July, is growing in popularity.

The hotel has a good-sized garden and a TV lounge for guests. The conservatory restaurant serves lunches and a more extensive à la carte evening menu based on local produce. Live music is often staged at the weekend.

The guest rooms are on the first floor and are comfortably furnished with TV, hair dryer, trouser press and hot drinks facilities as standard. A full cooked breakfast, along with toast, preserves and cereals is provided. Children are welcome to stay and will no doubt love the safe sandy beaches that are within walking distance of the hotel. Coastal walks, pony trekking and fishing can all be enjoyed nearby, too.
P

RHANDIRMWYN
Royal Oak
SA20 0NY

- ▶ Off A40 between Brecon and Llandeilo
- T (01550) 760201
- W rhandirmwyn.com
- Beer range varies
- One double, one twin, one family room, all en-suite, two single rooms with shared facilities
- £ ££
- Lunchtime and evening meals
- Accepted

This traditional village pub with exposed stone walls and tiled floors is a frequent local CAMRA Pub of the Year, offering a choice of at least four real ales that change frequently. It also stocks a good range of bottled beers and some 40 malt whiskies.

In a fairly remote spot, the inn was built as a hunting lodge for a local landowner, and is now a centre for community activities, attracting walkers, cyclists and birdwatchers visiting the nearby RSPB sanctuary. Guest bedrooms are decorated in country style with pine furnishings. The three larger rooms have en-suite facilities and TV and benefit from fine views of the Towy Valley. The single rooms are more basic, but inexpensive (£22.50). Pets are welcome. In the morning there is a choice of croissants, a fried breakfast or kippers. The wholesome food here is recommended; snacks and main meals are available every day.

The surrounding countryside is simply beautiful – rivers, lakes, gorges and waterfalls – while spring visitors can enjoy the multitude of bluebells. For something a little different you can visit the Dolaucothi Gold Mines (NT) in nearby Pumsaint that were first used in Roman times.

Q P

TALYBONT
White Lion
SY24 5ER

- ▶ On A487 between Aberystwyth and Machynlleth
- T (01970) 832245
- F (01970) 832658
- Banks's Original, Bitter; guest beers
- One double, two twin, one family room (one double, two single beds), all en-suite
- £ ££
- Lunchtime and evening meals
- Accepted

The White Lion is open all day until 1am daily (midnight on Sunday), so there is plenty of time to enjoy its excellent Banks's ales and excellent food – the pub is listed in CAMRA's Good Pub Food guide. You must try the lobster, crab or trout, caught by one of the pub's regulars, or the sausages that come in myriad flavours from the local butcher. The food here is good value – around £15 for two courses – and naturally the same high quality is maintained at breakfast. You can fill up on a full cooked meal or opt for the vegetarian alternative, or mackerel, with cereal, toast and preserves.

This small hotel has recently been refurbished; the public bar, once a butcher's shop, has retained the meat-hanging hooks on the ceiling along with its original slate floor. There is also a snug area, a family room with pool, darts and video games and a small restaurant. The pub hosts frequent music and poetry evenings. Guest rooms all have a television and hospitality tray. Pets can be accommodated. Buses from Aberystwyth and Bangor stop outside the pub. Close to Nant-y-Moch fishing lakes, permits can be obtained locally.

Q P

Channel Islands

ALDERNEY

Georgian House Hotel

Victoria Street, GY9 3UF

▶ Centre of St Anne
T (01481) 822471
W georgianhousealderney.com
Beer range varies
Four double/twin rooms, all en-suite
£ £££-££££
Lunchtime and evening meals and snacks
Accepted

This fine Georgian building is located in St Anne, the tiny island's main town. Open throughout the year, the friendly bar is popular with locals and visitors alike. For dining there is the elegant Walpole Room and the splendid Orangery where the floor to ceiling windows open fully to give a view of the award-winning garden, popular in summer for alfresco meals.

Food is excellent here, from the home-made biscuits served with morning coffee to the platters of fruits de mer that are the house speciality. The hotel imports many of its wines direct from French vineyards, while its real ale mostly comes from Randalls in Guernsey or Ringwood in Hampshire. The hotel stages regular live entertainment.

The guest bedrooms are named after some of the rocks that surround Alderney and are colour co-ordinated with regency-striped wallpaper. Coque Lihou (dark red), Ortac (blue) and La Ronde (gold) have en-suite bathrooms, while Verte Tete (green) has a shower. The spacious, comfortable rooms are equipped with satellite TV and tea and coffee making facilities. A full English breakfast is provided. ❀

GUERNSEY

Fleur du Jardin

Kings Mills, Castel, GY5 7JT

T (01481) 257996
W fleurdujardin.com
Fuller's London Pride; Jersey Guernsey Sunbeam
Ten double, six twin, one family room, all en-suite
£ £££-££££
Lunchtime and evening meals
Accepted

Within easy reach of the island's airport, this charming stone-built hotel enjoys an enviable setting in its own extensive grounds with a private outdoor swimming pool. Dating back to the 15th century, the building combines original features such as exposed beams, granite walls and open fires with modern comforts.

The well-appointed guest rooms are equipped with TV, tea and coffee making facilities and hair dryer. In the morning you can help yourself to the breakfast buffet then order from a cooked menu – a full hot breakfast, grilled kipper or smoked haddock. The hotel enjoys a good reputation for its food. Local produce is the mainstay of the beamed restaurant, decorated with watercolours of the area and warmed by a log fire in winter. An extensive menu, light meals and snacks are also served in the traditional bar that is busy all year round with locals as well as tourists.

Visitors benefit from the island's mild climate and can enjoy walks through quiet country lanes around the hotel, while just a little further away are some of Guernsey's best beaches. Bicycles can be hired locally and are possibly the best transport for exploring the surroundings.

Q ❀ P

Isle of Man

LAXEY
Bridge Inn
6 New Road, IM4 7PH

▶ On Ramsey road
T (01624) 862414
F (01624) 862779
W manxtaverns.co.im
Bushy's Mild, Bitter; guest beer
One double, two twin, two family, three single rooms, all en-suite; some wheelchair accessible
£ ££
No main meals served
Accepted

On the east coast, Laxey is a small fishing village with a little bay and harbour that is now mostly home to pleasure craft. The village boasts the world's largest waterwheel (built in 1854), which has been well preserved and is still in working order. This used to be a mining area and walks in the glen follow routes around the old mine workings. The cellar of the Bridge Inn was transformed into a morgue after the Snaefell mining disaster of 1897 when 20 men perished and the pub's lounge is now reputed to be haunted by ghostly figures.

Around 120 years old, the inn was newly built around the time of the mining accident, and has recently been refurbished to a high standard throughout. An established community local, the lounge bar is a convivial meeting place with a projection television for sporting events, and there is a function room that stages live music.

The guest rooms are simply decorated and furnished, equipped with TV and tea and coffee making facilities. Local produce on the breakfast menu includes the full English or Manx kippers and free-range farm eggs.

P

PORT ERIN
Falcon's Nest Hotel
The Promenade, IM9 6AF

T (01624) 834077
W falconsnesthotel.co.uk
Bushy's Bitter; Okells Bitter; guest beers
Fifteen double, eight twin, nine family, three single rooms, all en-suite
£ ££ (low season) £££ (high season)
Lunchtime and evening meals and snacks
Accepted

You can't miss the Falcon's Nest Hotel – this distinctive white-painted free house enjoys a prominent position overlooking the bay and the headland at Port Erin. Some public rooms and several bedrooms benefit from superb sea views.

The restaurant in the former ballroom has been beautifully restored to show off its original Victorian features. The menu specialises in local seafood such as Manx queenies. Meals and snacks can also be taken in the bar and stylish conservatories, and packed lunches are available. Real ale is served in the lounge, not the bar.

Children are welcome in this family-run hotel, which offers a baby listening service. The comfortable guest rooms have tea and coffee making facilities, TV, hair dryer and free Wifi Internet access. A full Manx breakfast is served buffet style from 8am (Manx kippers are available) or guests can request a continental breakfast tray for earlier departures. Most dietary requirements can be catered for.

The hotel will happily book your flight or ferry from the mainland as well as car hire, heritage passes and other tickets. Local attractions include the sheltered sandy beach just below the hotel, the railway museum and the island's steam railway.

Q P

PORT ST MARY
Albert Hotel
Athol Street, IM9 5DS

- ▶ By the bus terminal
- T (01624) 832118
- Bushy's Ruby Mild, Old Bushy Tail; Okells Bitter; guest beer
- One double, two twin rooms, all en-suite
- £ ££
- Lunchtime and evening meals
- Accepted

Situated next to the bus terminal, the Albert is convenient for those travelling by public transport. It also benefits from fine views over the inner harbour and bay of Port St Mary. This is a very traditional pub – pool and darts are played in the busy public bar where there is a juke box; the cosy lounge is nautically themed. Both bars are warmed by open fires.

Featuring in CAMRA's Good Pub Food guide, unpretentious home-cooked food is served in the bar, while a more inventive menu is offered in the restaurant. A list of fish dishes is on the specials board and desserts chalked up daily. Special dietary requirements can be catered for with a little notice. Local produce is used as much as possible in all meals.

The hotel's comfortable, traditional style continues in the en-suite guest bedrooms, which are well decorated and equipped. Young children cannot be accommodated. Visitors can enjoy sandy beaches and coastal walks – the clifftop trail south to the Calf of Man is recommended. Port St Mary is a popular yachting centre and home to the Isle of Man Yacht Club HQ.
Q ♣ P

SULBY
Sulby Glen Hotel
Main Road, IM7 2HR

- ▶ On A3 towards Peel at crossroads
- T (01624) 897240
- W sulbyglenhotel.net
- Bushy's Bitter; Okells Bitter; guest beers
- Five double, three twin, three single rooms, all en-suite
- £ ££
- Lunchtime and evening meals and snacks
- Accepted

The doorways in the Sulby Glen are over 8ft high – designed to accommodate the 'Sulby Giant', Arthur Caley, a 19th-century Manx worthy who drank at the inn. This traditional country hotel benefits from uninterrupted views of the glen and mountains and is within walking distance of Curragh Wildlife Park. Standing on the Sulby Strait section of the Isle of Man TT course, the hotel is an ideal choice for fans of the famous motorcycle race.

The bedrooms have recently been upgraded to four diamond rating, so guests can be assured of a comfortable stay; children are welcome. The inn is listed in CAMRA's Good Pub Food guide, and the Landlord's Bistro, warmed by an open fire, offers a varied menu that makes the most of local fish and seafood, particularly Manx Queenies – scallops. All the meat served here originates on the island. Vegetarian, vegan and wheat-free diets can be accommodated and children are offered their own menu. At breakfast you can tuck into Manx kippers, a full cooked meal with your choice of eggs, or a vegetarian alternative. Q ♣ P

BEER STYLES

Deepen your appreciation of cask ale with this run-down on the main styles available.

Mild

Mild was once the most popular style of beer but was overtaken by Bitter from the 1950s. It was developed in the 18th and 19th centuries as a less aggressively bitter style of beer than porter and stout. Early Milds were much stronger that modern interpretations, which tend to fall in the 3% to 3.5% category, though there are stronger versions, such as Gale's Festival Mild and Sarah Hughes' Dark Ruby. Mild ale is usually dark brown in colour, due to the use of well-roasted malts or roasted barley, but there are paler versions, such as Banks's Original, Timothy Taylor's Golden Best and McMullen's AK. Look for rich malty aromas and flavours with hints of dark fruit, chocolate, coffee and caramel and a gentle underpinning of hop bitterness. (SHOWN BELOW)

Old Ale

Old Ale recalls the type of beer brewed before the Industrial Revolution, stored for months or even years in unlined wooden vessels known as tuns. The beer would pick up some lactic sourness as a result of wild yeasts, lactobacilli and tannins in the wood. The result was a beer dubbed 'stale' by drinkers: it was one of the components of the early, blended Porters. The style has re-emerged in recent years, due primarily to the fame of Theakston's Old Peculier, Gale's Prize Old Ale and Thomas Hardy's Ale, the last saved from oblivion by O'Hanlon's Brewery in Devon. Old Ales, contrary to expectation, do not have to be especially strong: they can be no more than 4% alcohol, though the Gale's and O'Hanlon's versions are considerably stronger. Neither

MILD

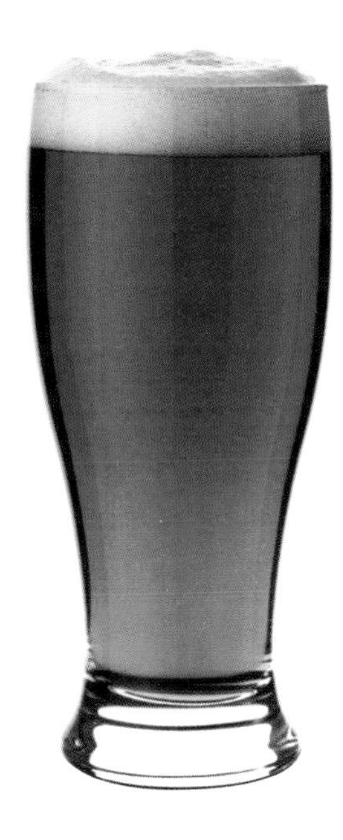

BITTER

do they have to be dark: Old Ale can be pale and burst with lush sappy malt, tart fruit and spicy hop notes. Darker versions will have a more profound malt character with powerful hints of roasted grain, dark fruit, polished leather and fresh tobacco. The hallmark of the style remains a lengthy period of maturation, often in bottle rather than bulk vessels.

Bitter

Towards the end of the 19th century, brewers built large estates of tied pubs. They moved away from vatted beers stored for many months and developed 'running beers' that could be served after a few days' storage in pub cellars. Draught Mild was a 'running beer' along with a new type that was dubbed Bitter by drinkers. Bitter grew out of Pale Ale but was generally deep bronze to copper in colour due to the use of slightly darker malts such as crystal that give the beer fullness of palate. Best is a stronger version of Bitter but there is considerable crossover. Bitter falls into the 3.4% to 3.9% band, with Best Bitter 4% upwards but a number of brewers label their ordinary Bitters 'Best'. A further development of Bitter comes in the shape of Extra or Special Strong Bitters of 5% or more: familiar examples of this style include Fuller's ESB and Greene King Abbot. With ordinary Bitter, look for a spicy, peppery and grassy hop character, a powerful bitterness, tangy fruit and juicy and nutty malt. With Best and Strong Bitters, malt and fruit character will tend to dominate but hop aroma and bitterness are still crucial to the style, often achieved by 'late hopping' in the brewery or adding hops to casks as they leave for pubs. (SHOWN ABOVE)

Golden Ales

This new style of pale, well-hopped and quenching beer developed in the 1980s as independent brewers attempted to win

GOLDEN ALE

younger drinkers from heavily-promoted lager brands. The first in the field were Exmoor Gold and Hop Back Summer Lightning, though many micros and regionals now make their versions of the style. Strengths will range from 3.5% to 5%. The hallmark will be the biscuity and juicy malt character derived from pale malts, underscored by tart citrus fruit and peppery hops, often with the addition of hints of vanilla and sweetcorn. Above all, such beers are quenching and served cool.

IPA and Pale Ale

India Pale Ale changed the face of brewing early in the 19th century. The new technologies of the Industrial Revolution enabled brewers to use pale malts to fashion beers that were genuinely golden or pale bronze in colour. First brewed in London and Burton-on-Trent for the colonial market, IPAs were strong in alcohol and high in hops: the preservative character of the hops helped keep the beers in good condition during long sea journeys. Beers with less alcohol and hops were developed for the domestic market and were known as Pale Ale. Today Pale Ale is usually a bottled version of Bitter, though historically the styles are different. Marston's Pedigree is an example of Burton Pale Ale, not Bitter, while the same brewery's Old Empire is a fascinating interpretation of a Victorian IPA. So-called IPAs with strengths of around 3.5% are not true to style. Look for juicy malt, citrus fruit and a big spicy, peppery, bitter hop character, with strengths of 4% upwards.

Porter and Stout

Porter was a London style that turned the brewing industry upside down early in the 18th century. It was a dark brown beer – 19th-century versions became jet black – that was originally a blend of brown ale, pale ale and 'stale' or well-matured ale. It acquired the name Porter as a result of its popularity among London's street-market workers. The strongest versions of Porter were known as Stout Porter, reduced over the years to simply Stout. Such vast quantities of Porter and Stout flooded into Ireland from London and Bristol that a Dublin brewer named Arthur Guinness decided to fashion his own interpretation of the style. Guinness in Dublin blended some unmalted roasted barley and in so doing produced a style known as Dry Irish Stout. Restrictions on making roasted malts in Britain during World War One led to the demise of Porter and Stout and left the market to the Irish. In recent years, smaller craft brewers in Britain have rekindled an interest in the style, though in keeping with modern drinking habits, strengths have been reduced. Look for profound dark and roasted malt character with raisin and sultana fruit, espresso or cappuccino coffee, liquorice and molasses.

Barley Wine

Barley Wine is a style that dates from the 18th and 19th centuries when England was often at war with France and it was the duty of patriots, usually from the upper classes, to drink ale rather than Claret. Barley Wine had to be strong – often between 10% and 12% – and was stored for prodigious periods of as long at 18 months or two years. When country houses had their own small breweries, it was often the task of the butler to brew ale that was drunk from cut-glass goblets at the dining table. The biggest-

IPA STOUT BARLEY WINE

selling Barley Wine for years was Whitbread's 10.9% Gold Label, now available only in cans. Bass's No 1 Barley Wine (10.5%) is occasionally brewed in Burton-on-Trent, stored in cask for 12 months and made available to CAMRA beer festivals. Fuller's Vintage Ale (8.5%) is a bottle-conditioned version of its Golden Pride and is brewed with different varieties of malts and hops every year. Many micro-brewers now produce their interpretations of the style. Expect massive sweet malt and ripe fruit of the pear drop, orange and lemon type, with darker fruits, chocolate and coffee if darker malts are used. Hop rates are generous and produce bitterness and peppery, grassy and floral notes.

Scottish Beers

Historically, Scottish beers tend to be darker, sweeter and less heavily hopped than English and Welsh ales: a cold climate demands warming beers. But many of the new craft breweries produce beers lighter in colour and with generous hop rates. The traditional, classic styles are Light, low in strength and so-called even when dark in colour, also known as 60/-, Heavy or 70/-, Export or 80/- and a strong Wee Heavy, similar to a barley wine, and also labelled 90/-. In the 19th century, beers were invoiced according to strength, using the now defunct currency of the shilling.

80/-

Maps

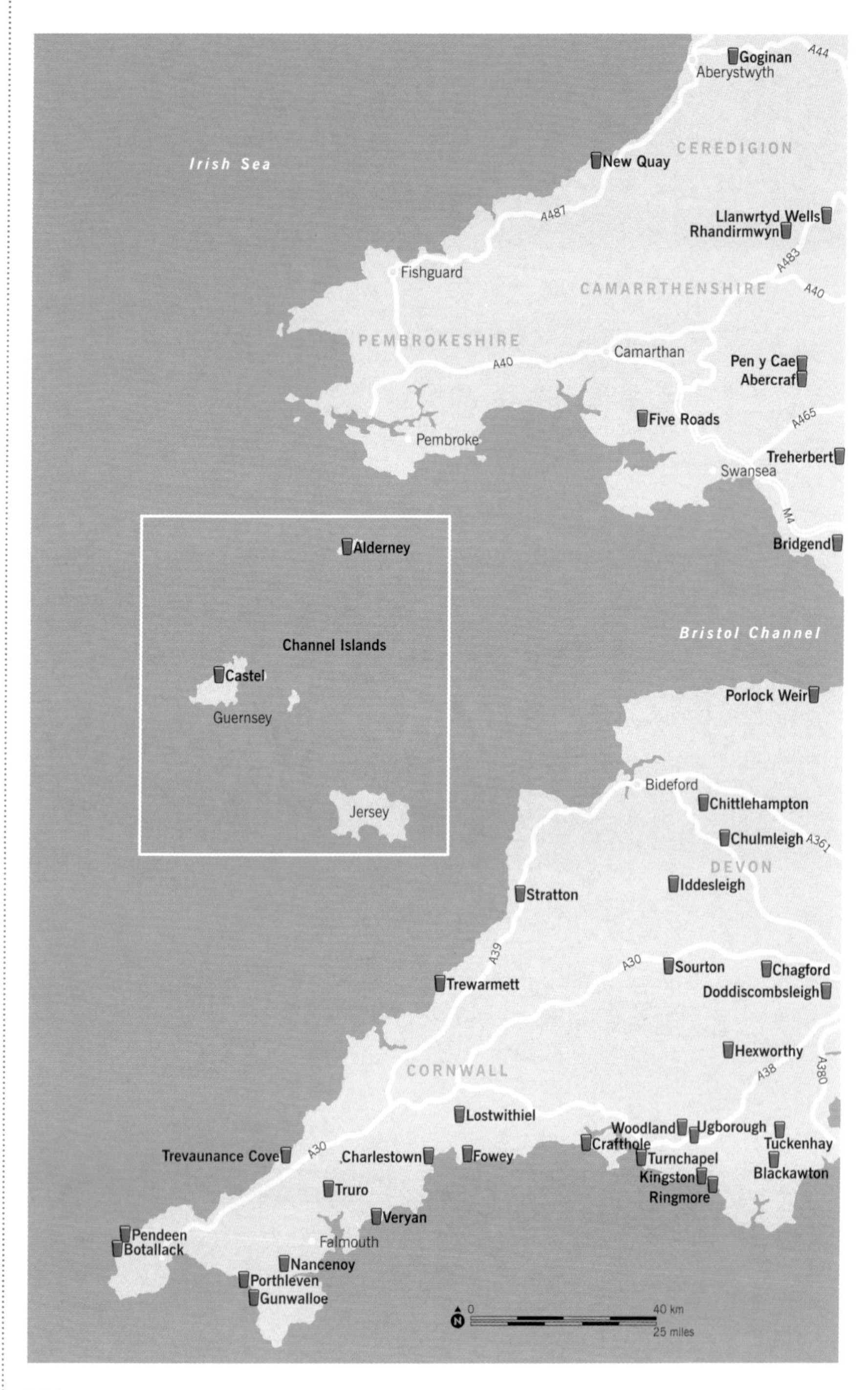
Goginan
A44
Aberystwyth
CEREDIGION
Irish Sea
New Quay
A487
Llanwrtyd Wells
Rhandirmwyn
A483
Fishguard
CAMARRTHENSHIRE
A40
PEMBROKESHIRE
Camarthan
A40
Pen y Cae
Abercraf
Five Roads
A465
Pembroke
Treherbert
Swansea
M4
Bridgend
Alderney
Bristol Channel
Channel Islands
Castel
Guernsey
Porlock Weir
Bideford
Chittlehampton
Jersey
Chulmleigh
A361
DEVON
Stratton
Iddesleigh
A39
A30
Sourton
Chagford
Trewarmett
Doddiscombsleigh
Hexworthy
CORNWALL
A38
A380
Lostwithiel
Woodland
Ugborough
Tuckenhay
Crafthole
Trevaunance Cove
A30
Charlestown
Fowey
Turnchapel
Blackawton
Kingston
Truro
Ringmore
Veryan
Pendeen
Botallack
Falmouth
Nancenoy
Porthleven
Gunwalloe
0
40 km
25 miles

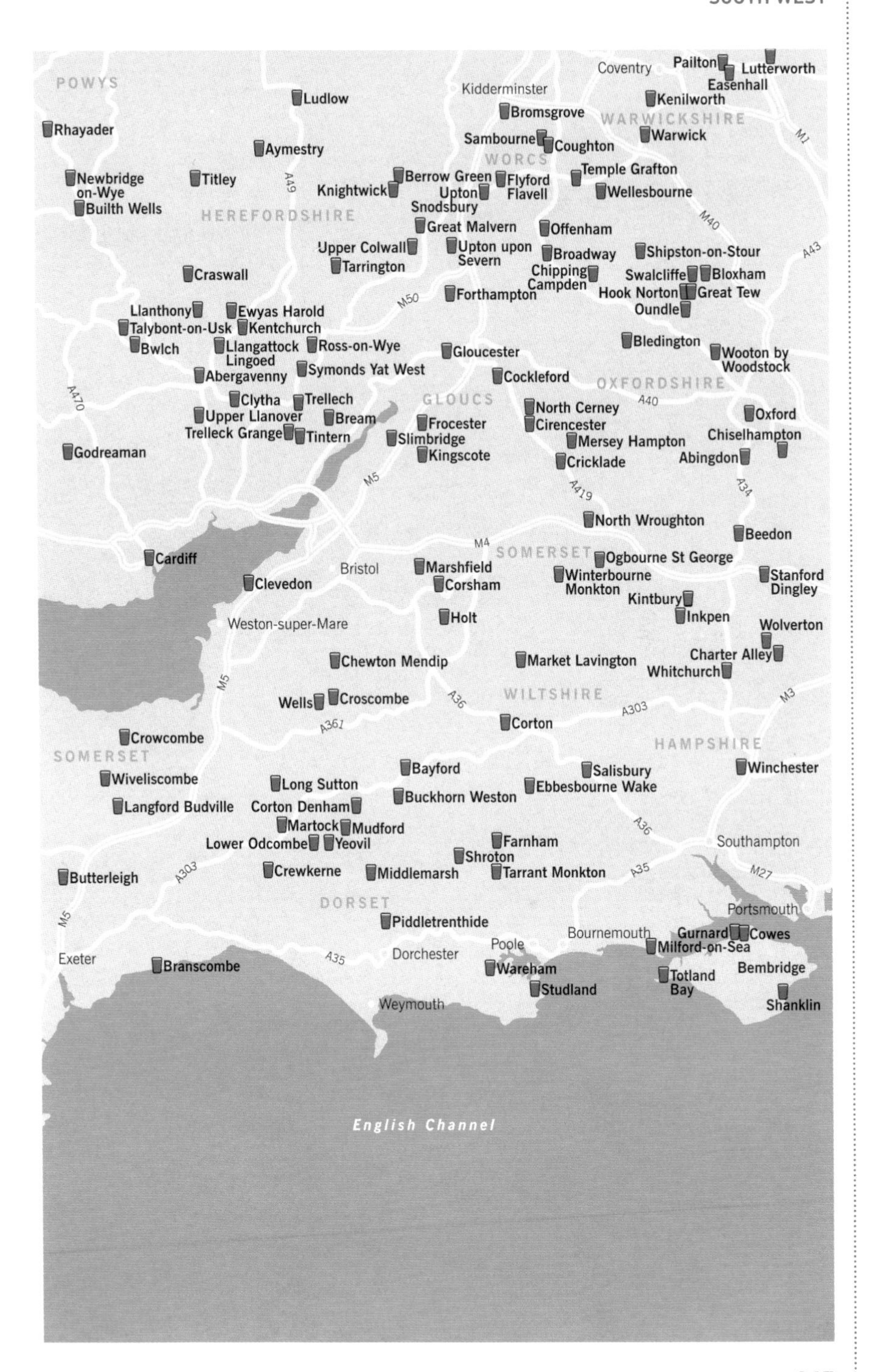
POWYS
Rhayader
Ludlow
Kidderminster
Coventry
Pailton
Lutterworth
Easenhall
Kenilworth
Bromsgrove
WARWICKSHIRE
Warwick
Sambourne
Coughton
Aymestry
WORCS
Temple Grafton
Newbridge on-Wye
Titley
Knightwick
Berrow Green
Upton Snodsbury
Flyford Flavell
Wellesbourne
Builth Wells
HEREFORDSHIRE
Great Malvern
Offenham
Upper Colwall
Upton upon Severn
Broadway
Shipston-on-Stour
Tarrington
Chipping Campden
Swalcliffe
Bloxham
Craswall
Forthampton
Hook Norton
Great Tew
Oundle
Llanthony
Ewyas Harold
Talybont-on-Usk
Kentchurch
Bwlch
Llangattock Lingoed
Ross-on-Wye
Gloucester
Bledington
Wooton by Woodstock
Abergavenny
Symonds Yat West
Cockleford
OXFORDSHIRE
Clytha
Trellech
GLOUCS
North Cerney
Upper Llanover
Bream
Frocester
Cirencester
Oxford
Trelleck Grange
Tintern
Slimbridge
Mersey Hampton
Chiselhampton
Godreaman
Kingscote
Cricklade
Abingdon
North Wroughton
Beedon
Cardiff
SOMERSET
Ogbourne St George
Bristol
Marshfield
Clevedon
Corsham
Winterbourne Monkton
Stanford Dingley
Kintbury
Inkpen
Weston-super-Mare
Holt
Wolverton
Chewton Mendip
Market Lavington
Charter Alley
Whitchurch
Wells
Croscombe
WILTSHIRE
Corton
Crowcombe
SOMERSET
HAMPSHIRE
Bayford
Salisbury
Winchester
Wiveliscombe
Long Sutton
Ebbesbourne Wake
Langford Budville
Corton Denham
Buckhorn Weston
Martock
Mudford
Lower Odcombe
Yeovil
Farnham
Southampton
Shroton
Butterleigh
Crewkerne
Middlemarsh
Tarrant Monkton
DORSET
Portsmouth
Piddletrenthide
Bournemouth
Gurnard
Cowes
Poole
Milford-on-Sea
Exeter
Branscombe
Dorchester
Wareham
Totland Bay
Bembridge
Studland
Weymouth
Shanklin
English Channel

Ripley
Ashbourne
Hulland Ward
Kimberley
Flintham
Lowdham
A17
Oasby
Grantham
M6
STAFFORDSHIRE
Derby
A52
A41
Eccleshall
Newton Solney
Needwood
Hartshorne
Colton
Handsacre
A1
LEICESTERSHIRE
Little Bytham
Somerby
A16
Shifnal
Coalbrookdale
Ironbridge
Tamworth
Market Bosworth
Leicester
Stamford
Walsall
Bridgnorth
Medbourne
Dudley
Birmingham
SHROPSHIRE
NORTHAMPTONSHIRE
Oundle
Stilton
Pailton
Lutterworth
Easenhall
Arthingworth
Ludlow
Kidderminster
Coventry
Kenilworth
Kettering
Bromsgrove
WARWICKSHIRE
Sambourne
Coughton
Warwick
Brampton
M1
WORCS
Northampton
A1
Berrow Green
Flyford Flavell
Temple Grafton
Knightwick
Upton Snodsbury
Wellesbourne
Great Malvern
Offenham
M40
Ireland
Upper Colwall
Upton upon Severn
Sherington
Houghton Conquest
Broadway
Shipston-on-Stour
A43
Salford
Tarrington
Chipping Campden
Swalcliffe
Bloxham
A5
M1
Astwick
Hook Norton
Great Tew
BEDFORDSHIRE
M50
Forthampton
Oundle
Streatley
Great Offley
Ross-on-Wye
Bledington
BUCKINGHAMSHIRE
Gloucester
Wooton by Woodstock
Denham
Whipsnade
Symonds Yat West
Cockleford
Aylesbury
Monmouth
OXFORDSHIRE
Aldbury
Trellech
GLOUCS
North Cerney
A40
Oxford
Bream
Frocester
Cirencester
Tintern
Slimbridge
Mersey Hampton
Chiselhampton
Chesham
Amersham
Kingscote
Cricklade
Abingdon
Radlett
Chalfont St Giles
M5
A419
A34
M40
Kingwood
North Wroughton
Henley-on-Thames
Beedon
Maidenhead
M4
SOMERSET
M4
Bristol
Marshfield
Ogbourne St George
Corsham
Winterbourne Monkton
Stanford Dingley
Kintbury
Newbury
M25
Holt
Inkpen
Hersham
Wolverton
SURREY
Charter Alley
Chewton Mendip
Market Lavington
Whitchurch
Dorking
M3
Gomshall
Croscombe
Wells
A36
WILTSHIRE
Peaslake
A303
Corton
HAMPSHIRE
Bayford
Salisbury
Winchester
A3
Mannings Heath
Ebbesbourne Wake
Buckhorn Weston
Corton Denham
West Chiltington
Mudford
A36
WEST SUSSEX
Yeovil
Farnham
Southampton
Charlton
Amberley
Shroton
Middlemarsh
Tarrant Monkton
A35
M27
East Ashling
A27
DORSET
Portsmouth
Piddletrenthide
Gurnard
Cowes
Poole
Milford-on-Sea
A35
Dorchester
Bournemouth
Wareham
Bembridge
Totland Bay
English Channel
Studland
Shanklin
Weymouth

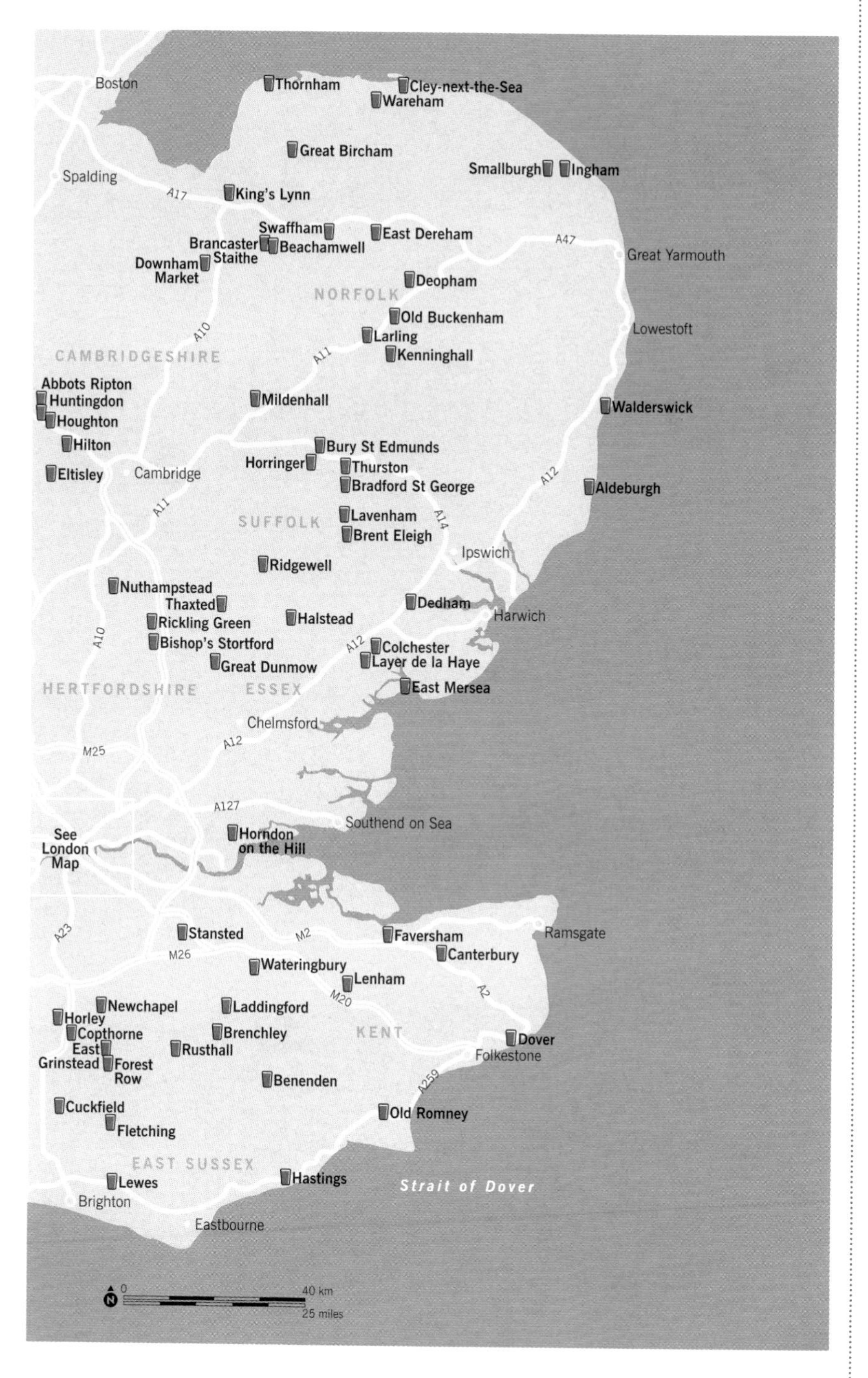
Boston
Thornham
Cley-next-the-Sea
Wareham
Great Bircham
Spalding
Smallburgh
Ingham
A17
King's Lynn
Swaffham
East Dereham
A47
Brancaster Staithe
Beachamwell
Great Yarmouth
Downham Market
Deopham
NORFOLK
Old Buckenham
A10
Lowestoft
Larling
A11
CAMBRIDGESHIRE
Kenninghall
Abbots Ripton
Huntingdon
Mildenhall
Houghton
Walderswick
Hilton
Bury St Edmunds
Horringer
Thurston
Eltisley
Cambridge
Bradford St George
A12
Aldeburgh
A11
Lavenham
A14
SUFFOLK
Brent Eleigh
Ipswich
Ridgewell
Nuthampstead
Thaxted
Dedham
Rickling Green
Halstead
Harwich
A10
Bishop's Stortford
A12
Colchester
Layer de la Haye
Great Dunmow
HERTFORDSHIRE
ESSEX
East Mersea
Chelmsford
M25
A12
A127
Southend on Sea
See London Map
Horndon on the Hill
A23
Stansted
M2
Faversham
Ramsgate
M26
Canterbury
Wateringbury
Lenham
A2
M20
Newchapel
Laddingford
Horley
KENT
Copthorne
Brenchley
Dover
East Grinstead
Rusthall
Folkestone
Forest Row
Benenden
A259
Cuckfield
Old Romney
Fletching
EAST SUSSEX
Lewes
Hastings
Strait of Dover
Brighton
Eastbourne
0
40 km
25 miles

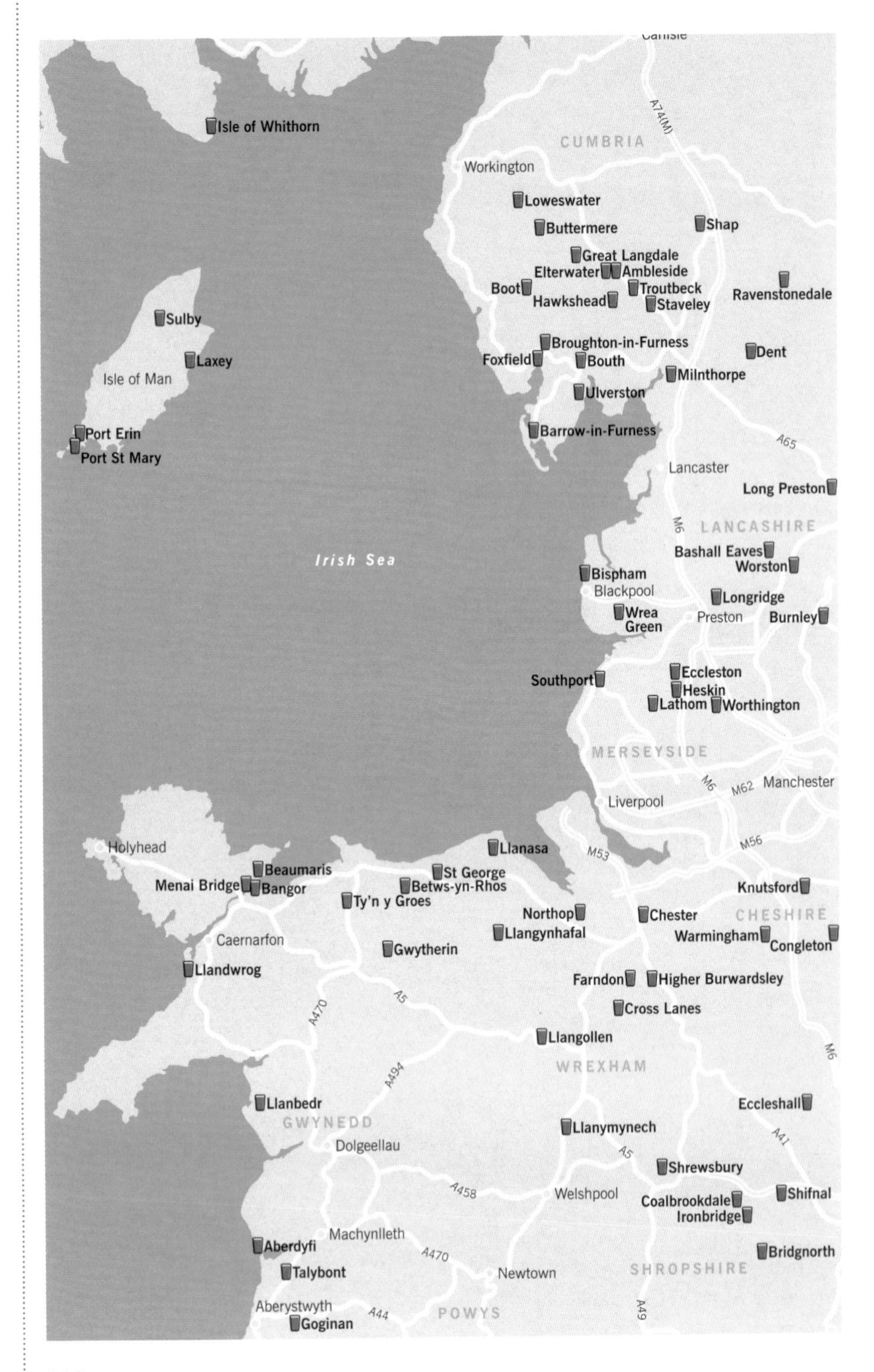
Isle of Whithorn
CUMBRIA
A74(M)
Workington
Loweswater
Buttermere
Shap
Great Langdale
Elterwater
Ambleside
Boot
Troutbeck
Hawkshead
Staveley
Ravenstonedale
Sulby
Broughton-in-Furness
Foxfield
Bouth
Dent
Laxey
Isle of Man
Milnthorpe
Ulverston
Port Erin
Port St Mary
Barrow-in-Furness
A65
Lancaster
Long Preston
M6
LANCASHIRE
Bashall Eaves
Irish Sea
Worston
Bispham
Blackpool
Longridge
Wrea Green
Preston
Burnley
Southport
Eccleston
Heskin
Lathom
Worthington
MERSEYSIDE
M6
M62
Manchester
Liverpool
Holyhead
Llanasa
M53
M56
Beaumaris
St George
Menai Bridge
Bangor
Betws-yn-Rhos
Ty'n y Groes
Knutsford
Northop
Chester
CHESHIRE
Llangynhafal
Warmingham
Congleton
Caernarfon
Gwytherin
Llandwrog
Farndon
Higher Burwardsley
A470
A5
Cross Lanes
Llangollen
M6
WREXHAM
A494
Llanbedr
Eccleshall
GWYNEDD
Llanymynech
A41
Dolgeellau
A5
Shrewsbury
A458
Welshpool
Coalbrookdale
Shifnal
Ironbridge
Machynlleth
Aberdyfi
A470
Bridgnorth
Talybont
Newtown
SHROPSHIRE
Aberystwyth
A44
POWYS
A49
Goginan

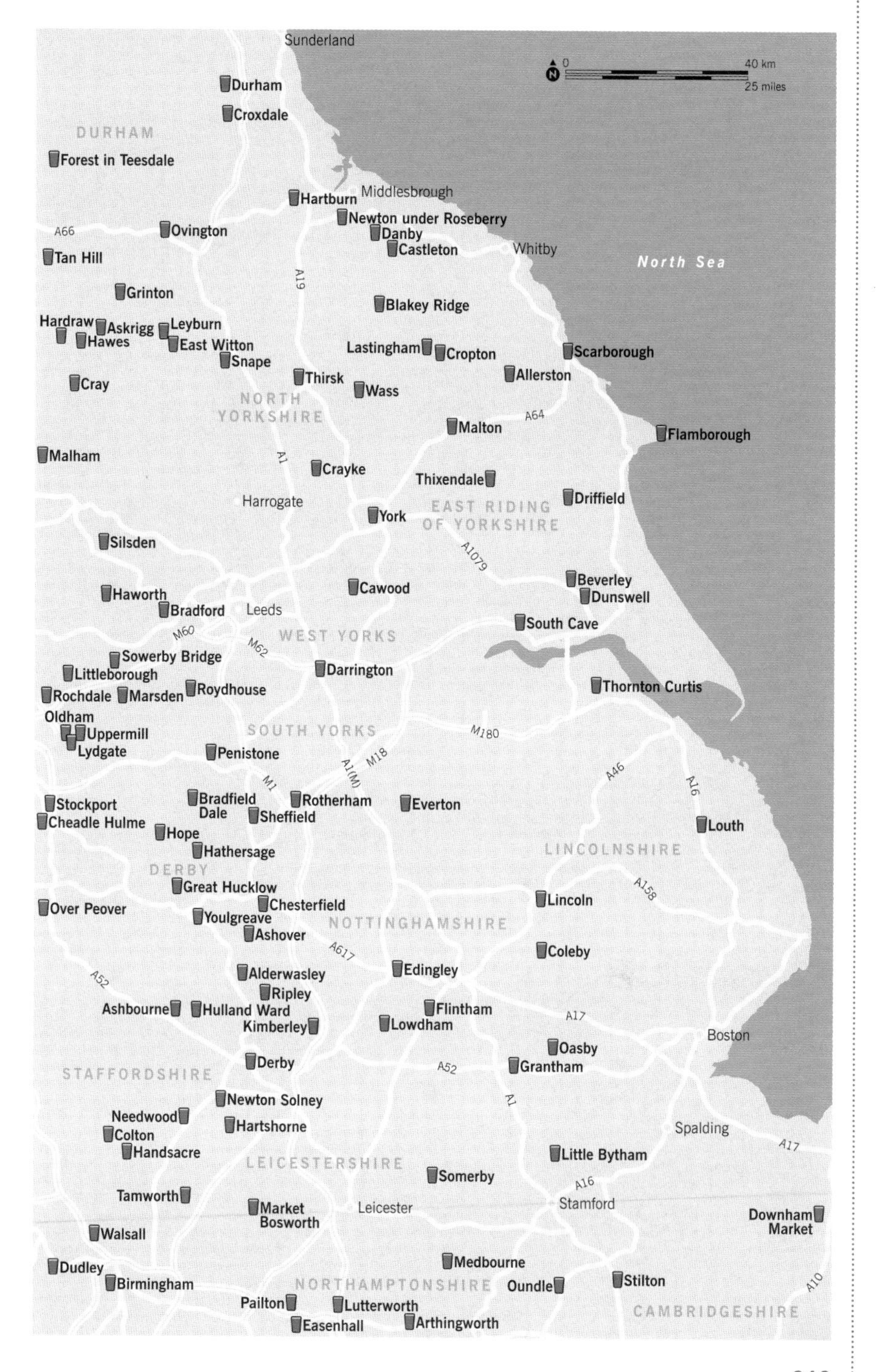
Sunderland
0
40 km
25 miles
Durham
Croxdale
DURHAM
Forest in Teesdale
Hartburn
Middlesbrough
Newton under Roseberry
Danby
Castleton
Whitby
North Sea
A66
Ovington
Tan Hill
A19
Grinton
Blakey Ridge
Hardraw
Askrigg
Leyburn
Hawes
East Witton
Snape
Lastingham
Cropton
Scarborough
Thirsk
Allerston
Cray
Wass
NORTH YORKSHIRE
A64
Malton
Flamborough
Malham
A1
Crayke
Thixendale
Driffield
Harrogate
York
EAST RIDING OF YORKSHIRE
Silsden
A1079
Beverley
Cawood
Dunswell
Haworth
Bradford
Leeds
South Cave
M60
WEST YORKS
M62
Sowerby Bridge
Darrington
Littleborough
Thornton Curtis
Rochdale
Marsden
Roydhouse
Oldham
SOUTH YORKS
M180
Uppermill
Lydgate
Penistone
M18
A1(M)
A46
M1
A16
Stockport
Bradfield Dale
Rotherham
Everton
Cheadle Hulme
Sheffield
Louth
Hope
Hathersage
LINCOLNSHIRE
DERBY
A158
Great Hucklow
Lincoln
Over Peover
Chesterfield
Youlgreave
NOTTINGHAMSHIRE
Ashover
A617
Coleby
Edingley
A52
Alderwasley
Ripley
Ashbourne
Hulland Ward
Flintham
A17
Kimberley
Lowdham
Boston
Oasby
Derby
A52
Grantham
STAFFORDSHIRE
Newton Solney
A1
Needwood
Hartshorne
Colton
Spalding
Handsacre
Little Bytham
A17
LEICESTERSHIRE
Somerby
A16
Tamworth
Market Bosworth
Leicester
Stamford
Downham Market
Walsall
Medbourne
Dudley
Stilton
Birmingham
NORTHAMPTONSHIRE
Oundle
A10
Pailton
Lutterworth
CAMBRIDGESHIRE
Easenhall
Arthingworth

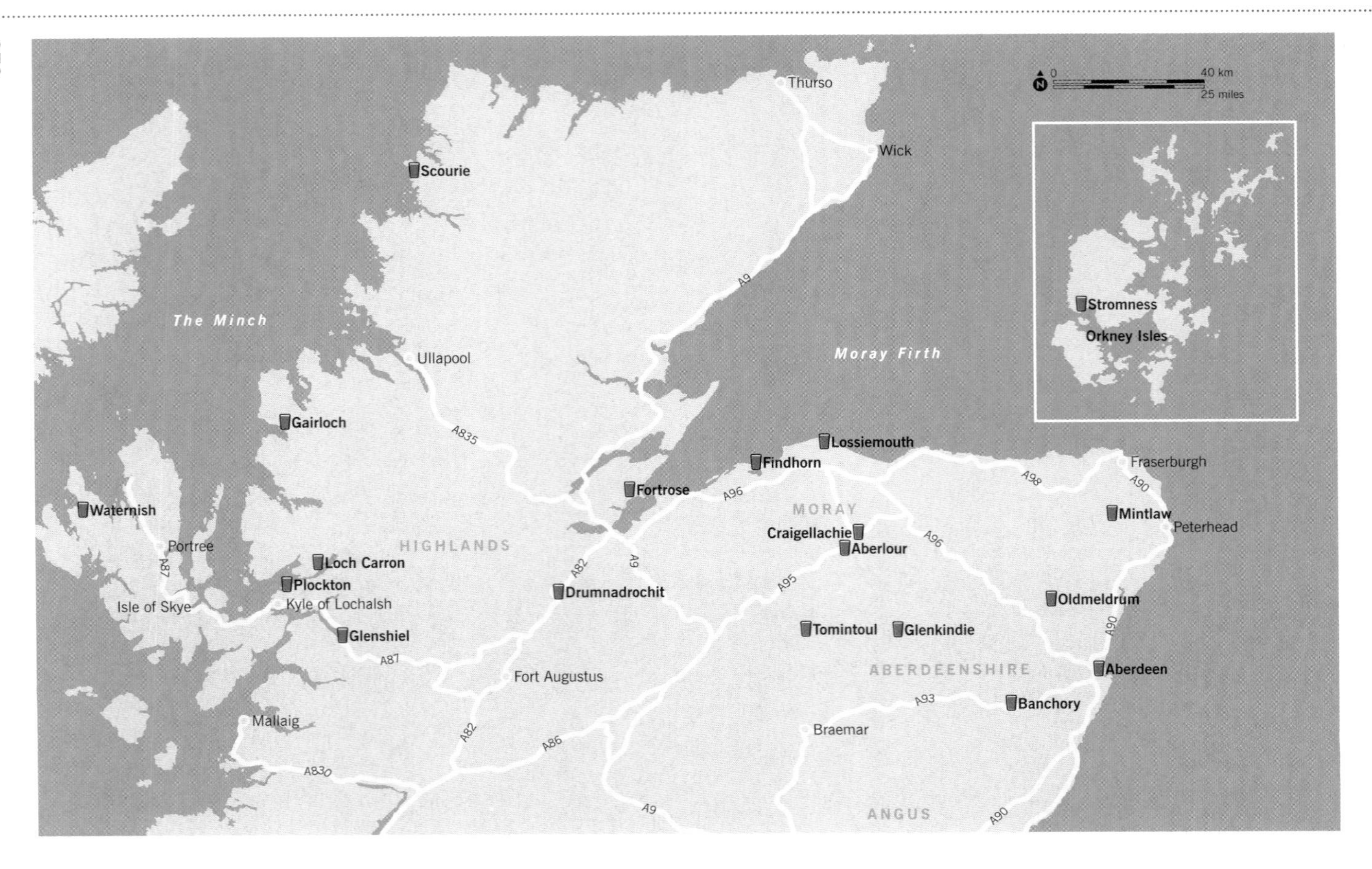

0
40 km
25 miles
Stromness
Orkney Isles
Thurso
Wick
Scourie
The Minch
Ullapool
Moray Firth
Gairloch
A835
A9
Lossiemouth
Findhorn
Fortrose
A96
Fraserburgh
A98
A90
Mintlaw
Peterhead
MORAY
Craigellachie
Aberlour
A96
Waternish
Portree
HIGHLANDS
Loch Carron
Plockton
A87
Isle of Skye
Kyle of Lochalsh
A82
A9
Drumnadrochit
A95
Oldmeldrum
Glenshiel
Tomintoul
Glenkindie
A87
Fort Augustus
ABERDEENSHIRE
Aberdeen
A93
Banchory
Mallaig
A82
A86
Braemar
A830
A9
ANGUS
A90

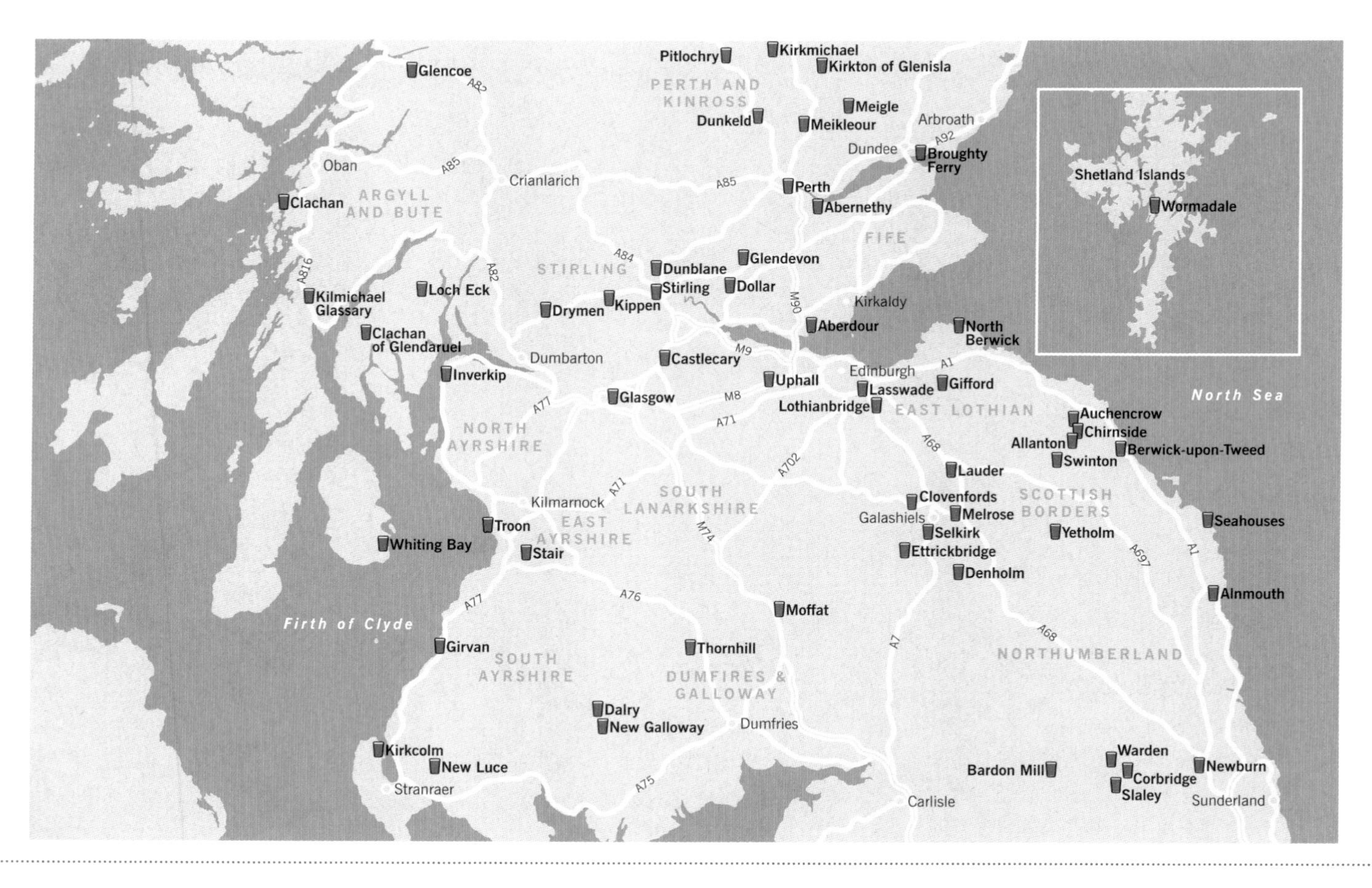
Shetland Islands
Wormadale
North Sea
Firth of Clyde
PERTH AND KINROSS
FIFE
EAST LOTHIAN
SCOTTISH BORDERS
NORTHUMBERLAND
STIRLING
ARGYLL AND BUTE
NORTH AYRSHIRE
EAST AYRSHIRE
SOUTH LANARKSHIRE
SOUTH AYRSHIRE
DUMFIRES & GALLOWAY
Pitlochry
Kirkmichael
Kirkton of Glenisla
Glencoe
Dunkeld
Meigle
Meikleour
Arbroath
Dundee
Broughty Ferry
Oban
Crianlarich
Perth
Abernethy
Clachan
Glendevon
Dunblane
Stirling
Dollar
Kilmichael Glassary
Loch Eck
Drymen
Kippen
Kirkaldy
Aberdour
North Berwick
Clachan of Glendaruel
Dumbarton
Castlecary
Inverkip
Edinburgh
Uphall
Lasswade
Gifford
Glasgow
Lothianbridge
Auchencrow
Chirnside
Allanton
Swinton
Berwick-upon-Tweed
Lauder
Clovenfords
Kilmarnock
Galashiels
Melrose
Troon
Whiting Bay
Selkirk
Yetholm
Seahouses
Stair
Ettrickbridge
Denholm
Alnmouth
Moffat
Girvan
Thornhill
Dalry
New Galloway
Dumfries
Kirkcolm
New Luce
Stranraer
Bardon Mill
Warden
Corbridge
Slaley
Newburn
Sunderland
Carlisle
A82
A85
A92
A816
A84
M90
M9
A1
M8
A77
A71
A68
A702
M74
A697
A76
A7
A75

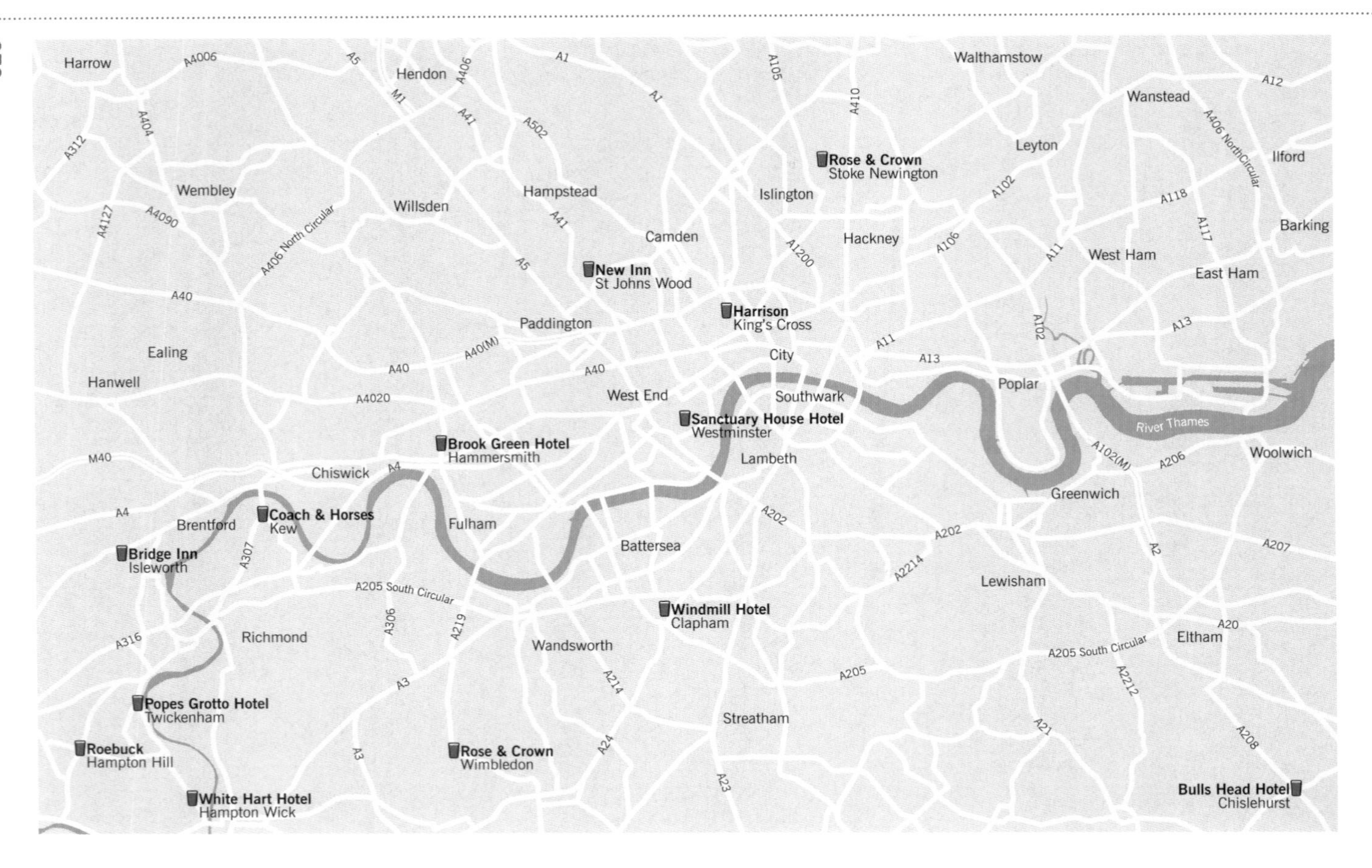

Harrow
Hendon
Walthamstow
Wanstead
Leyton
Ilford
Barking
Rose & Crown
Stoke Newington
Wembley
Willsden
Hampstead
Islington
Camden
Hackney
West Ham
East Ham
New Inn
St Johns Wood
Harrison
King's Cross
Paddington
Ealing
City
Hanwell
West End
Southwark
Poplar
Sanctuary House Hotel
Westminster
River Thames
Brook Green Hotel
Hammersmith
Lambeth
Woolwich
Chiswick
Greenwich
Coach & Horses
Kew
Brentford
Fulham
Bridge Inn
Isleworth
Battersea
Lewisham
Windmill Hotel
Clapham
Richmond
Wandsworth
Eltham
Popes Grotto Hotel
Twickenham
Streatham
Roebuck
Hampton Hill
Rose & Crown
Wimbledon
White Hart Hotel
Hampton Wick
Bulls Head Hotel
Chislehurst
A4006
A5
A1
A105
A410
A12
M1
A406
A41
A502
A406 NorthCircular
A312
A404
A102
A118
A4127
A4090
A406 North Circular
A117
A1200
A106
A11
A40
A40(M)
A13
A4020
M40
A4
A102(M)
A206
A202
A2
A207
A307
A2214
A205 South Circular
A306
A219
A20
A316
A3
A214
A205
A2212
A21
A208
A24
A23

NOTES

NOTES

NOTES

Readers' Recommendations

Every year sees many of the country's pubs change hands. A new licensee can bring improvements or even disaster to the finest establishments! While most details were checked before going to press, errors will inevitably occur and changes come thick and fast. If you come across listed pubs which have changed or if you find an undiscovered gem, let us know and we will investigate it for the next edition.

Photocopy and complete this form and send it to:
Beer, Bed & Breakfast Readers' Recommendations,
230 Hatfield Road, St Albans, Herts, AL1 4LW
(or fax 01727 848795 / email books@camra.org.uk)

Your name/contact details ______________________________
(not for publication)

____

____

Pub ______________________________
(name & address)

____

______________________________ Postcode ______________

Telephone ______________ Fax ______________

Email ______________________________

Web ______________________________

Brief description of pub for inclusion or reasons for excluding it ______________

____

____

____

____

Beer served ______________________________

____

____

It takes all sorts to Campaign for Real Ale

CAMRA, the Campaign for Real Ale, is an independent not-for-profit, volunteer-led consumer group. We actively campaign for full pints and more flexible licensing hours, as well as protecting the 'local' pub and lobbying government to champion pub-goers' rights.

CAMRA has 84,000 members from all ages and backgrounds, brought together by a common belief in the issues that CAMRA deals with and their love of good quality British beer. From just £20 a year, that's less than a pint a month, you can join CAMRA and enjoy the following benefits:

A monthly colour newspaper informing you about beer and pub news and detailing events and beer festivals around the country.

Free or reduced entry to over 140 national, regional and local beer festivals.

Money off many of our publications including the Good Beer Guide and the Good Bottled Beer Guide.

Access to a members-only section of our national website, **www.camra.org.uk**, which gives up-to-the-minute news stories and includes a special offer section with regular features saving money on beer and trips away.

The opportunity to campaign to save pubs under threat of closure, for pubs to be open when people want to drink and a reduction in beer duty that will help Britain's brewing industry survive.

Log onto **www.camra.org.uk** forCAMRA membership information.

Do you feel passionately about your pint? Then why not join CAMRA

Just fill in the application form (or a photocopy of it) and the Direct Debit form on the next page to receive three months' membership FREE!

If you wish to join but do not want to pay by Direct Debit, please fill in the application form below and send a cheque, payable to CAMRA, to CAMRA, 230 Hatfield Road, St Albans, Hertfordshire, AL1 4LW.

Please tick appropriate box	DIRECT DEBIT		NON DIRECT DEBIT	
Single Membership (UK & EU)	£20	☐	£22	☐
For under-26 Membership	£11	☐	£13	☐
For 60 and over Membership	£11	☐	£13	☐

For partners' joint membership add £5 (Partner must live at the same address).
Life membership information is available on request.

If you join by Direct Debit you will receive three months' membership extra, free!

Title ______________ Surname ______________________________

Forename(s) ____

Address ____

______________________________ Postcode __________________

Date of Birth ______________ Email address __________________

Signature ____

Partner's details (for Joint Membership)

Title ______________ Surname ______________________________

Forename(s) ____

Date of Birth ______________ Email address __________________

Please tick here ☐ if you would like to receive occasional emails from CAMRA (at no point will your details be released to a third party).
Find out more about CAMRA at **www.camra.org.uk** Telephone 01727 867201

CAMPAIGN FOR REAL ALE

Instruction to your Bank or Building Society to pay by Direct Debit

Please fill in the form and send to: Campaign for Real Ale Ltd. 230 Hatfield Road, St. Albans, Herts. AL1 4LW

Name and full postal address of your Bank or Building Society

To The Manager — Bank or Building Society

Address

Postcode

Originator's Identification Number

9	2	6	1	2	9

FOR CAMRA OFFICIAL USE ONLY
This is not part of the instruction to your Bank or Building Society

Membership Number

Name

Postcode

Name (s) of Account Holder (s)

Bank or Building Society account number

Branch Sort Code

Reference Number

Instruction to your Bank or Building Society
Please pay CAMRA Direct Debits from the account detailed on this Instruction subject to the safeguards assured by the Direct Debit Guarantee. I understand that this instruction may remain with CAMRA and, if so, will be passed electronically to my Bank/Building Society

Signature(s)

Date

Banks and Building Societies may not accept Direct Debit Instructions for some types of account

detached and retained this section

DIRECT Debit

This Guarantee should be detached and retained by the payer.

The Direct Debit Guarantee

- This Guarantee is offered by all Banks and Building Societies that take part in the Direct Debit Scheme. The efficiency and security of the Scheme is monitored and protected by your own Bank or Building Society.
- If the amounts to be paid or the payment dates change CAMRA will notify you 10 working days in advance of your account being debited or as otherwise agreed.
- If an error is made by CAMRA or your Bank or Building Society, you are guaranteed a full and immediate refund from your branch of the amount paid.
- You can cancel a Direct Debit at any time by writing to your Bank or Building Society. Please also send a copy of your letter to us.

Books for beer lovers

CAMRA Books, the publishing arm of the Campaign for Real Ale, is the leading publisher of books on beer and pubs. Key titles include:

Good Beer Guide

Editor: ROGER PROTZ

The Good Beer Guide is the only guide you will need to find the right pint, in the right place, every time. It's the original and the best independent guide to around 4,500 pubs throughout the UK; in 2002 it was named as one of the Guardian newspapers books of the year and the Sun newspaper rated the 2004 edition in the top 20 books of all time! This annual publication is a comprehensive and informative guide to the best real ale pubs in the UK, researched and written exclusively by CAMRA members and fully updated every year

Good Pub Food

SUSAN NOWAK & JILL ADAM

This fully revised sixth edition of Good Pub Food singles out over 600 real ale pubs in England, Wales, Scotland and Northern Ireland, which also specialise in fine cuisine. All are highlighted on easy to use maps and have a full description of their location, ales, menus, prices, vegetarian selections and facilities. Both Susan Nowak and Jill Adam have been involved in editing and compiling CAMRA guides for over 20 years.

£14.99 ISBN 978 1 85249 214 4

An Appetite For Ale

FIONA BECKETT / WILL BECKETT

A beer and food revolution is under way in Britain and award-winning food writer Fiona Beckett and her publican son, Will, have joined forces to write the first cookbook to explore this exciting new food phenomenon that celebrates beer as a culinary tour de force. This collection of more than 100 simple and approachable recipes has been specially created to show the versatility and fantastic flavour that ale has to offer. With sections on Snacks, Spreads and Dips, Soups, Pasta and Risotto, Seafood, Chicken and other Birds, Meat Feasts, Spicy Foods, Bread and Cheese and Sweet Treats it provides countless ideas for using beer from around the world. With an open mind, a bottle opener and a well-stocked larder, this exciting book will allow you to enjoy real food, real ale and real flavour. Published September 2007.

£16.99 ISBN 978 1 85249 234 2

The Book of Beer Knowledge

JEFF EVANS

A unique collection of entertaining trivia and essential wisdom, this is the perfect gift for beer lovers everywhere. Fully revised and updated it includes more than 200 entries cover everything from the fictional 'celebrity landlords' of soap pubs to the harsh facts detailing the world's biggest brewers; from bizarre beer names to the serious subject of fermentation.

£9.99 ISBN 978 1 85249 198 7

CAMRA's London Pub Walks

BOB STEEL

CAMRA's London Pub Walks enables you to explore the entire city while never being far away from a decent pint. A practical pocket-sized guide, it includes 30 walks around more than 180 pubs serving fine real ale, from the heart of the City and the bustling West End to majestic riverside routes and the leafy common of Wimbledon. The perfect companion for a day out discovering real London.

£8.99 ISBN 978 1 85249 216 8

300 Beers To Try Before You Die

ROGER PROTZ

300 beers from around the world, handpicked by award-winning journalist, author and broadcaster Roger Protz to try before you die! A comprehensive portfolio of top beers from the smallest micro-breweries in the United States to family-run British breweries and the world's largest brands. This book is indispensable for both beer novices and aficionados.

£14.99 ISBN 978 1 85249 213 7

CAMRA's Good Cider Guide

Now in its 5th edition, this title features more than 600 traditional cider producers and outlets in the UK and is an essential volume for anyone wishing to become a cider connoisseur. The popularity of real cider is permanently rising as more and more people discover how deliciously mellow, aromatic and intoxicating the flavours of naturally-produced cider can be. CAMRA's Good Cider Guide, revised and updated, offers a county-by-county directory of UK cider producers and outlets and provides unique, in-depth knowledge for the discerning cider consumer.

£10.99 ISBN 978 1 85249 195 6

Good Bottled Beer Guide

EDITOR: JEFF EVANS

This fully updated and expanded sixth edition is the bible for all aficionados of real ale in a bottle. It is a unique and comprehensive guide to the huge number of beers now available in supermarkets, off-licences and via the internet in the UK. Nearly 800 bottle-conditioned beers are profiled including bitters, lagers, milds, wheat beers, stouts, porters, fruit beers and barley wines.

£10.99 ISBN 978 1 85249 226 7

Good Beer Guide Prague & The Czech Republic

EVAN RAIL

This fully updated and expanded version of a collectible classic is the first new edition to be produced by CAMRA for 10 years! It is the definitive guide for visitors to the Czech Republic and compulsory reading for fans of great beer, featuring more than 100 Czech breweries, 400 different beers and over 100 great places to try them. It includes listings of brewery-hotels and regional attractions for planning complete vacations outside of the capital, sections on historical background, how to get there and what to expect, as well as detailed descriptions of the 12 most common Czech beer styles.

£12.99 ISBN 978 1 85249 233 5

Beer Lover's Guide to Cricket

ROGER PROTZ

There are many books about cricket and many on beer, but this is the first book to bring the two subjects together. Leading beer writer and cricket enthusiast Roger Protz has visited the major grounds of all the First Class counties and gives in-depth profiles of them – their history, museums, and memorabilia, plus listings of the best real ale pubs to visit within easy reach of each ground and details of the cask ales available. This fully illustrated book also features individual sections on the birth of the modern game of cricket and the history of each featured ground, making it an essential purchase for any cricket fan.

£16.99 ISBN 978 1 85249 227 4

Order these and other CAMRA books online at **www.camra.org.uk/books**, ask at your local bookstore, or contact:
CAMRA, 230 Hatfield Road, St Albans, AL1 4LW. Telephone 01727 867201